THE NEW NATURALIS

A SURVEY OF BRITISH NATUR

YORKSHIRE DALES

*

The aim of this series is to interest the general reader in the wildlife of Britain by recapturing the enquiring spirit of the old naturalists. The editors believe that the natural pride of the British public in the native flora and fauna, to which must be added concern for their conservation, is best fostered by maintaining a high standard of accuracy combined with clarity of exposition in presenting the results of modern scientific research.

THE NEW NATURALIST LIBRARY

YORKSHIRE DALES

JOHN LEE

This edition published in 2015 by William Collins,
an imprint of HarperCollins Publishers

HarperCollins Publishers
1 London Bridge Street
London SE1 9GF

WilliamCollinsBooks.com

First published 2015

A CIP catalogue record for this book is available
from the British Library.

Set in FF Nexus

Edited and designed by
D & N Publishing
Baydon, Wiltshire

Printed in Hong Kong by Printing Express

Hardback
ISBN 978-0-00-750369-8

Paperback
ISBN 978-0-00-750370-4

Contents

Editors' Preface

The Yorkshire Dales, which became a National Park more than 60 years ago, is an iconic English landscape that is long overdue the literary and scientific attention of the New Naturalist series, and so we are delighted that Professor John Lee, an ecologist long familiar with the area, has now filled this need with characteristic style and rigour. Readers will find that the natural history of the Dales is known in great detail, even by the high standards expected in these islands and of this series. This is thanks to the unflagging attentions of professionals and amateurs alike. With the universities of Lancaster, Manchester, Sheffield, Leeds, York and Durham arrayed around its borders, the academic pantheon of British natural history has quartered and catalogued these uplands and valleys for a century. Within the borders of the National Park, Malham Tarn Field Centre has schooled and sheltered many thousands of naturalists and students. The area is also the happy hunting ground of the redoubtable Yorkshire 'Naturalists' Union. It was even once the haunt of two secret societies of botanists, so clandestine that they were unknown even to each other, though both were dedicated to the same end of protecting Britain's last surviving Lady's Slipper Orchids. All of this and more is unearthed by Professor Lee.

Though in places the landform of the Dales could be described as well-upholstered, in others the underlying geology grins through its surface with bared limestone teeth. Scoured for millions of years by ice and rock, the Dales landscape has also been quarried and mined for centuries by pick and shovel. In fact John Lee suggests that, in part at least, the Dales present a post-industrial landscape. The other human influence to have shaped the landscape is of course farming, which has waxed and waned under the influence of climate since the Neolithic. Place names ending in *–ley* tell us that the first Anglo-Saxon farmers probably created their fields in forest clearings, while place names with the *–ton* suffix were villages founded at a later date. A century later, Scandinavian immigrants named their settlements *–thwaite, –sett* and *–scale* and left us the words that have become as evocative of the area as the landforms they describe: *beck, fell, scar* and *dale*. If you know how to read them, the very stone walls speak: dry-stone walls with a continuous cap of rock forming a ledge that projects away from the field were designed to prevent Wolves leaping them into enclosures full of sheep. The Wolves are long gone, but the sheep remain and the walls now invite you to enter by stile and gate. Let John Lee escort you into these rich pastures.

Author's Foreword and Acknowledgements

My first very brief encounter with the Yorkshire Dales came in 1958 on a coach journey from Keighley with brother Terry and my soon to be sister-in-law Hilary en route to a walking holiday in the Lake District. In those days the old Keighley to Kendal turnpike, now the A65, climbed up Giggleswick Scar on the South Craven Fault before affording excellent views of Ingleborough as it skirted the edge of the then very new National Park. My next encounter came at the end of my first year as an undergraduate in the Botany Department at the University of Sheffield in 1962. After the first-year exams the department organised a series of day excursions to broaden our knowledge of plants and the habitats in which they grow, and one of these was to Malham. For a southerner with a keen interest in plants and landscape, this was a truly magical experience, helped by a glorious early-June day. The beck emerging from the base of the Cove, the steep climb up the side to view the limestone pavements above it, and the walk up the Watlowes dry valley past Water Sinks to the Tarn itself are etched in the memory, as are views of Tarn Moss, the woods and the mires.

It was a day for this southerner to encounter new plants, including Baneberry in the pavements, Jacob's-ladder on the damp screes and, most attractive of all, the mass of pink flowers of Bird's-eye Primrose in the mires and flushes.

Students in the Botany Department and its successor Animal and Plant Sciences Department were and are fortunate to be exposed to a strong ecological tradition cemented when A. R. Clapham succeeded W. H. Pearsall as professor of botany in 1944. By the early 1960s there were not only the soon to be distinguished young ecologists, Derek Anderson, Philip Grime and Ian Rorison in the department, but also outstanding individuals in other fields. This latter group included David Read, John Webster and Harold Woolhouse, all of whom had a strong interest in ecology but a centre of gravity in mycology or plant physiology. The arrival of J. L. Harley, a former research student of Sir Arthur Tansley, as the second professor in the mid-1960s further enhanced the scholarship, immediately making it the centre of excellence in mycorrhizal research that it remains today under the leadership of Sir David Read and Jonathan Leake. Jack Harley was an old boy of Leeds Grammar School and was familiar with the Dales from his youth. His survey of Colt Park and Ling Gill woods in upper Ribblesdale formed the basis of Tansley's account of them in his classic work *The British Islands and Their Vegetation*, published in 1939. But it was John Webster who got me actively involved with the natural history of Yorkshire through encouraging me to join the Yorkshire Naturalists' Union and, in particular, its Mycology (now Fungi and Lichens) section.

Forays were the major part of this section's activities, and one of these provided my first visit to Richmond and the northern Dales. The section at that time contained an admirable mix of expert professional mycologists such as John Webster, Roy Watling and Tom Hering and outstanding amateurs such as Willis Bramley. But it also attracted botanists with more general interests, including John Lovis and Arthur Sledge. Arthur Sledge was another Leeds Grammar School old boy, but one who spent his whole career in the University of Leeds Botany Department. He was expert in fern taxonomy, but his knowledge of plants in general and of the Yorkshire flora in particular was very extensive. So fungal forays at this period were more than the mere pursuit of mycological specimens, and helped me to learn much more about the county's range of habitats and plants.

During this period I was also very fortunate to marry into a Westmorland farming family. Harold Wright farmed an area to the south of the county which included a sheep run over what is now Clawthorpe Fell National Nature Reserve, covering some magnificent areas of limestone pavement, and he helped me to establish a grazing exclosure study on one of these. This not only taught me about the rate at which vegetation developed above the gryke surface once sheep grazing was removed, but also demonstrated the extreme sensitivity of the lichens on the clint surfaces to the drip from galvanised wire netting.

The Yorkshire Dales National Park is only a short drive from Clawthorpe, and my wife Barbara and I began to make excursions there from the mid-1960s onwards. In 1967 I was appointed to an assistant lectureship in the Botany Department of the Victoria University of Manchester. There I had the great good fortune to have D. H. Valentine as my first head of department. David Valentine was a plant taxonomist with an extensive knowledge of the northern Pennines, particularly of the Teesdale flora. He had arrived from Durham the year previously and was keen to promote plant ecology in the department. I also had the great good fortune to share an office with Clive Stace for my first three years in Manchester, and to have John Tallis as an ecological colleague. Together they taught me much about the British flora and vegetation history. In those less pressurised academic days it was possible occasionally to fit in brief excursions to familiarise ourselves with the flora of northern England and Wales, and three of these took us to see *Cypripedium calceolus, Dryas octopetala* and *Saxifraga oppositifolia* in flower in the Dales. There were also day trips with student parties to various sites in Ribblesdale and Chapel-le-Dale, including Scar Close and Colt Park.

As my career developed, much of my UK research became centred on the Peak District, which was closer at hand than the Dales, even when I moved back to Sheffield in 1994. But one friend in particular, Kathleen Firth, encouraged me to take a much greater interest in the Dales again. When Kath retired from teaching in Altrincham, she moved to Langcliffe and got actively involved in volunteering for English Nature at Colt Park. Although I was not able to renew my interest in the Dales immediately, my retirement to the Lyth Valley in south Cumbria gave me the opportunity, but alas not before Kath had died.

This book is the result of many happy hours spent exploring the Dales in recent years, discussions with scientists, land managers and fellow Dales enthusiasts and, of course, reading the extensive scientific literature on the region. It begins with a chapter introducing the Yorkshire Dales National Park, its climate and its soils, as well as describing briefly how legislation has affected both land use and conservation since the Second World War. It is followed by two chapters describing the landscape and how geological history and human activities have shaped the National Park the visitor sees today. A series of chapters essentially describing the major habitats follows, with diversions to consider the most iconic plant of the Dales, the Lady's Slipper Orchid, and some important animal groups. The emphasis in these latter chapters on birds, mammals and Lepidoptera is on change, and the book concludes with a chapter looking to the future. Although I have concentrated on the National Park, not least because the facts are most easy to assemble for its habitats, I have also strayed to take examples from both further north and south within the Pennine chain when published ecological studies are not available from within the park. I have also strayed occasionally into Nidderdale and the North York Moors for other examples.

I could not have completed this work without the generous help and support of many people and organisations. In particular I am most grateful for the unstinting support of Ian Court of the Yorkshire Dales National Park Authority, Colin Newlands of Natural England, and Peter Welsh of the National

Trust. They have provided me with many leads, introductions and literature, as well as patiently answering my many questions. In addition, Ian and Colin have greatly improved the drafts of several chapters. I am also very grateful to all those who have given me permission to reproduce figures and tables from their publications, especially to the Field Studies Council, which has been so important in promoting and publishing research on the Dales, and to Robin Sutton at the Malham Field Centre for helping me with several enquiries.

Much of the fun in writing this book has come in the form of field excursions, some organised, such as those that formed part of the Flora of the Dales and Swaledale festivals, and some informal. In the latter category I am particularly grateful to Roger and Pauline Meade and to Alistair Headley for sharing with me many ecological delights. Alistair and Roger have very considerable ecological knowledge and experience, which I have endeavoured to mine, and they have also commented on, corrected and markedly improved early drafts of several chapters. Roger has also kindly provided several photographs.

Many people have given me much help in preparing and/or commenting on individual chapters. Simon Bottrell commented on and much improved an early draft of the Geology and Geomorphology chapter. Tom Lord kindly allowed me to reproduce his work on medieval dry-stone walls and his photograph of the barbed point of a reindeer antler, one of the earliest pieces of evidence for human activity in the Dales. He also helped me understand the possible effects of future changes in agri-environment schemes on the Dales. Colin Newlands allowed me access to Natural England's documents on the Ribblesdale and Wharfedale woodlands, and I had most helpful discussion, with Donald Pigott on woodlands in general, and on the status of lime species in the Dales in particular. Tim Laurie kindly provided me with information about the relict woodlands of Swaledale, and gave me access to an unpublished pollen diagram from Ellerton Moor. Ian Court provided valuable information on both Red Squirrel and Dormouse investigations.

The Lady's Slipper Orchid chapter has benefitted from input by Margaret Hartley of the Wharfedale Naturalists Society, including information on the group of naturalists around Arthur Raistrick. Elizabeth Shorrock generously trawled through unpublished documents and letters in her possession for relevant information, and allowed me to quote from a letter to her and her husband Brian about the rediscovery of the orchid. I am also much indebted to John Lovis for providing information about Arthur Sledge, the secret society formed to protect the orchid, and early attempts to obtain seed from the surviving plant. Philip Oswald kindly provided further illumination of the strict secrecy used to protect the orchid in the early post-war period, and how this secrecy was broken. He also made valuable comments to improve the text. Colin Newlands showed me letters which have recently come to light from the son of Willie Jarman, the person credited with rediscovering the orchid in 1930. Thanks are due to Rob Petley-Jones, who guards the voluminous files on the orchid held by Natural England, for allowing me access to them, and particular thanks go to Peter Corkhill, not only for answering so many questions about his considerable involvement in the efforts to conserve the orchid, but also for saving me days of labour by helping me search the files. Donald Pigott also most helpfully provided much background information about early attempts to conserve the orchid, and his great wealth of knowledge on the ecology of the Dales was always made readily available, to my considerable benefit. Andrew Watkinson provided reminiscences of his time as a temporary warden for the orchid when he was a student at the University of York in 1972, as well as making valuable suggestions to improve the chapter. Lastly, my colleagues David Read and Jonathan Leake helped to clarify the current position of the orchid's mycorrhizal fungi. Jonathan also considerably improved my description of soils in Chapter 1.

Colin Newlands allowed me to browse the voluminous documents on the Ingleborough limestone pavements at Colt Park Barn, and also commented on the chapter describing them, as well as providing access to unpublished research on hay meadows. I am also very grateful to Ashley Lyons and her colleagues at Edge Hill University for allowing me to quote some of their unpublished results on the effects of grazing on the biodiversity of calcareous grasslands, and to Kevin Walker of the Botanical Society of Britain and Ireland and Mark Lynes, both of whom kindly answered a number of questions, including on the status and distribution of *Alchemilla minima* and *Dryas octopetala* in these grasslands. David Baines of the Game & Wildlife Conservation Trust answered many questions on moorland management and bird populations, and Roger Meade much improved my description of the blanket mires.

I have had much help with the chapter on Tarns and Wetlands. George Hinton has most kindly allowed me to present his latest research on macrophyte productivity and inorganic carbon uptake in Malham Tarn. Deborah Millward helped me with questions about Semer Water, and Emily Alderton kindly allowed me to quote some of her unpublished data on Otter spraints at Malham Tarn. Allan Pentecost answered various queries about Malham and Fountain's Fell tarns, and made valuable suggestions to improve the chapter. My colleague Philip Warren made a number of very helpful suggestions on the manuscript, as did Roger Meade, all of which greatly improved the end result. Brian Shorrock answered questions on bird populations on Malham Tarn as well as informing me of the discovery of a population of Small Pearl-bordered Fritillaries on Ha Mire. Paul Ashton and Clive Stace helped me understand the current status of *Carex flava* in the Malham fens. Alistair Headley commented on an early version of the manuscript, and also most kindly provided me with access to unpublished information on Swarth Moor. Graham Proudlove made many helpful suggestions and corrections to improve the chapter on Rivers and Caves.

I am greatly indebted to Brian Shorrock for answering my many questions on bird populations and how these have changed over recent decades. Both he and Ian Court provided many suggestions for the improvement of this chapter, as did my colleagues Tim Birkhead and Ben Hatchwell. Ian Court also provided many vital inputs to the Mammals, Moths and Butterflies chapter, and Colin Howes and Charles Fletcher have also been invaluable, providing me with a wealth of information and giving me many suggestions on how to improve the chapter. Paul Millard and Terry Whitaker have also most kindly provided unpublished information on their ongoing studies, Paul of moths in Wharfedale and Terry of both butterflies and moths at various sites in the Dales.

I am very grateful to all those who have kindly allowed me to reproduce their photographs, including Phillip Cribb and Falgunee Sarker.

I have received much encouragement and support from friends, including Sheila and Donald Pigott and Margaret and Martin Wilson. Martin read through much of the text, and made many suggestions for its improvement, but sadly died before he could see the book in print. I am also particularly indebted to Julia Koppitz of HarperCollins for her help and advice at every stage, and to Hugh Brazier and David Price-Goodfellow for their efficiency and for the many suggested improvements to this book during the publication process, all of which have greatly enhanced the end result. But of course, despite all this expert help in the preparation of the book, any errors and omissions are entirely due to me.

When I told Sir John Lawton, the then Chairman of the Yorkshire Wildlife Trust, that I was considering embarking on a New Naturalist on the Dales, his immediate response was that it would take a year out of my life. Over many years I have always found John to be right on most things, but I can report that the book has taken rather longer than one year.

Besides the great help I have received from so many people, I have benefited greatly from the unstinting support of my family. Richard, Robin and Peter have helped at various times, and at very short notice, with queries about photography, word processing and software. Barbara has accompanied me on many field excursions as well as allowing me unfettered time and space to complete the book. She has kept my spirits up when they have flagged, encouraged me at every stage and helped me in many other ways. I could not have finished the task without her.

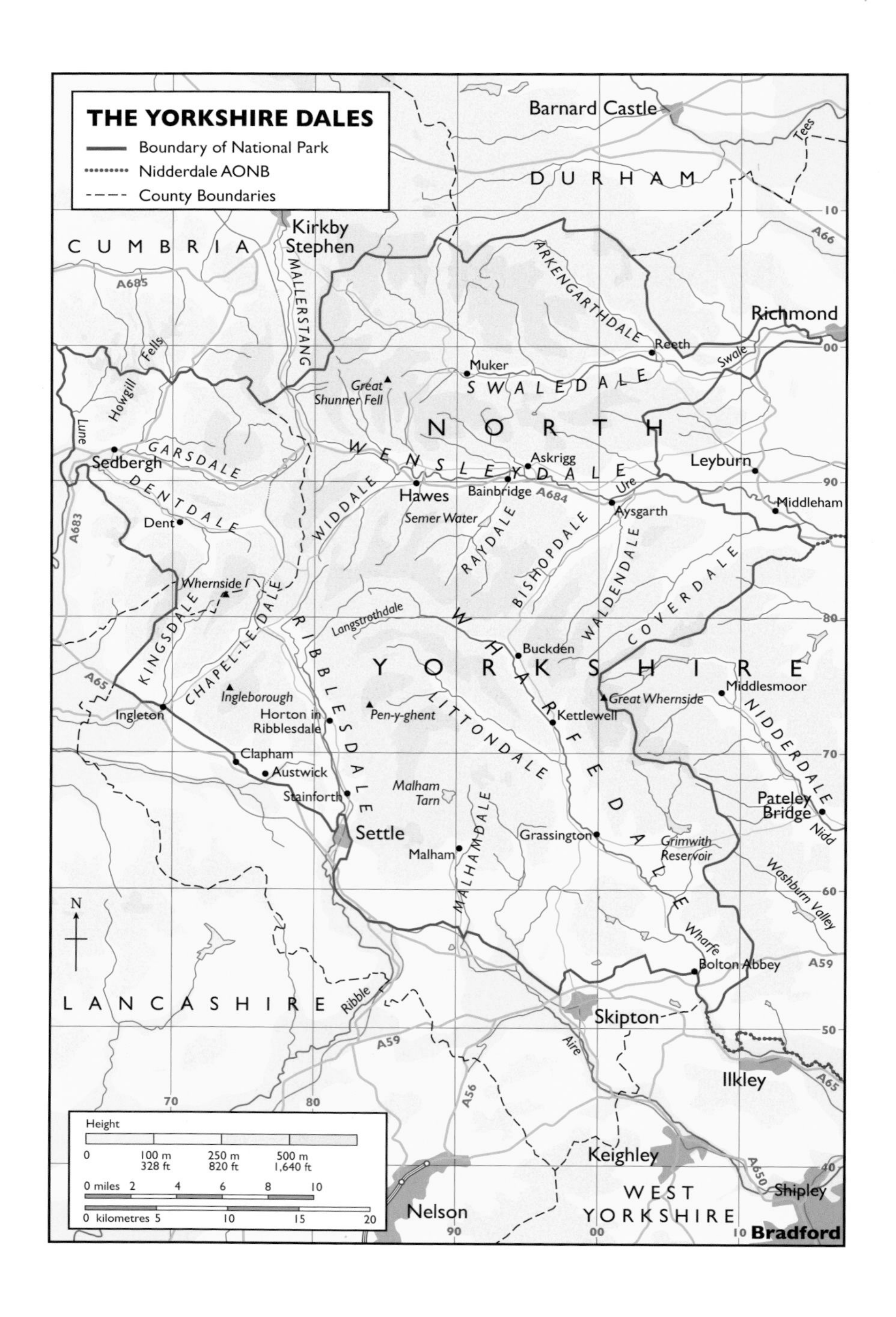
THE YORKSHIRE DALES
Boundary of National Park
Nidderdale AONB
County Boundaries
Barnard Castle
Tees
DURHAM
CUMBRIA
Kirkby Stephen
A66
A685
MALLERSTANG
ARKENGARTHDALE
Richmond
Reeth
Swale
Muker
Great Shunner Fell
SWALEDALE
Howgill Fells
Lune
NORTH
Sedbergh
GARSDALE
WENSLEYDALE
Askrigg
Leyburn
DENTDALE
Hawes
Bainbridge
A684
Ure
Middleham
Aysgarth
A683
Dent
Semer Water
WIDDALE
RAYDALE
BISHOPDALE
WALDENDALE
COVERDALE
Whernside
KINGSDALE
CHAPEL-LE-DALE
Langstrothdale
RIBBLESDALE
WHARFEDALE
Buckden
YORKSHIRE
A65
Ingleborough
Great Whernside
Middlesmoor
Ingleton
Horton in Ribblesdale
Pen-y-ghent
LITTONDALE
Kettlewell
NIDDERDALE
Clapham
Austwick
Malham Tarn
Pateley Bridge
Stainforth
Nidd
Settle
MALHAMDALE
Grassington
Grimwith Reservoir
Malham
Washburn Valley
N
Wharfe
Bolton Abbey
A59
LANCASHIRE
Ribble
Skipton
A59
Aire
A56
Ilkley
A65
Height
0
100 m 328 ft
250 m 820 ft
500 m 1,640 ft
0 miles 2 4 6 8 10
0 kilometres 5 10 15 20
Keighley
A650
Shipley
Nelson
WEST YORKSHIRE
Bradford
10
00
90
80
70
60
50
40
70
80
90
00
10

CHAPTER 1

The National Park

The small market town of Skipton is approximately halfway along the Pennine chain which stretches north from Derbyshire to the Scottish border. Immediately to the north of the town, and for some 110 kilometres (70 miles) towards Stainmore, lie the Yorkshire Dales, one of our best-loved National Parks. On the west the Park is bounded by the market towns of Settle and Sedbergh, and on the east by Richmond and Leyburn. All but Sedbergh, the largest town in the National Park, lie just outside its current boundary. The Dales, as they are popularly known, consist of a series of valleys interspersed with often rounded hills rising to 736 metres (2,415 feet) on Whernside, the highest point.

When it was first designated in 1954, the whole National Park was within the historic county of Yorkshire, forming part of the North and West Ridings. Today, following the reorganisation of local government in 1974, the National Park is mostly in North Yorkshire, with the region around Sedbergh, including Dentdale and Garsdale, being part of Cumbria. In North Yorkshire, the Dales are further divided into two administrative regions: Craven in the south and west, and Richmondshire in the north and east. Both have ancient origins. Craven is mentioned in the Domesday Book, where it refers to a much larger area than today's administrative region, stretching as far west as the Lancashire coast. A castle was established at Richmond in 1071 by Alan the Red of Brittany, and his estates around the castle, reaching as far north as the River Tees, became known as Richmond Shire. The National Park does not cover all of either the ancient or the current administrative areas. Essentially it covers the hills and dales of the upland part of the region (Fig. 1), with the lower parts of the famous river valleys of Aire, Ribble, Swale, Ure and Wharfe falling outside, as does Nidderdale on its eastern boundary, which was designated an Area of Outstanding Natural Beauty (AONB) in 1994. A major reason for the exclusion of the moors of upper Nidderdale from the National Park in 1954 was opposition from Bradford Corporation Water Board, concerned that access might provide a risk to public health (Speakman, 2014). The wealth of ecological information available on the National Park forms the basis of this book, but examples are also taken from Nidderdale and elsewhere in northern England where they help us to understand the factors affecting animal and plant populations in the region.

The landscape we see today has been moulded by successive glaciations during the last 2.5 million years, leaving exposures of predominantly Carboniferous-age rocks (359–299 million years old) at the surface, covered in other places by glacial till and wind-blown deposits known as loess from the end of the Last glaciation. What distinguishes the Dales from the Pennine hills immediately to the south is that many of these exposed scars and benches on the valley sides are formed of Carboniferous limestone rather than of rocks giving rise to acidic soils. Carboniferous limestone is also exposed much further to the

FIG 1. Upper Wharfedale in mid-May, near Buckden, looking south. The village is just visible in the distance on the extreme left of the photograph.

south, in the White Peak of Derbyshire, but this region was not covered by the most recent glaciation, and largely lacks the extensive bare limestone pavements which are such a remarkable landscape feature of the Dales. The pavements, grey scars and many, many miles of limestone walls are attractive landscape features for most visitors today, as are the rivers with their waterfalls which have helped to deepen the valleys following the glacial retreat. But limestone country has a special pull for naturalists over and above the delights of the landscape itself, and the Dales represent the largest exposure of Carboniferous limestone rocks in any region of the Pennines. Their rich diversity of habitats and assemblages of plants and animals have provided a great attraction for naturalists over several centuries.

TOPOGRAPHY AND CLIMATE

Although the National Park is named for the dales themselves, the hills into which they are cut are just as important. The Three Peaks of Ingleborough, Pen-y-ghent and Whernside near the head of Ribblesdale have been a magnet for walkers for generations, particularly those from Bradford, Leeds and the industrial towns around them. None of these hills is very high in comparison to the nearby Lakeland mountains, but their proximity to one another, and their imposing forms in the landscape, provide an irresistible challenge, particularly for those many people drawn to complete the Three Peaks Walk. And these are just three of 20 hills in the National Park over 600 metres which help to make it a most popular centre for walkers. The Pennine Way traverses the National Park south to north and includes the summit of Pen-y-ghent. The Coast-to-Coast walk crosses the northern edge of the National Park over Great Shunner Fell to Richmond. In contrast, the Dales Way, which runs northwest from Ilkley to Sedbergh and beyond, largely keeps to the river valleys.

The major northern dales of Swaledale and Wensleydale lie more or less west to east below the Pennine watershed, whereas the southern dales are orientated approximately north to south. The Ribble eventually flows westwards into the Irish Sea, as do the rivers in the northwest corner of the National Park which join the Rivers Eden and Lune, but all the other rivers and their tributaries flow eventually southeastward into the Humber. The National Park covers essentially the upland areas of these river valleys and their catchments. From the mouth of the Lune it is approximately 40 kilometres down the prevailing southwesterly wind to the summit of Whernside (Fig. 2) with a rise in altitude of over 700 metres. Similarly on the eastern edge of the National Park there is a rapid fall in altitude from the high fells above Swaledale and Wensleydale to the Vale of

Mowbray. This means that the climate shows considerable local variation both across and within the Dales, not least because of the theoretical 0.6 °C fall in air temperature for every 100-metre rise in altitude, the so-called adiabatic lapse rate effect. In the cloudy oceanic climate of northern England the lapse rate may be even higher at 0.65 °C for every 100 metres. Hill tops are windier than sheltered valley bottoms and receive more precipitation as moist air moving across them is cooled, but the orographic enhancement of precipitation in the Dales is not as great as in the nearby Lake District with its higher hills and closer proximity to the coast. As well as the major effects of topography on climate, local features can also have marked effects on microclimates; for example south-facing dale sides receive a greater amount of solar radiation energy and are warmer than north-facing ones, which are cooler and more moist, with often far-reaching effects on the vegetation.

Some of these effects can be seen from records in the Malham region. Early records of precipitation were made at Tarn House from 1870, but these were

FIG 2. Whernside (736 metres), one of the Three Peaks and the highest point in the Yorkshire Dales National Park, viewed from Southerscales limestone pavement.

discontinued in 1928, and it was not until the Field Studies Council established a field centre there in 1948 that weather recording began again. The Malham weather station is at 395 metres, and Gordon Manley (1979) estimated that the mean annual temperature recorded there in the 1950s was 0.3 °C above that expected at this altitude by extrapolation from the nearest lowland stations. He attributed this to local topographical features, including the fact that measurements were made on a south-facing slope, only 100 metres from Malham Tarn (Fig. 3). Some shelter from trees around the house also affects air movement, diminishing the fall in temperature on quiet clear nights and, on fine sunny days, increasing the rise in temperature. He concluded that at the Malham weather station this resulted in fewer air frosts than might be expected. Differences in topography can have a marked effect on the incidence of frost, with for example large saucer-shaped depressions in the landscape making frost hollows in which the incidence of late frosts in their bases is much higher than on their rims. These frosts can have a marked detrimental effect on plants fresh into growth.

FIG 3. The only long-term meteorological station in the National Park is on the south-facing slope above Malham Tarn and immediately below Tarn House.

In 1963 Manley established a thermograph on Fountains Fell at 660 metres (Fig. 4), 1 kilometre south of the summit cairn, and 5 kilometres northwest of the Malham Field Centre. Temperature records were made from May 1963 to December 1968. The mean annual air temperature was 2.1 °C colder on Fountains Fell than at Malham, representing an apparent very rapid fall in temperature with altitude of 0.79 °C per 100 metres (Table 1). There was a greater number of days with air frosts at the higher altitude (130 days per annum at Fountains Fell, compared to 80 at Malham), and both locations had markedly more frosts than Ilkley, 30 kilometres away in lower Wharfedale, where there were 57 days of air frosts per annum. Manley also estimated that snow lay on the ground at Fountains Fell for 80 days per annum on average, approximately double the length of snow lie at Malham.

Temperature has a marked effect on plant growth, and effectively determines the length of the growing season. This is usually taken to be the period in which the air temperature exceeds 5.5 °C, the temperature at which common lowland pasture grasses begin growth. Whereas in mild winters, at sheltered lowlands sites close to the coast, growth can occur almost throughout the year, on Fountains Fell Manley estimated that the growing season was only the 22

FIG 4. Fountains Fell from Lower Winskill Farm, Langcliffe, showing the ridge on which Gordon Manley established a temporary thermograph in 1963.

TABLE 1. Average temperatures for Malham Tarn House and Fountains Fell (the latter approximate) reduced to the period 1941–1970, from Manley (1979).

	Average temperature (°C)											
	Jan	Feb	Mar	Apr	May	Jun	Jul	Aug	Sep	Oct	Nov	Dec
Malham Tarn (395 m)	0.9	1.1	2.9	5.7	8.7	11.7	12.9	12.7	10.9	7.9	4.1	2.1
Fountains Fell (660 m)	−1.0	−1.0	0.5	3.0	6.0	9.5	10.5	10.5	9.2	6.0	2.0	0.0

weeks between 10 May and 15 October. Temperature has a marked effect both on vegetative growth and on the ability of plants to set seed. Prince (1976) grew barley on similar soils at Lancaster (53 metres) and Malham (495 metres). He found that barley grains attained a much higher maximum weight, and a month earlier, at Lancaster than at Malham (Fig. 5). At Malham the minimum grain water content was not achieved until late September, five weeks after similar water contents were achieved at Lancaster. This is a striking demonstration of the unsuitability of the Craven uplands for the growth of cereal crops, although in the past oats were an important crop on many farms. Other cereals were also formerly grown in the region, particularly in the lower and warmer parts of the dales. Millward

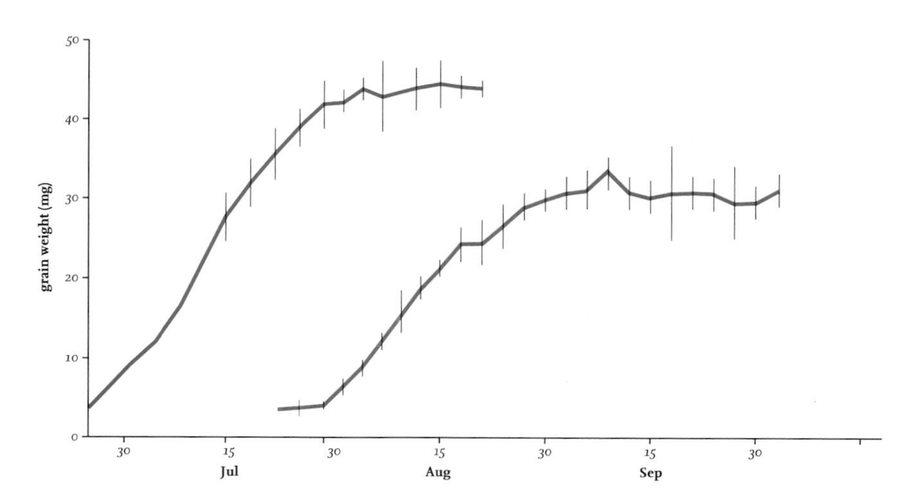

FIG 5. Accumulation of dry matter by barley grains from plants grown at Malham (red) and Lancaster (blue) in 1970. The error bars show 95 per cent confidence limits. From Prince (1976).

(1988) recorded that when the national corn acreage peaked in the 1850s, only 3 per cent of the 18,000 acres (7,300 ha) in lower Wensleydale was arable, and the 81,000 acres (33,000 ha) in the upper dale would have had considerably less. Temperature has a marked effect on tree growth too, and woodland is rarely found above altitudes at which the mean temperature does not exceed 10 °C for a minimum of two summer months. Based on Manley's observations on Fountains Fell, tree growth today should be possible almost everywhere in the National Park, and the largely treeless landscape we see today is the result of the demands of human populations and their grazing animals.

In recent decades there has been increasing concern about climate warming. Burt & Horton (2003) analysed the daily weather record made at Malham in the period 1961–2000. They showed that the annual mean temperature increased by nearly 1 °C over the period, with winters showing the greatest seasonal warming. Although the duration of snow lie was not quantified, this almost certainly declined in response to the winter warming. There were fewer air and ground frosts towards the end of the period, but July and August were the only months to remain entirely frost-free since 1959. The warmest year on record was 1997, with a mean air temperature of 8.2 °C. Rainfall records in the late nineteenth and early twentieth centuries allowed these workers to reconstruct precipitation data from 1860 to 2000. This showed an annual average of 1,502 mm, and a trend for the winter months (December, January and February) to become wetter and the summer months (June, July and August) to become drier (Table 2), but no overall trend in annual precipitation over this period. Up until 2011, the wettest year recorded was 2000, with 2,097 mm, and the driest was 1975, with 1,124 mm.

The trend to wetter winters increases the risk of flooding in the river valleys draining the National Park, particularly because this is the period of the year when evaporation from wet surfaces and plant leaves is at a minimum. The excess of precipitation over potential evaporation determines water movement down through soils and into the aquifers. An estimate of this has been made for

TABLE 2. Total winter and summer rainfall at Malham Tarn, and winter : summer rainfall ratio, by decade. From Burt & Horton (2003).

Decade	*1960s*	*1970s*	*1980s*	*1990s*
Total winter rainfall (mm)	3,786	4,134	4,698	4,743
Total summer rainfall (mm)	3,349	3,097	3,299	3,038
Winter : summer ratio	1.13	1.33	1.42	1.56

Widdybank Fell, at an altitude of 510 metres in the north Pennines. During the period 1968–75 the average annual rainfall was 1,523 mm, very similar to the long-term annual average for Malham. Precipitation exceeded potential evaporation in every month, and in annual total by 1,186 mm. Effectively this means that for every square metre of ground on average at least 1,186 litres percolated through the soil per year (Pigott, 1978). These data suggest that over much of the upland regions of the National Park, even with the slightly higher mean temperatures today, precipitation will continue to greatly exceed evaporation.

The Malham record is the only long climate data set for the National Park, although another recording site has been established at Colt Park on Ingleborough and, most recently, Lee Schofield has established a network of automatic weather stations across the Dales. However, using the long-term Malham record, some of the variation in climate across the Dales can be judged by a comparison with similar records from the lowland stations closest to the eastern edge of the National Park, at Dishforth and Leeming. Data held by the Met Office for all three sites for the period 1981–2010 show that both lowland sites (*c.*50 metres above sea level) have similar mean annual precipitation (*c.*642 mm) – less than half that at Malham (1,550 mm). These lowland sites are in the rain shadow to the east of the Pennines, and are warmer than the Craven uplands (annual mean maximum temperatures close to 13.3 °C as against 10.5 °C for Malham) with fewer frost days (*c.*54 as against 73 at Malham). The climatic variation along the west–east lying dales can also be judged from some precipitation measurements made in Wensleydale (Millward, 1988). She records mean precipitation figures ranging from 1,942 mm at the top of Widdale to 764 mm at Leyburn. Weather records were also made by the station-masters at Ribblehead for a period from 1938. The wettest year from these records up until the mid-1950s was 1954, with a total of 2,781 mm (Hartley & Ingilby, 1956).

SOILS

Climate exerts a considerable effect on soils, not least through temperature particularly affecting biological activity, and through the excess of precipitation over evaporation. Soils within the National Park vary considerably in depth, from scarcely more than a centimetre deep under plants beginning to colonise bare Carboniferous limestone rocks to peat overlying shales and gritstone which may be several metres deep. They also vary considerably in their chemical characteristics, with shallow limestone soils having a pH close to neutrality (pH 7) as the result of the slow dissolution of the calcium carbonate rock, to bog peat a thousand times more acid with a pH approaching 4. This difference in chemical characteristics also influences the organic matter content and the organisms involved in incorporating plant litter into the soils. Soils close to neutrality and with a high base status (readily available calcium, magnesium, potassium and sodium ions) contain mull humus. This is an intimate mixture of mineral particles and organic matter produced as the result of the activities of the soil fauna, which in the shallowest limestone soils is mainly composed of mites (Acarina) and springtails (Collembola). Mites and springtails can be staggeringly abundant. In soils at Malham, Wood (1967) estimated densities of these organisms between 167,000 and 282,000 per square metre. In deeper soils, still with a high base status, other groups of organisms become important, including large earthworms. In contrast, in freely drained acidic soils, where the bases are largely replaced by hydrogen and aluminium, plant matter in various stages of decomposition is present, often above the mineral soil, and the resulting humus is not intimately mixed with that soil. This is mor humus, in which faunal activity is low and large earthworms are absent. Where strongly acidic soils become waterlogged, a further restriction on the decomposition of organic matter occurs. The soil becomes anaerobic, restricting the activity of many fungi and bacteria, and organic matter accumulates as peat.

The great excess of precipitation over evaporation, particularly in the hills, means that all the soils are subject to a strong leaching tendency, except on slopes where leaching losses may be replaced by down-slope movement of elements from above. If the leaching losses of bases are greater than their replacement from decomposition, weathering processes and inputs from up slope, then the soils become acidic. The thin soils (< 10 cm deep) over limestone are perhaps least susceptible to leaching, partly because they are subject to periodic spring and summer droughts which help to reverse the downward movement of water through the soil capillaries. These are rendzinas, in which the black mull humus is mixed with limestone fragments throughout.

Brown earths are deeper soils developed on superficial mineral deposits over the limestone. Where the parent material is rich in calcium carbonate, so-called mesotrophic brown earth soils occur. These contain mull humus and are only mildly acidic (pH c.6). Many of the lowland pastures are on mesotrophic brown earth soils, where the soil nutrient losses due to livestock harvest and leaching are often counterbalanced by liming. Earthworms, potworms (Enchytraeidae) and nematodes are active in completely mixing the organic and mineral matter in these soils, and Moles (Talpa europaea) are often conspicuously present. Where the soils are less rich in calcium carbonate, the bases can readily be lost by leaching, and oligotrophic brown earths develop. These contain mor humus and are much more acidic than mesotrophic brown earths (pH < 5). Faunal activity is low in these soils and there is typically no earthworm activity in the upper layers, leading to strong surface accumulation of humus.

Podzols are more extreme acidic and leached soils. These are often developed on freely drained soils on coarse sandy material such as over Millstone Grit. They also contain mor humus, and their acidity is linked to the depletion of base cations by intense leaching. The surface layer of the mineral soil is strongly acidic ($pH < 4$) and appears grey with bleached sand grains as a result of the mobilisation and leaching of iron. Iron and some humus accumulate deeper in the soil, where an impervious iron pan or diffuse ochre deposits can develop. When an iron pan is strongly developed this impedes drainage so that soils can become permanently waterlogged and peat develops. Seasonal waterlogging can affect other soils, particularly those developed on shales or in shallow depressions or close to water courses. This gives rise to anaerobic conditions in which respiration by plant roots and soil microorganisms leads to the reduction of iron from the orange-brown ferric to the blue-grey ferrous state, and oxygen release from air-conducting roots leads to localised oxidation. These soils are known as gleys, and often contain blue-grey and orange mottling reflecting their changing reduction and oxidation status.

In some parts of the National Park, mineral veins rich in heavy metals, notably in lead, have been deposited within joints and fractures in the sedimentary rocks.

FIG 6. Spoil largely devoid of vegetation at Ox Close Special Area of Conservation near Carperby, Wensleydale, a relic of the once major lead-mining industry.

Where these occur at the surface they have mostly been exploited by a mining industry dating back to at least Roman times, so little in the way of natural colonisation and soil development can now be observed. However, there are large areas of metal-rich spoil resulting from both surface ore extraction and mining activities, and these are almost always sparsely colonised (Fig. 6). The thin skeletal soils which have developed in some places on these spoils are rich in lead and other heavy metals and are toxic to many organisms, but have a characteristic, very impoverished flora adapted to this hostile environment.

THE NATIONAL PARK, AGRICULTURE AND ENVIRONMENT

The National Parks movement had its origins in the late nineteenth century as a means of protecting outstanding landscapes for public enjoyment, but it was only in the period immediately following the Second World War that they became a reality in England and Wales following an Act of Parliament in 1949. The National Parks and Access to the Countryside Act established the National Parks Commission, the body for the designation of National Parks, and for Areas of Outstanding Natural Beauty. The Peak District National Park, established in 1950, was the very first National Park, but it was quickly followed by ten others including, in 1954, the Yorkshire Dales National Park. The Act also established the Nature Conservancy, which was given powers to set up National Nature Reserves (NNRs) to protect the most important habitats, and also to establish Sites of Special Scientific Interest (SSSIs), and to enter into management agreements with their owners or occupiers. SSSIs are areas with significant physical environmental features, such as topographical or geological ones, or with important plant and animal communities.

The post-war period was also notable for another Act of Parliament destined to have a major effect on the early National Parks. In line with successive governments' policy up until the 1980s, the emphasis was on increased agricultural production (Condliffe, 2009). Most of these National Parks were situated in the uplands and therefore much affected by the 1946 Hill Farming Act. This was designed to stimulate livestock production and profitable farming in the uplands, providing subsidies for hill cattle and sheep, and 50 per cent grant aid to improve 'Mountain, hill and heath land which is suitable for the use for the maintenance of sheep of a hardy kind'. Improvements included lime and fertiliser addition as well as drainage. The latter included digging open channels, known as grips, in peatland to improve heather growth for both sheep and Red Grouse (*Lagopus lagopus scoticus*). It was perhaps not immediately realised that the 1946 Hill Farming Act was to a degree detrimental to some of the provisions of the 1949 Act. However, it was clear by the 1970s that many upland SSSIs were being adversely affected by agricultural practices such as overgrazing and drainage, and further legislation was required for their protection.

The 1981 Wildlife and Countryside Act required owners or occupiers of SSSIs to notify the Nature Conservancy Council in advance of any proposed action aimed at increasing agricultural productivity such as drainage or inorganic fertiliser addition which might damage the site. Under this Act, National Park Authorities were also charged with mapping all areas of mountain, moor and heath, which then became ineligible for agricultural improvement grants. The 1980s marked a turning point in upland conservation. For although farmers still received headage-based subsidies from the European Commission's Common Agricultural Policy (CAP) Less Favoured Areas scheme, which encouraged high sheep and cattle numbers, the 1986 Agriculture Act provided in selected areas for the introduction of voluntary Environmentally Sensitive Area (ESA) agri-environment schemes. The Pennine Dales ESA, including most of the Yorkshire Dales National Park, was designated in 1985 and extended in 1987.

The ESA schemes rewarded farmers willing to farm less intensively. These could be awarded under three main headings: first, to conserve and enhance the natural beauty of an area; second, to conserve the flora and fauna, and geological and physiographic features; third, to protect buildings of archaeological, architectural or historic interest where particular agricultural practice was likely to aid their conservation. Although these schemes were broadly successful in terms of environmental benefits, they were not always popular with the farming community, and sheep numbers in the Dales continued to rise into the 1990s. They also had the disadvantage that the schemes were not available outside ESAs. In 1991, as a development of the schemes, the Countryside Commission, the successor body to the National Parks Commission, introduced the Countryside Stewardship Scheme (CSS), which was available to all landowners and managers, not just farmers, but with no automatic right of entry. Entry became competitive and based on environmental benefits.

Whilst ESA and CSS schemes offered considerable potential benefits, and were available at several tiers of entry, giving more money for more restrictions on farming practice, they were not always conducive to maximising environmental improvements and, with this in mind, in 1993 English Nature (the successor body to the Nature Conservancy Council) introduced the Wildlife Enhancement Scheme (WES) for SSSIs. This scheme allowed for specialist site-specific optimal management approaches. The several schemes (ESA, CSS and WES) were subsequently progressively phased out in favour of Environmental Stewardship

Schemes. These are available at Entry Level Stewardship and Higher Level Stewardship. Currently 231,439 hectares of the Yorkshire Dales are targeted for Higher Level Stewardship. In the hills, this scheme includes the Uplands Entry Level Scheme, first introduced in 2010 when it replaced the Hill Farm Allowance, which rewards upland farmers with higher payments to provide a greater commitment to environmental management in England's Severely Disadvantaged Areas, which includes most of the Yorkshire Dales. A new three-tier environmental land management system will be introduced from 2016 to replace the Environmental Stewardship Schemes, providing funding for farmers and land managers to deliver benefits for wildlife, to improve water quality and to create woodlands.

The year 2001 was a watershed in terms upland agriculture in the United Kingdom. It was the outbreak of foot and mouth disease in that year which led to the slaughter of cattle and sheep in many areas of northern England, including in parts of the Dales, and which resulted in a reassessment of the importance of agriculture in the rural economy. Footpaths were closed, and at first visitors were strongly discouraged for fear of the further spread of the disease; this soon began to have an effect on the tourist industry and helped to emphasise that, in several of our National Parks, tourism was much the more important part of the rural economy. It also had the short-term effect of eliminating entirely grazing by domestic livestock from large areas of the uplands, the most obvious initial response of which was increased flowering of many species. In the longer term some farmers chose to re-evaluate their business options, so that, for example, sheep numbers, which had already peaked during the 1990s, began to decline. Another consequence of the foot and mouth outbreak, and the perceived mishandling of it by the Ministry of Agriculture, Fisheries and Food, came in June 2001 when that department was merged with part of the Department of Environment, Transport and the Regions, and a small part of the Home Office, to create the Department of Environment, Food and Rural Affairs (Defra); this for the first time brought environmental and agricultural interests into the same ministry. A later change saw the merger of English Nature with the Countryside Agency (the successor body of the Countryside Commission) to establish Natural England. Natural England is the government's advisor on the natural environment, managing National Nature Reserves and notifying SSSIs, but also responsible for designating National Parks and Areas of Outstanding Natural Beauty as well as for managing England's green farming schemes. Another important change came with the 1995 Environment Act, which created the Environment Agency in part as the successor body to the National Rivers Authority and Her Majesty's Inspectorate of Pollution, with responsibilities including air and water quality, and flood protection.

An international landmark in environmental conservation was provided by the 1992 Earth Summit in Rio de Janeiro at which governments promised to 'develop national strategies, plans or programmes for the conservation and sustainable use of biological diversity ...' This led to the European Community Habitats Directive of the same year, which required member states to establish a network of important high-quality conservation sites, Special Areas of Conservation (SACs), to protect species and habitats of European importance. The Ingleborough Complex, the Craven Limestone Complex, which includes Malham Tarn, and Ox Close near Carperby are three SACs subsequently designated which lie wholly within the National Park, with parts of the North Pennine Meadows, North Pennine Moors and the River Eden SACs also included. The Earth Summit was followed in 1994 by the United Kingdom government's publication of the *UK Biodiversity Action Plan* (UK BAP), which encouraged the development of local biodiversity action plans. *Nature in the Dales: a Biodiversity Action Plan for the Yorkshire Dales National Park* was produced in 2000 by the National Park Authority in consultation with the Dales Biodiversity Forum. The key aims of the costed programme were:

To conserve and, where practicable, enhance:

(a) the overall populations and natural ranges of native species and the quality and range of habitats in the Yorkshire Dales.
(b) the biodiversity value of nationally and internationally important and threatened species and habitats.
(c) the biodiversity value of species and habitats that are characteristic of the Yorkshire Dales National Park.
(d) the biodiversity of natural and semi-natural habitats where this has been diminished over recent decades.

Continuing progress with these aims was provided in 2011 by the publication by the Yorkshire Dales Biodiversity Forum of *Nature in the Dales: 2020 Vision*. The primary aims of this second Biodiversity Action Plan were: 'To get 95 per cent of the area of priority habitats in the Yorkshire Dales National Park into "good" condition by 2020' and 'To get 95 per cent of the populations of priority species in the Yorkshire Dales National Park into a stable or increasing condition by 2020'. The Yorkshire Dales Biodiversity Forum brings together the interests and expertise of landowners and managers, the statutory bodies and naturalists helping to provide a primary and continuing focus on conservation in the living landscape which is the National Park.

LANDSCAPE AND NATURAL HISTORY

What makes the Dales so special? For many visitors it is the landscape itself and the villages within it. Other regions of Britain have a pastoral landscape with river valleys containing farms and villages where lowland fields bounded by dry-stone walls are common, and rough grassland and moorland cover the hills above. Other National Parks, most notably the Peak District, occupy at least in part a land surface formed over limestone bedrock. But the Dales are unique in having the largest exposure of Carboniferous limestone in the country and, as a result of successive glacial periods, forming the finest so-called glacio-karst landscape in Britain. The stepped dale sides (Fig. 7) with their limestone cliffs, screes and pavements, plucked and cleared by the ice of the Devensian or Last glaciation, are striking landscape features, as are the distinctive grit-capped summits of Ingleborough and Pen-y-ghent. This unrivalled landscape is matched

FIG 7. An example of the stepped landscape of the Dales: cliffs, screes and pavements on the side of the glaciated trough of Chapel-le-Dale.

FIG 8. The view of Ingleborough from the northwest. The cliffs below the summit are famed for their assemblage of arctic–alpine species.

below ground by a myriad of cave systems – including one, the Three Counties cave system, which is amongst the longest yet explored in the world. Some of these caves, such as White Scar Cave in Chapel-le-Dale, are tourist attractions, and others, such as the Victoria Cave near Settle, have provided evidence of a long history of human populations in the area from at least 12,500 BCE. And the caves and the landscape above provide geomorphologists with a 'laboratory' for the study of landforms and the processes that have formed them.

But what is so special about the Dales for the naturalist? For many it is the large exposure of Carboniferous limestone and the range of different habitats that it gives rise to. Limestone pavements can be found elsewhere in Britain, but nowhere so extensively or at such high altitudes as, for example, on Ingleborough. These pavements with their unique flora are amongst the most prized by naturalists. The limestone cliffs exposed below the summits of Ingleborough and Pen-y-ghent are famed for the presence of arctic–alpine species at or near their southern limit in England (Fig. 8). The northern calcareous grassland community which is found extensively within the National Park is very restricted in its distribution elsewhere in England, and the Dales are also famed as the last refuge in Britain of the Lady's Slipper Orchid (*Cypripedium calceolus*). The close juxtaposition of contrasting communities adds to the natural history interest. For example, where islands of peat or grassland on a shallow layer of glacial drift lie close to exposed limestone, the naturalist can pass within a stride or two from acidic mire, grassland or heath to calcareous grassland or pavement, with their very different floras and soil faunas.

Although vertical drainage abounds in limestone districts, the National Park still contains two large freshwater bodies, Malham Tarn and Semer Water, the last remnants of the many lakes which filled the bottom of the dales as the ice melted following the Devensian glaciation. The former is the largest marl lake in England, and it has been internationally famous since 1971 as a Ramsar site for its wetland communities and surrounding mires, but it has attracted naturalists for at least 200 years. These two lakes and many of the becks and rivers draining the National Park provide an English stronghold for the threatened native White-clawed Crayfish (*Austropotamobius pallipes*). Interest in the biodiversity of the rivers also extends into the caves below ground through which many streams flow, and which contain a distinctive fauna.

The extensive blanket mires on the higher hills are noted as breeding grounds for Golden Plover (*Pluvialis apricaria*) and Dunlin (*Calidris alpina*), while Wigeon (*Anas penelope*) nest beside a few small upland tarns. Ring Ouzels (*Turdus torquatus*), though declining, are still an important summer visitor to the mosaic of upland grasslands and heaths. The grasslands, heaths and mires also support important populations of butterflies and moths, including the Northern Brown Argus (*Aricia artaxerxes*) and Small Pearl-bordered Fritillary (*Boloria selene*) butterflies and the Least Minor moth (*Photedes captiuncula*). Only about 4 per cent of the National Park is covered in woodland, and only a small proportion of this is little-disturbed ancient or semi-natural woodland. However, this includes some of the most important habitats such as Strid Wood, the fragment of Sessile Oak (*Quercus petraea*) woodland at Bolton Abbey in Wharfedale (Fig. 9), and the sub-alpine Ash (*Fraxinus excelsior*) woodlands of Colt Park and Ling Gill in upper Ribblesdale. In the northwest of the National Park more recent plantation woodlands provide a stronghold for the Red Squirrel (*Sciurus vulgaris*), and the ancient Freeholders' Wood in Wensleydale is the site of an experiment to reintroduce the Hazel Dormouse (*Muscardinus avellanarius*). Experiments have also underpinned the attempts to increase the area of flower-rich hay meadows. The Dales contain nearly half the upland hay meadows in England, but these meadows currently represent less than 1 per cent of grassland in the National

FIG 9. A rare example in the Dales of remnant Sessile Oak woodland, above the Strid, Bolton Abbey, Wharfedale.

FIG 10. An example of species-rich hay meadow at Lower Winskill Farm, Langcliffe, one of the most important habitats but covering less than 1 per cent of grassland in the National Park.

Park. Those few remaining ones are of outstanding national natural history interest, and provide a major attraction for both naturalists and other visitors (Fig. 10).

The diversity of habitats and their rich biodiversity are perhaps unrivalled in any other National Park in Britain. But to fully appreciate the present-day plant and animal communities, their status and the constraints upon them, it is important to have an appreciation of the geology and landscape history of the National Park, including the role that human populations have played in modifying and shaping their environment. The next two chapters therefore discuss these topics, after which the book follows a habitat-based approach with diversions to consider one individual plant, the Lady's Slipper Orchid, and some animal groups. A theme running through the book is change, and this extends to the future both in terms of possible climate scenarios and in the proposed extensions to the National Park, both of which are discussed in the final chapter.

CHAPTER 2

The Making of the Landscape – Geology and Geomorphology

GEOLOGY

From many vantage points a visitor to the Yorkshire Dales sees a landscape in which the exposed rocks were formed in the Carboniferous period, 359 to 299 million years ago. The limestones, grits, sandstones and shales exposed at the surface over most of the National Park nearly all date from this period (see e.g. Waltham, 2007), and they have in common the fact that they are all sedimentary rocks formed in a shallow sea when what subsequently became the British Isles was situated near the equator. But this is only part of the story. To the northwest, that part of the Howgill Fells rising above Sedbergh, and within the National Park, is formed of Silurian slates and sandstones; and elsewhere, perhaps most notably around the Ingleborough massif, there are locally small exposures of older rocks of the Ordovician and Silurian ages. Therefore to fully understand the present landscape it is necessary to delve a little further back into the geological history than the Carboniferous.

Most of what are known by geologists as basement rocks in the Dales belong to the Ordovician and Silurian periods, 485 to 419 million years ago (Fig. 11), but Soper and Dunning (2005) provided evidence suggesting an older, Precambrian origin in the Ingleton Group of rocks. All these basement rocks are sedimentary, formed in a deep ocean known as the Iapetus Ocean, and built up to a considerable depth of several kilometres. Over time this great weight of sediments was compressed into rock in the form of shales, sandstones and grits, depending on the predominant particle sizes in the original sediments

Quaternary	
Neogene	25 million years BP
Palaeogene	63 million years BP
Cretaceous	136 million years BP
Jurassic	190 million years BP
Triassic	225 million years BP
Permian	280 million years BP
Carboniferous	345 million years BP
Devonian	410 million years BP
Silurian	440 million years BP
Ordovician	530 million years BP
Cambrian	570 million years BP
Pre-Cambrian	

Rocks and superfical deposits from geological time periods represented in the Dales

FIG 11. Geological time, with shading representing periods or parts of periods showing rocks and superficial Quaternary deposits exposed in the Yorkshire Dales. Adapted from Wilson (1992).

as the result of diagenesis, the process by which sediments are lithified into sedimentary rocks. These basement rocks were important because they provided the surface on which the younger sedimentary rocks of the Carboniferous period were laid down, and to an extent dictated how this occurred. Today, the whole of the Dales region sits on a section of these basement rocks which has become known as the Askrigg Block.

The Devonian period (419 to 359 million years ago) which followed the Silurian was a period in which tectonic plate movements progressively closed the Iapetus Ocean and produced a major mountain-building phase known as the Caledonian orogeny. It involved immense pressure and complex folding in the rocks caused by earth movements, and resulted in massive mountain-building activity. This folding of the basement rocks can be seen today in the vertical beds of Ordovician and Silurian rocks exposed near Ingleton and Horton-in-Ribblesdale. Another result of this immense pressure deep down around 450 million years ago was to cause some rocks to melt, producing a granite mass known as the Wensleydale Granite, and this would rise from the earth's crust both underlying and uplifting the Askrigg Block. The upper surface of this granite intrusion is inclined slightly to the north-northeast, which is also reflected in the overlying sedimentary rocks.

As the Devonian period progressed, in less than 50 million years the mountains became heavily eroded to produce an arid lowland, and only near Sedbergh are there exposed any rocks (conglomerates) of this age in the National Park (see e.g. Wilson, 1992). At the beginning of the Carboniferous period, the old eroded Devonian land surface was covered by a warm sea, and in places older rocks were exposed. This resulted in Carboniferous sediments beginning to accumulate on Silurian or Ordovician rocks. Geologists call this an unconformity. An unconformity arises where rocks of one age rest directly on very much older ones, often with markedly different orientation of the beds. An excellent example of such an unconformity can be observed at Thornton Force, on the Kingsdale Beck above Ingleton (Fig. 12). Here the lip of the waterfall is provided by the near-horizontal strata of the Great Scar Limestone. At the base of the limestone is a metre thickness of conglomerate formed from cobbles washed by waves on an early Carboniferous tropical beach. This sits directly on the much older (by *c.*200 million years), darker and vertically bedded Lower Ordovician slates into which the stream has cut a small basin. An important feature of these basement rocks is that they are impermeable, and they therefore mark the downward limit of groundwater movement through the limestone above.

FIG 12. Thornton Force, a waterfall on the Kingsdale Beck where water cascades over the Carboniferous limestone, which lies directly on the basement rocks formed of Ordovician slates.

The Great Scar Limestone is the oldest Carboniferous limestone, and it is particularly prominent in the southern part of the Dales where it reaches 200 metres in thickness and forms some of the major and much-loved landscape features such as Malham Cove, Gordale Scar (Fig. 13), Kilnsey Crag and the unrivalled limestone pavements on the Ingleborough benches. It was deposited across the whole of the Askrigg Block, where to the north it is *c*.280 metres thick, but the shallow north-northeast dip of the latter across the Dales results today in only very limited exposures of this rock on the floor of Wensleydale, and no exposure at all in Swaledale, where it is buried beneath younger rocks of the Yoredale series (Fig. 14). This limestone deposition was the result of the Askrigg Block sinking slowly into a shallow tropical sea in which corals, crinoids, bivalves and many other small organisms abounded. The remnants of these organisms, rich in calcium carbonate, were broken down to produce a sediment which over time was re-crystallised to form a strong limestone.

The considerable depth of the Great Scar Limestone has resulted from the slow subsidence of the Askrigg Block over a long period of time, allowing sediment accumulation to continue in the shallow tropical sea. A certain amount of irregularity in the subsidence process and changes in sea level may

FIG 13. Gordale Scar, cliffs of Great Scar Limestone rising *c*.150 metres above the valley floor supporting woodland fragments, notably of Yew (*Taxus baccata*) on ledges inaccessible to sheep.

have interrupted the steady sedimentation, and narrow bands of shale found today in the limestone may possibly result from volcanic ash deposition in this period.

Geologists recognise several subdivisions within the Great Scar Limestone (see e.g. Waters & Lowe, 2013 for fuller detail). The basal layer observable is a conglomerate known as the Chapel House Limestone, which sits directly on the basement rocks. On this is deposited the grey Kilnsey Limestone, followed successively by the paler Cove Limestone and the Gordale Limestone of the Malham Formation, all named after the prominent landscape features which they help to form.

At the time that the Great Scar Limestone was being formed, the Askrigg Block was bounded to the north by the Stainmore Trough, and to the south by the deep Craven Basin. At this southern interface, barrier reef formation occurred similar to those observable in tropical regions today. Today this has resulted in a series of reef knolls forming steep isolated limestone hills of Cracoe Limestone between Settle and Burnsall in lower Wharfedale. Contemporaneous sedimentation in the Craven Basin itself has also produced limestone beds, and these form Haw Bank and other hills near Skipton.

FIG 14. The Valley of the Wild River, the Swale below Keld cutting through strata belonging to the Wensleydale or Yoredale series.

Later in the Carboniferous a cyclical series of changes became established in the seas which formed the Great Scar Limestone. This reflected repeated changes in sea level and in the deposition of sediments from a huge river delta which drained a major landmass to the north, and extended southward from what is now Scotland to encompass the shallow tropical sea. The clear tropical sea resulted in a limestone formation which is rich in brachiopod, coral and crinoid fossils, but as the water became progressively shallower, mud and sand carried by the major river system were deposited in the delta. These deposits have subsequently become lithified into shales and sandstones. The shales are often also rich in bivalve, brachiopod and bryozoa fossils. Another cycle was initiated by renewed subsidence, again producing oceanic conditions suitable for the growth of corals, crinoids and other benthic organisms and resulting eventually in limestone formation. These cycles are known as cyclothems, and 11 of them occur in rocks of this period in the Dales – rocks that are referred to as the Yoredale or Wensleydale series. In some cyclothems the deltaic deposits have produced conditions suitable for the growth of swamp forests, resulting in narrow coal seams. The limestone bands range from 1 to 60 metres in thickness and were given names by geologists and lead miners in the nineteenth century. The oldest of these, directly above the Great Scar Limestone, is the Hawes Limestone, and the youngest is the Main Limestone, which forms prominent scars high on Ingleborough, Pen-y-ghent and Whernside. Overall the limestones amount to approximately a quarter of these Yoredale series rocks, and provide the most erosion-resistant beds.

The rocks of the Yoredale series have played an important part in determining the Dales landscape, not least because they underlie nearly half of the National Park. They form the bulk of Ingleborough, Pen-y-ghent and Whernside above the Great Scar Limestone benches, excluding the summit caps, and almost the entire surface slopes of Swaledale and Wensleydale. Their differential resistance to erosion, from the least resistant shales to the most resistant limestones, has resulted in the stepped landscape of these and other dale sides. The erosion-resistant limestones form the scars, and the benches below them result from the erosion of the shales, which has undercut the more resistant rocks above. The differential erosion resistance of the rocks is responsible for some of the most spectacular waterfalls. The Aysgarth Falls in Wensleydale result from the River Ure flowing over outcrops of the Hawes and Gayle limestones which form the lips of the falls. Further up Wensleydale the Hardraw Beck falls 28 metres from a lip of the Hardrow Limestone into a plunge pool formed in the underlying shale, exposing a complete cyclothem (Fig. 15). The Hardrow Limestone forms a 7-metre cap at the top of the waterfall. Immediately below this is 4 metres of sandstone and 4 metres of finer sandstones, siltstones

FIG 15. Hardraw Force, where the beck falls 28 metres over a single cyclothem of Yoredale rocks from a lip of resistant limestone into a plunge pool formed in shale.

and mudstones. The plunge pool is formed in the top 13 metres of the underlying laminated shales. Hardraw Force has been subject to waterfall retreat as the shales have undercut the more erosion-resistant rocks above, causing their collapse. It is estimated that the 250-metre-long rocky gorge and valley below the waterfall are the result of erosion and waterfall retreat since the end of the Last or Devensian glaciation. Cotter Force is another upper Wensleydale waterfall in which this cyclothem is exposed.

The Yoredale sandstones are not particularly prominent in landscape terms. They vary considerably in thickness, from thin beds with a metre or less exposed (for example, in several Wensleydale waterfalls), to the more massive beds forming much of the pedestal of Ingleborough and Whernside. In Wensleydale, particularly around Hawes, these sandstones have been mined as a source of flagstones for both paving and roof-slating.

Chert beds also occur in the Yoredale rocks, interspersed by mudstones, and these beds may be as much as 40 metres thick. Chert is formed when silica replaces carbonate in limestone beds, but exactly what provided the source of silica here remains uncertain. Chert beds occur above the Main Limestone: the lower bed is known as the Main Chert and the upper is the Richmond Chert. The chert is exposed in Swaledale and Wensleydale, and forms the cliff top of Fremington Edge above Arkengarthdale (Fig. 16).

FIG 16. Fremington Edge, with its old lead and chert workings on the skyline above Reeth.

FIG 17. A major tourist attraction, the River Wharfe cutting through a strong bed of Millstone Grit at the Strid, Bolton Abbey.

Later in the Carboniferous period, *c.*325 million years ago, the river delta continued to expand and large amounts of sand and mud were deposited on top of the Yoredale sediments. This has resulted in the hard, coarse sandstones and shales which form the Millstone Grit series. Locally swamp conditions were created which resulted in the production of coal seams. The high moors of the northern and eastern Dales are underlain by these grits, which have largely been eroded from the south and west of the Dales as the result of the subsequent uplift of the Askrigg Block. The Grassington Grit is a bed 50 metres thick found towards the base of the Millstone Grit series on which the extensive moorlands between Nidderdale and Wharfedale have developed. It is perhaps most easily observed in the Strid, where the River Wharfe cuts into a strong bed of grit (Fig. 17). The Grassington Grit is also important, as it forms the protective cap over the Yoredale series rocks on the summits of Ingleborough, Pen-y-ghent, Whernside and several other hills. Later in the Millstone Grit series the Brimham Grits were deposited. Near Pateley Bridge in Nidderdale these form the isolated tors which are the Brimham Rocks. Erosion of the joints in the rocks is their probable cause, although exactly how this erosion has occurred, and why these prominent landscape features have been produced here and nowhere else in the surrounding grit moorlands, remains something of a mystery.

The Millstone Grit series was followed by swamp conditions, which produced the Coal Measures. These rocks have been lost by erosion in the Dales, although coals formed in the Craven Basin have been exploited near Ingleton.

The Grassington Grit caps on Ingleborough and Whernside are about 700 metres above sea level. To the south and west of Ingleton, buried deep in the ground, lie the younger rocks of the Coal Measures: these are found approximately 400 metres below sea level, with the Grit below that. This large vertical displacement of contemporaneous rocks is the result of extensive faulting along the southern boundary of the Askrigg Block. This fault zone runs approximately northwest to southeast and contains several broadly parallel faults including the North, Middle and South Craven faults (Fig. 18). On its western edge another major fault, the Dent Fault, runs approximately north–south, separating the Askrigg Block from the Ordovician and Silurian rocks of the Howgill Fells. The northern and eastern edges of the Block are less well defined, although faults, notably the Stockdale Fault, also occur in the northern part of the National Park. The faulting which caused the huge displacement between the rocks on the Askrigg Block and those in the Craven Basin was particularly active in the Carboniferous, notably at the beginning and end of the period, but probably had its origins much earlier at the time of plate collisions causing stresses in the basement rocks. However, it is thought that the North and South Craven faults continued to be active into at least the Triassic period, 252 to 201 million years ago. The displacement, particularly in the Carboniferous, must have been associated with much strong and sustained earthquake activity.

The faults mark the boundary between the limestone country of the Craven Uplands and the shales of the Craven Lowlands. The North Craven Fault runs from west of Ingleton to beyond Pateley Bridge and is the longest of the three major faults. The South Craven Fault lies close to the North Craven fault south of Ingleton but diverges from it to the southeast below the Craven Lowlands. The Middle Craven Fault extends from the South Craven Fault at Settle into Wharfedale. Perhaps the most remarkable landscape feature demonstrating the faults is Giggleswick Scar, where the now wooded limestone scarp of the South Craven Fault overlooks the farmland on the Craven Lowlands (Fig. 19). But the faults have had major effects on the landscape elsewhere. For example, Malham Cove probably had its origins as a fault scarp on the Middle Craven Fault, although today it has retreated 600 metres to the north. Lines of weakness in the Gordale Limestone linking the North Craven and Middle Craven faults have been exploited in the development of the Watlowes dry valley above Malham Cove and the Gordale gorge. Although it is rarely easy to observe fault exposures, because of subsequent erosion, an excellent small exposure of the North Craven Fault can be seen in Swilla Glen on

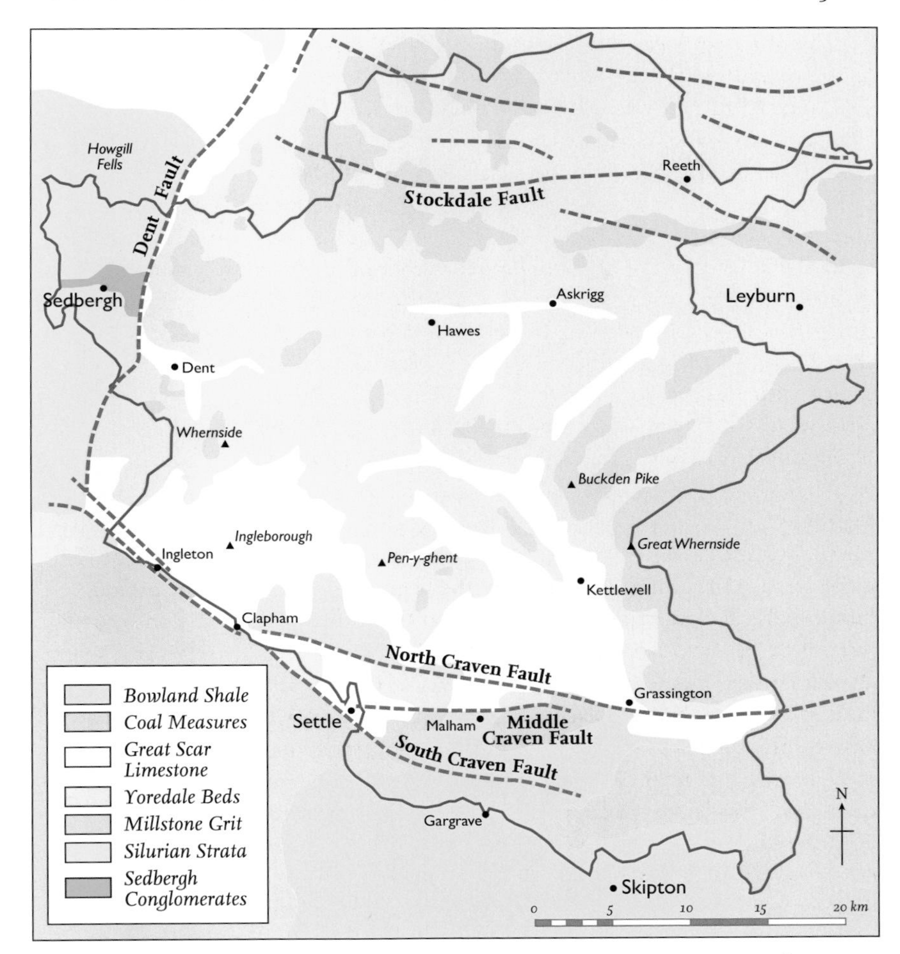

FIG 18. A simplified geological map of the Yorkshire Dales, showing the major small towns and villages, and some of the highest hills. (Yorkshire Dales National Park Authority)

the Ingleton Waterfalls walk exposed where Ordovician mudstones below the fault have slipped away from below the Great Scar Limestone. But minor faults occur across the Dales, some of which have resulted in major cave and pothole features such as the Gaping Gill Main Chamber.

Faults in the Carboniferous rocks are also important in determining the mineral wealth of the Dales. Mineral veins were deposited in rock fractures from hot mineral solutions rising from far below at the end of the Carboniferous

FIG 19. Giggleswick Scar, at the extreme western edge of the National Park near Settle. Here the wooded scarp of the South Craven Fault overlooks fields formed over shales on the western side of the fault.

period. These mineral solutions resulted from the deep sediments accumulated in the Craven and the Stainmore basins to the west and to the north of the Askrigg Block. As the sediments accumulated and were turned into rock at great depths, a strong brine solution, approximately six times as concentrated as seawater, was squeezed out under great pressure. It reached temperatures in excess of 100 °C as a result of heating from deep in the Earth's crust. These hot brines were able to carry minerals in solution upwards and away from the sediments. The solutions rose along fractures and permeable beds to regions of lower pressure within the Askrigg Block. As the solutions cooled and the minerals came out of solution, open faults were both the major route and also the centres of deposition, but some of the precipitation also involved interaction between the fluid and the limestone surfaces. The deposition of these minerals occurred at the end of the Carboniferous and in early Permian times, which began 298 million years ago when the Dales were covered by considerable depths of Millstone Grit and Coal Measure shales which have long since been eroded away, but which provided a barrier to the further upward movement of the mineral-bearing solutions. The lead ore galena is economically the most important mineral found in these veins, where it is associated with other gangue minerals including fluorite and baryte.

GEOMORPHOLOGY

It is perhaps hard today to appreciate that ice covered much of the Dales as recently as 17,000 years ago, but if we are to understand how the present landscape evolved we have to acknowledge the major erosive effects of glaciation.

The Pleistocene epoch, which began about 2.588 million years ago, marks the onset of the northern hemisphere glaciation and the beginning of the Quaternary period. The Pleistocene is characterised by a series of major cold periods when glaciers extended from the north, interspersed with warmer periods or interglacials which led to glacial retreat, driven primarily by astronomical forcing of solar radiation associated with repeating changes in the earth's motion, the so called Milankovitch cycles. Within these glacial periods there were also some short-lived fluctuations called interstadials, when warmer conditions caused the ice to retreat, and colder stadials in which the ice advanced again. Historically four major glacial periods were recognised, although now over 11 major glacial events have been identified. The second major historic cold period, the Anglian, which lasted from 480,000 to 430,000 years ago, resulted in the largest ice advance, covering all of Britain north of a line between the Thames and the Bristol Channel. The surface of the ice sheets emanating from Scandinavia was as much as 1,200 metres above sea level and thus more than capable of entombing the whole of the Dales. The individual dales themselves were in existence before the Anglian glaciation; for example, though it was subsequently reshaped, Ribblesdale may have had its origins as far back as 2 million years ago, but ice sheets of this magnitude have massive erosive power as they move slowly down the valleys, deepening them by scouring the soils and rocks. Most recent estimates suggest that the dale floors have been lowered by c.200 metres in the last 1.3 million years largely as the result of glacial erosion.

Today it is difficult to observe effects of the Anglian glaciation, because of later erosion events, most particularly during the Last or Devensian glaciation. The Last Glacial Maximum occurred between 26,500 and 19,000 years ago. During this period ice again entombed all of the Dales. Ice reaching the Dales from the north flowed into major ice streams moving south through the Irish Sea and the Vale of York, but recent research has shown that an ice centre was also established over high ground (> 600 metres) on Baugh Fell and Wild Boar Fell at the head of Wensleydale (Mitchell, 2013). The Devensian ice streams did not extend as far as those during the Anglian glaciation, reaching only as far south as the Midlands and not engulfing the Peak District. As the climate began to ameliorate about 17,000 years ago the glaciers slowly retreated northwards, revealing an ice-scoured landscape, many features of which are readily observable in the Dales today.

There was a brief cooling later, between c.13,000 and 11,500 years ago, resulting in some resurgence of glaciation in Scotland, but few glaciers formed in the Dales at that time, and these were small corrie glaciers in high basins such as on Great Coum and Whernside which had little direct effect on the wider landscape. However, during this period, periglacial conditions would have enhanced physical weathering processes through repeated freezing and thawing, causing instability on steep slopes and further scree development. This cold period marks the end of the Pleistocene and the beginning of the Post-glacial or Holocene, the period in which humans have come increasingly to affect both the landscape and the climate.

Ribblehead is a good place to begin an appreciation of the massive power of the Devensian glaciers and how this has affected the Dales landscape. To the east the view towards Birkwith is over a large number of small, rounded hills (Fig. 20). These are drumlins, features produced when glacial till is deposited by slow-moving ice. They have a characteristic whaleback shape, usually slightly steeper at one end and drawn out in the direction of the depositing ice flow. These small hills vary in size but frequently are between 400–700 metres long, 20–30 metres high and 200–300 metres wide. This large drumlin field is one of

FIG 20. The major drumlin field of small hills between Ribblehead and Birkwith: the view looking east from Colt Park Barn near Ribblehead.

the finest in the country, and the immense amount of till which it contains is a salutary reminder of the power of the Devensian glaciers to shape the landscape by removing and grinding weak rock strata, and transporting the debris downstream. Exactly how drumlins are deposited and shaped by the ice is still a matter of some debate, but the pattern and shape of the Ribblehead field suggests that they were formed by ice moving slowly south from Newby Head with another flow from Cam Fell. Another large drumlin field is found at Garsdale Head. The ice movement accelerated as it flowed into Ribblesdale and Chapel-le-Dale, producing conditions much less suitable for drumlin formation, and scouring the Ingleborough Great Scar Limestone pavements.

On the smaller scale, evidence for glacial transport can be found in the many erratic boulders carried from their source strata and deposited elsewhere. Often this is observable today where gritstone or greywacke boulders have been deposited on limestone benches. The most remarkable example of this form of glacial transport is found at Norber on the south side of Ingleborough, where hundreds of these erratics occur together (Fig. 21). In this case the greywacke boulders have not been transported very far. They have come from Silurian rock

FIG 21. One of many glacial erratic Silurian greywackes at Norber perched on a Carboniferous limestone plinth. The greywacke boulder was transported by a glacier from nearby Crummackdale, and it protects the underlying limestone from the eroding effects of precipitation, resulting in the formation of the plinth.

outcrops in nearby Crummackdale and were carried by the glacier flowing down that dale onto a shoulder of Carboniferous limestone at Norber Scar.

It was once thought that during the Devensian glaciers in the Dales were largely confined to the valleys, and that ice did not cover the hill tops which were then effectively nunataks, small rocky peaks appearing through the ice, and possibly acting as refugia for the most cold-tolerant organisms. More recently this has been shown to be erroneous except during the early stages of glaciation, when ice was building over the plateau, and again during deglaciation (see e.g. Mitchell, 2013). Computer-generated models suggest in fact that, at the Last Glacial Maximum, ice may have exceeded 800 metres in thickness over the plateau, but as the ice sheet subsequently shrank with the margins retreating towards the Dales ice centre around Baugh Fell, summits further away such as Ingleborough and Whernside did indeed become exposed as nunatuks.

The Dales ice centre was active during deglaciation, feeding the glaciers in the individual dales. These glaciers carried large amounts of till, depositing some as terminal moraines as the ice stagnated and began to melt, and also as lateral moraines, a combination of till gouged out along the edge of the glacier and debris falling from the hillsides above. Examples of both moraines occur in several dales, but one of the best can be found in Kingsdale. Here the terminal moraine is now a prominent grassy ridge at the foot of the dale called Raven Ray which has been breached by the Kingsdale Beck (Fig. 22). Braida Garth farm stands on a terrace which, together with Wackenburgh Hill, forms a lateral moraine.

When the glaciers began to stagnate and retreat, much of the land above them not covered with ice was still permanently frozen. As the summers slowly warmed, this resulted in repeated freezing and thawing cycles, perhaps over centuries, a process which causes stone sorting on shallow slopes and instability on steep ones as well as rock fragmentation and scree formation. The inherent structure of the Yoredale rocks exposed them to this, particularly where they were situated on glacially over-steepened slopes. The weaker shales collapsed, undermining the stronger limestones and sandstones and causing land slippage. Ancient landslides, now covered in vegetation, are today prominent features on several at least of the higher hills such as Kisdon, Ingleborough, Penhill and Whernside. Less spectacular is the general slumping of soils at this time when the melted surface layers of the soil slipped over the frozen subsurface to form solifluction terraces on many steep slopes.

The considerable flow of meltwater discharges as the ice sheets decayed produced large quantities of fine sediments which were deposited in the surrounding lowlands, extending on the west into what is now the Irish Sea. As

FIG 22. Looking south along Kingsdale, showing in the distance the terminal moraine of Raven Ray at its western end. The Kingsdale Beck does not now flow above ground through much of the dale in dry weather, but over time, together with the rising from Keld Head, it has breached the terminal moraine.

these deposits dried, large areas of bare sediments were exposed under periglacial conditions. The net result was that strong winds picked up and redistributed some of these sediments back onto the Dales in the form of a layer of loess.

Today the larger dales are classic U-shaped glaciated troughs, many with rivers running down them and only very slowly eroding the valley floors (Fig. 23). But the retreating glaciers produced large volumes of fresh water which in many dales for a time resulted in shallow glacial lakes impounded behind their terminal moraines. Only one of these moraine-impounded lakes survives today, Semer Water in Raydale, and this is much reduced from its original size. This reflects the fact that shallow lakes are only temporary features of the landscape since they become filled in with sediment or, as in several cases in the Dales, are lost by water cutting a new channel in the moraine and lowering the lake level, as has happpened through the terminal moraine in Wensleydale above the site of Aysgarth High Force. Evidence for the existence of these ancient lakes is seen in the sediment fans found in some dale bottoms. These were formed where becks carried outwash sands and gravels into ancient shallow lakes or wetlands;

FIG 23. Littondale, an example of the classic U-shaped glaciated troughs which form the major dales.

FIG 24. The Gordale Beck, the best tufa-depositing stream in Britain, descending the tufa cascade in the gorge at Gordale Scar.

examples can be found in Littondale and Wharfedale, and several of the villages, such as Arncliffe and Kettlewell, now sit on them. The large sub-glacial flows of meltwater were made more powerful by the fact that they flowed over largely frozen surfaces which restricted water movement below ground. They were responsible for creating, or helping to reshape, some of the more remarkable present-day landscape features. At Goredale a large meltwater flow gouged out the valley and cut through fault weaknesses in the limestone linking the North Craven Fault to the Middle Craven Fault, enlarging caves in the process, and eventually creating the gorge as the caves collapsed. The Gordale Beck which now occupies the valley is still eroding the gorge, but has none of the power of the glacial outwash (Fig. 24). Malham Cove is thought to have been originally associated with the Middle Craven Fault and probably started life as a waterfall. It has now retreated 600 metres to the north of the fault, and waterfall erosion alone is most unlikely to have been responsible. This form of erosion would have produced a narrow gorge quite unlike the Cove today. Probably the Cove is largely a result of Pleistocene ice events. A glacier descending down the now dry Watlowes valley from the present region of Malham Tarn weakened and removed blocks of limestone. Major outwash events followed as the glacier melted, and destructive torrents of water flowed over the exposed limestone to produce the cove we see today.

THE KARST LANDSCAPE

Karst is the German word for the Slovenian region of Kras, a bare and stony limestone area, and it has become the general term for all limestone landforms worldwide. The Dales provide the finest example of this landform in the United Kingdom. Chalk and limestone have a characteristic not shared with other rocks: they are slightly soluble in rainwater; and this solubility is raised as the temperature of the water falls and as the carbon dioxide in solution increases as the result of respiration by plant roots and soil microorganisms. Soil carbon dioxide concentrations may be more than an order of magnitude greater than those in air, considerably enhancing the erosive power of the drainage water. The result is that drainage sinks into the ground, and no water exists on the surface. In limestone districts this is achieved by the water penetrating and eroding fissures until it reaches impervious rocks below the limestone strata. These fissures typically form where lines of weakness in the limestone exist along joints and bedding planes. But small fractures in the rock also occur particularly in the vicinity of faults. Drainage in karst regions is essentially vertical, contrasting with that on impervious rocks, where it is organised into surface rivers. The Dales limestone is an example of so-called glaciokarst, where the land surface has been recently and extensively modified by glacial action.

Carboniferous limestone is commonly greater than 98 per cent calcite (calcium carbonate), which slowly dissolves in the percolating water leaving little or no solid material. Thus the movement of water vertically through the limestone strata slowly lowers the rock surface and widens the fissures. A demonstration of the surface lowering can be seen where erratic boulders have been deposited on limestone benches. At Norber, the large erratic boulders today sit on small plinths, the result of the protection that the boulders give the underlying limestone from the eroding effects of precipitation (see Fig. 21). The height of these pedestals has been used to calculate the denudation of the limestone surface during the Holocene, but to a degree at least this is complicated by a number of factors. These include estimating the age of the erratics, whether or not they were embedded initially in a layer of glacial till which has subsequently been eroded, the importance of past periglacial conditions including snow lie, and unquantifiable amounts of drip and wind-blown rain reaching the pedestals during the Holocene.

It is perhaps not surprising therefore that estimates of surface lowering in the Dales have varied between 13 and 46 mm per thousand years. The latest mean estimate of the age of the erratics themselves has been obtained using cosmogenic (^{36}Cl) analysis, a technique which allows an estimate of the length of time that a rock has been exposed at or near the earth's surface. Cosmic rays cause the production of the rare chlorine-36 isotope in rock crystals which accumulate, and the concentration of this isotope is used to estimate the length of exposure. This investigation produced a mean age for the erratics of 17.9 ± 1.0 thousand years (Wilson *et al.*, 2012). These workers adapted the technique to study surface lowering of a nearby limestone pavement at Moughton, 3 kilometres north-northeast of Norber, which they assumed had been exposed at the same time as the Norber erratics. They estimated that the limestone pavement surface at Moughton had been lowered by an average of 33 ± 10 cm over the last 17.9 thousand years. Marjorie Sweeting (1973) used another method to estimate the denudation of the limestone surface in northwest Yorkshire, measurements of the calcium content of drainage waters. This produced a much larger estimate of the rate of surface lowering of 4.9–5.0 cm per thousand years. Clearly there will be and will have been considerable variation in denudation rates over both space and time depending on factors such as the extent and nature of the glacial till and/or loess cover over the limestone, climatic conditions and plant colonisation (see e.g. Waltham, 2013). Bare limestone areas will have denuded more slowly than those covered by vegetation, as will areas covered in lime-rich glacial till compared to those covered in acidic soils or peat. Direct measurement of surface loss from buried limestone tablets illustrates this latter point. Steven Trudgill (1985) estimated that the surface loss of these tablets in calcareous soils at Cowside near Malham ranged between 20 and 40 mm per thousand years, whereas the figure for those buried in acid soils at nearby Darnbrook was between 100 and 600 mm.

Solution processes produce remarkable features in karst landforms both on the surface and underground, which together help to make the Dales of outstanding interest not only to environmental scientists but also to cavers and visitors in general. These include dolines and swallow holes, as well as caves and limestone pavements.

Dolines are closed hollows, typically bowl-shaped, which are circular or elliptical in plan. They vary in size from a metre or two in depth and a dozen or so metres in diameter to much larger structures which may be hundreds of metres in diameter. They are typically found where glacial drift or loess covers the limestone, and can occur as isolated structures, but are often found in large groups. Several forms are recognised, including solution, collapse and subsidence dolines, but all are essentially depressions formed as the result of water sinking underground.

In solution dolines water infiltrates fissures in the rock and these are slowly enlarged. This enlargement causes the surface around the fissures to be lowered, and settling occurs, forming a closed depression around the central drainage outlet. Frequently vegetation and soil obscure the underlying limestone. Examples of large solution dolines are the saucer-shaped depressions on Malham Moor, which are as much as a kilometre in diameter. Such large structures cannot have been formed by solution processes alone in the time since the Devensian ice retreated, and must pre-date this. They must have been covered by the Devensian ice, and to a degree modified by this through erosion and/or depositional processes. However, it is thought that the ice cover on the Malham High Country was largely static, so-called cold-based ice, which having little erosive power would not have drastically modified the pre-Devensian landform. Spectacular potholes such as Buttertubs, between Wensleydale and Swaledale, are another form of solution dolines.

Collapse dolines typically occur where caves immediately underlie the surface limestone beds. The cave roofs collapse when the percolating water causes their failure, resulting in steep cliff-like walls and a base filled with limestone blocks. Hull Pot on Pen-y-ghent is a good example of this form of doline; it is approximately 100 metres long, 20 metres deep and 10 metres wide (Fig. 25).

FIG 25. Hull Pot on Pen-y-ghent, showing the vertical walls of a large collapse doline.

Subsidence or alluvial dolines occur where limestones are covered with superficial deposits. Solution of the limestone occurs beneath the soil cover, enlarging joints into which soil particles subside, eventually resulting in shallow crater-like depressions. These are more popularly known as shake-holes and are very common feature of the Dales. Waltham & Tillotson (1989) recorded c.3,500 on Ingleborough alone, of which Braithwaite Wife Hole close to the Southerscales limestone pavements is an easily accessible example (Fig. 26). Ash Tree Hole on Leck Fell is a large example where partially vegetated slopes are still slumping into the depression. Shake-holes rarely occur singly, and are often grouped along major joints and faults.

Swallow holes are another important feature of the Dales. They occur where streams flowing across the Yoredale shales, or other impervious layers, reach the limestone and sink underground. The best-known example is Gaping Gill, where Fell Beck, draining the higher southwestern slopes of Ingleborough, falls nearly 100 metres down a shaft into a large cave. Other well-known examples include the Buttertubs potholes (Fig. 27), Hunt Pot on Pen-y-ghent and Goyden Pot in Nidderdale, but there are many more.

FIG 26. Braithwaite Wife Hole, an old conical subsidence doline 60 metres in diameter and 25 metres deep, Southerscales, Ingleborough.

FIG 27. The largest of the Buttertubs, a group of fluted potholes in the Main Limestone between Swaledale and Wensleydale.

The vertical drainage that characterises karst regions means that underground erosion features are vitally important components of this landform. Water percolating through small fissures, small faults and joints and along bedding planes in the limestone slowly enlarges them to create drainage routes, a process which may take millions of years, and thus may have been initiated long before the Devensian glaciation. But once these routes are established they may over time result in cave development, particularly so where shale bands occur in the limestone. Several possible reasons for cave development there include the fact that shale bands may contain iron pyrites, which produces sulphuric acid on oxidation, and this will corrode the limestone. The shale may also be less resistant to physical erosion than for example sparry limestones, and as a result it may be more easily removed to initiate cave formation. But much of cave development must come from the corrosive effect of carbon dioxide in the percolating water dissolving the limestone. However, exactly how the carbon dioxide concentration is maintained in fissures well below the surface limestone beds where the initial corrosive effects of the gas have taken place, particularly in saturated fissures with no access to the air, has been a matter of discussion.

Two forms of water flow underground are recognised. Where water flows in saturated fissures with no access to air, it may eventually be under considerable hydrostatic pressure and can even flow uphill. This is known as phreatic or forced flow. It frequently results in circular or elliptical passages in cross section, which can be interconnected as braided loops. If and when the water level in passages drops so that air enters, the flow is known as vadose or free flow, falling only under gravity. This leads to the passage being deepened both by erosion and by the corrosive effects of carbon dioxide dissolved in the water. The result is that circular or elliptical passages become more rectangular in shape as the stream deepens them, and the stream flows much as if it were on the surface, having for example meanders, pools and waterfalls.

Many cave systems have large chambers, which partly result from roof collapse, and here limestone blocks litter the floor. These caves may contain stalactites and stalagmites as the result of water dripping slowly from their roofs. These structures cannot form underwater, and result when water, enriched in carbon dioxide, loses the gas to the cave air causing some of the calcite to be precipitated. Stalactites come in a variety of forms, including as long hollow straw-like structures. Their growth depends on climatic conditions, which affect the rate of water seepage. Thus during the Pleistocene glaciations little or no water would have flowed, and no growth of these structures would have occurred. In addition these glaciations may have affected subsequent water seepage by removing some surface limestone beds, and thus changing postglacial seepage pathways. The concurrent removal of vegetation and soils which enrich carbon dioxide in the drainage water would also have reduced considerably the water's corrosive power. Stalactites and stalagmites can grow quite rapidly in suitable conditions. Sweeting (1973) recorded measurements of the Jockey Cap stalagmite in Clapham Cave. Between 1839 and 1873 it increased in height and width by 7.66 mm per year, and between 1873 and 1965 its height increased by 20 mm and its width by 200 mm. Banding within stalactites and stalagmites can be used to provide records of climate change. Stalagmites grow by deposit of layer upon layer, providing structures in longitudinal section similar to tree rings in cross section, the rate of growth being determined by environmental conditions.

The water which disappears underground, often through many swallow holes as well as seeping directly from the soil into the limestone, can travel a considerable distance before it reaches the surface again and, when it does, it usually appears in a very few resurgences. Leck Fell provides a good example. This area of limestone extends to 10 square kilometres over which there are at least 20 inlet streams, but all the water entering this area reappears in one major spring called Leck Beck Head. Austwick Beck Head is another major spring draining the western area of Ingleborough, where there are many potholes. An illustration of the complexity of water movement once it disappears underground can be provided by the outflow from Malham Tarn. This disappears underground at Water Sinks at the head of the Watlowes dry valley leading to the top of Malham Cove (Fig. 28).

FIG 28. Water Sinks, where the outflow stream from Malham Tarn is lost underground. The car park is a popular starting point for exploring the tarn. Tarn Woods, surrounding the Field Studies Council's Field Centre at Tarn House, is on the other side of the tarn.

It might be supposed that the water appearing from the spring at the base of the cove, 1.5 kilometres away, had its origin at Water Sinks (Fig. 29). Tracer and flood pulse studies have shown, however, that although some of the water that emerges at the cove has found its way from Water Sinks, the major source is Smelt Mill Sink, 2.5 kilometres to the northwest. Much of the water disappearing at Water Sinks reaches the surface at two springs a few metres apart at Aire Head, 3 kilometres south of the source.

Much of the water appearing from major springs may not be saturated with calcium carbonate, as a result of turbulent vadose flows through cave systems. However, phreatic flows may lead to springs at which water, supersaturated with calcite, vents carbon dioxide as it reaches the surface, a process assisted by algal and bryophyte photosynthesis. This leads to the formation of travertine or tufa, a soft porous rock formed of almost pure calcium carbonate. Tufa mounds and accumulations in streams are not particularly common in the Dales, and Pentecost (2013) lists a total of only *c.*50 sites within the National Park. Of these, Gordale Beck has the largest system of tufa deposition and is regarded as the best tufa-depositing stream in Britain. Among the more prominent tufa formations is the mossy cascade of Janet's Foss waterfall, below Gordale Bridge (Fig. 30).

Dry valleys lack, or only temporarily have, a watercourse. They are very numerous in karst areas, and have been formed by rivers and glaciers. Watlowes

FIG 29. Malham Cove Rising, source of Malham Beck below the cove. The major source of the water is Smelt Mill Sink, 2.5 kilometres away.

FIG 30. Janet's Foss waterfall, where the Gordale Beck falls over a mossy tufa screen.

FIG 31. Watlowes dry valley leading from Comb Scar to the top of Malham Cove. The valley was cut largely by sub-glacial streams at the end of the Devensian glaciation.

is glacial in origin, and when the ice began to melt, water would have flowed on the still frozen valley bottom and down over Malham Cove (Fig. 31). As we have seen, this no longer occurs, except at times of severe flood, and the water sinks into cave systems underground leaving the valley dry. Similarly, river-cut valleys commonly become dry in karst areas as drainage into cave systems below ground becomes established. Dolines are features of many dry valleys because water collecting in small pools sinks into fissures and joints causing solution of the limestone and eventually lowering of the surface.

Geomorphologists recognise many solutional features of limestone surfaces, and these are grouped under the general term karren. This relates to the patterns observed in the weathering limestone such as runnels and holes on bare rock or under a vegetation cover. For example rundkarren are smooth groves or channels, typically between 12 and 50 cm wide and deep, cut into the limestone under a vegetation cover. This and many other karren features can be found on limestone pavements, including the deep clefts or grykes which are known as kluftkarren, and the large residual blocks or clints which are flachkarren. Limestone pavements are one of the outstanding landscape and ecological features of the Dales, and their geomorphology is considered in more detail in Chapter 6.

CHAPTER 3

The Making of the Landscape – the Influence of Humans

Today, whether entering the Dales by train, car, bicycle or on foot, particularly from the northern towns and cities, it is easy for the visitor to think he or she is looking at a landscape relatively little influenced by man. Admittedly the fields with their walls and barns suggest that agriculture is important, but they have a timeless quality. However, few visitors will realise that most of these iconic structures are less than three hundred years old. Fewer visitors still will fully appreciate the role humans and their grazing animals have had on the landscape and its component natural history over several millennia. And even fewer visitors will be aware of the importance of past mining activities, particularly for lead, modifying the landscape at a time when parts of the Dales were essentially industrial centres. It is hard to appreciate that apart from the essential topography and landform dictated by geological history and Quaternary events, more or less everything that the visitor sees is the result of human activity, much of it fairly recent. Thus a knowledge of the past is a very important background to an understanding both of the present distribution of animals and plants and of their ecology.

EARLY INFLUENCES

In the Yorkshire Dales, as in every other part of Britain, humans have markedly influenced the landscape and the vegetation. Humans first reached the Dales as the climate warmed following the Devensian glaciation – exactly when is uncertain, but a bevel-based reindeer antler rod found in the Victoria Cave near

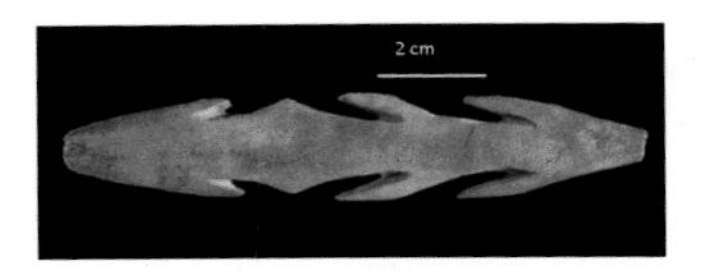

FIG 32. Later Upper Palaeolithic bilaterally barbed point of reindeer antler, from Victoria Cave in Ribblesdale. (Tom Lord)

Settle, and dated to *c.*12,500 BCE, towards the beginning of the Late-glacial or Windermere Interstadial, is the earliest evidence of human activity in the Dales. Later in the Interstadial, after 12,000 BCE, antler and bone objects found in Conistone Dib, Kinsey, Sewell's and Victoria Caves, including elk, reindeer and cut-marked wild horse bones, again indicate human presence (Fig. 32). However, there is no evidence from the caves for human activity in the cold Younger Dryas or Loch Lomond Stadial, which brought the Late-glacial Interstadial to an end in about 10,800 BCE (Lord & Howard, 2013), and it is doubtful whether small bands of hunters in the Late-glacial had any effect upon the landscape.

In the Holocene, as the climate ameliorated after the Younger Dryas Stadial, forests came to cover much of the land surface except perhaps on the more exposed upper reaches of the highest fells. These forest resources were first exploited by bands of hunter–gatherers in the later Mesolithic period (8000–3800 BCE). Bone tools and evidence of flint tools from these people have been discovered at various sites in the Dales including at Malham Tarn, while a Mesolithic site in Kingsdale yielded charcoal dated to between 6850 and 6640 BCE. Almost certainly these sites did not represent permanent occupancy during the middle Mesolithic, but rather summer camps of lowland people exploiting small game, birds and fruits, perhaps influenced by the fact that rising sea levels were progressively removing coastal hunting grounds to the west. Such hunter–gatherer activity would probably have had relatively little influence on plant and animal populations or on the landscape, but it is possible that locally there was some disturbance. Pollen analysis from Ingleborough has shown woodland clearance dated to the late Mesolithic (Swales, 1987), which may have been deliberately designed to attract grazing animals to clearings in order to aid hunting, and evidence for fire management to create these clearances at this period comes from relatively high levels of polyaromatic hydrocarbons in sediments from Semer Water (Chiverell *et al.*, 2008).

Evidence for Neolithic people (3900–2600 BCE) in the Dales comes from stone burial cairns, stone circles and wall footings as well as human remains. Cave excavations have also revealed pottery fragments, flints and worked bones which have been ascribed to the Neolithic. To what extent these people were farming as distinct from hunter–gathering is unclear. Certainly bone fragments indicate that they were still hunting, and probably there was no marked discontinuity between the end of hunter–gathering and its replacement by farming, rather a gradual shift in emphasis from one to the other over a considerable period of time. Pollen analysis has shown appreciable forest clearance in the period by fire and probably also by ring barking, but no evidence of domesticated cereal growing, at least in the uplands. This increase in grasslands suggests that the people were herders and traded animal products for grain, and it is probable that upland pastures were used on a seasonal basis. During this period it is also possible that some of the first upland enclosures were begun, and stone circles such as above Yockenthwaite in Wharfedale and at Ox Close above Carperby in Wensleydale give evidence of a complex social system.

In the Bronze Age (2600–600 BCE) pastoral farming in the Dales continued much as before, but the arrival of new tools must have accelerated the reduction in forest cover. It has been estimated that only 15 per cent of the total area remained as forest as early as 1500 BCE. This period marked the climatic optimum since the Last glaciation, and the generally warm climate was more conducive to cereal growing. Now came the period of first permanent settlements in the Craven uplands and probably also of the first attempts at land improvement for agriculture, such as clearing stones to create space for crops. Single or multi-family farmsteads were established to keep cattle and to grow wheat and barley. At this time there is evidence for the creation of small pounds for stock adjacent to dwellings, such as at Dew Bottoms on the limestone plateau above Cowside Beck. Burnt mounds are also a feature of this period in upland Britain. These low mounds range from 5 to 15 metres in diameter and contain ash, charcoal, sooty material and rock fragments. One in Kingsdale has been dated to 1500 BCE, but there is as yet no consensus as to their exact use.

As the late Bronze Age was replaced by the early Iron Age around 600 BCE, the new technology gradually allowed for more durable tools such as axes and knives, and for the replacement of wooden ards by iron-tipped ploughs. Although still primitive, these ploughs represented a considerable advance. The old ard (or scratch plough) had merely scratched the surface, but now it was possible to turn the soil over, allowing the easier sowing of old crops and the introduction of new ones. Further acceleration of woodland clearance will again have been at least partly caused by the availability of better tools. This was also a period in which drove roads became established for the first time, linking the farmsteads and their surrounding small enclosed fields with the higher pastures. During the Iron Age the climate deteriorated as the temperature cooled and precipitation increased, perhaps inducing the first primitive attempts at land drainage. Iron Age agricultural features observable today include fields readily seen from the limestone pavements above Malham Cove.

The coming of the Romans to the Dales around 70 CE is usually taken to signify the end of the Iron Age and the beginning of the Romano-British period. Little seems to have changed at this time in terms of agriculture and land use apart from the construction of roads such as that above Bainbridge in Wensleydale. These roads linked forts such as the major fort at Bainbridge and, with other forts and marching camps, they aided the subjugation of the native peoples. However, Elizabeth Livett's unpublished pollen diagram from Ellerton Moor above Swaledale suggests that this was a period when soil fertility declined as the result of podsolisation caused by leaching and overgrazing (Fleming, 1998). Heather moorland replaced grassland on the upper slopes of the dale, including on areas of late prehistoric coaxial field systems that extended above the limit of the present walled pastures.

THE MEDIEVAL PERIOD

After the withdrawal of the Roman garrisons in the late fourth and early fifth centuries, a series of small kingdoms was established in northern England and, by the sixth century, these had come under the control of Anglian warlords. There is little evidence that the end of Roman occupation led to a depopulation of the Dales, but the early medieval period included a rapid, if short-lived, climate deterioration in the middle sixth century which may have resulted in crop failures, famine and disease leading to depopulation and the subsequent abandonment of more marginal land. Elizabeth Livett's pollen diagram from Ellerton Moor shows a peak in arable cultivation about 320–410 CE followed by an increase in tree pollen. The latter increase peaked around 745–865 CE, suggesting some recovery of woodland although not back to pre-Iron Age forest cover.

From the seventh century onwards, as the climate warmed, the existing Romano-British peoples were slowly augmented by new Anglian settlers originating from northern Germany and southern Denmark. These people brought new arable farming and forestry skills including the use of oxen, and their settlements were probably the first Dales villages. These are found on the eastern edge of the Dales and can be recognised today in village names ending in *–ley*, from *leah* meaning a forest clearing. Higher up the Dales the village names are replaced by *–ton* suffixes, meaning village or farmstead, perhaps reflecting later immigration of Anglo-Saxon farmers into more open areas. Features of these villages included dwellings for a group of families, common fields for arable, common pasture and meadow, and drove ways for livestock across the arable fields. Some of the drove ways survive to this day as green lanes. Arable

FIG 33. Terraces like these, in sloping fields above the Malham Beck, formed the strip lynchets of former arable cultivation.

cultivation was often on sloping fields above the wet valley floor in which groups of terraces were developed typically up to 200 metres long and around 10 metres wide. These lynchets and similar structures produced by later medieval farmers are still readily observable today (Fig. 33). The higher fell land above the common arable fields and pastures was probably little used except for summer grazing and for harvesting of heather for thatching. The remaining woods were an important source of fuel and timber, but in many places they were also important as pastures for livestock as well as providing sources of winter fodder from pollarded trees (see e.g. Fleming, 1998).

By the eighth century the village pattern recognisable today had largely already been established. Later in the ninth and tenth centuries Viking-age movements of people infiltrated the Dales, the last of which came from the west and comprised pastoral farmers who established farmsteads perhaps in unoccupied land in the remote valley heads away from the Anglo-Saxon villages. They established small crofts, meadows and sheep folds close to their dwellings and utilised upland pastures for their flocks. They combined summer pastures on the hills with winter ones in the higher parts of the valleys, where place names of Scandinavian origin abound with suffixes such as *–thwaite*, *–sett* and *–scale*. The important Scandinavian influence in these regions is also apparent in landscape descriptors such as *beck*, *clint*, *crag*, *dale*, *fell* and *scar*.

THE NORMAN INFLUENCE

The 'Harrying of the North' which followed the Norman Conquest was designed to remove any threat to the south of the country. The effects on the countryside are difficult to assess, but the Domesday Book compiled in 1086 shows that most estates in the region were worth less than they had been in 1066, and many were 'waste', suggesting a decline in agricultural activity over the period perhaps as a direct result of the brutal subjugation. William installed new overlords in the region; as examples, Count Alan of Brittany was granted a large area including Swaledale and Wensleydale as part of the new Honour of Richmond, and Roger de Poitou became overlord of Craven. The Norman overlords were interested in hunting, and large areas of the upper dales, including much of the area of Norse settlement, were incorporated into free chase or hunting forest in which forest courts were responsible for deer management. The hunting forest required both woodland as cover for the game (Fallow, Red and Roe Deer and Wild Boar) and open grasslands for the hunt. The need to enhance deer stocks resulted in some reduction of sheep numbers so as to encourage regeneration of existing woodlands. This early conservation management was overseen by a warden with foresters under him and resulted in the establishment of some new settlements in the forests. For example, the village of Bainbridge was established to house the foresters in Wensleydale (Fig. 34).

FIG 34. Bainbridge, site of a Roman fort and a twelfth-century settlement to manage the forest of Wensleydale.

While the establishment of hunting forests was important, the most far-reaching effect on the landscape after the Conquest was the establishment of the monasteries during the twelfth century. Increasingly the baronial rulers granted large tracts of land to the monasteries; intercessional prayers would then ensure the landowners' paths to heaven. Cistercian monks were the first to settle in the Dales, founding Fountains Abbey in 1132 and Jervaulx in 1145. Bolton Abbey in Wharfedale was established by Augustinian canons in 1155. But equally important were monasteries remote from the Dales such as Bridlington, Byland and Furness, which were granted large landholdings; for example Bridlington owned much of Swaledale. These areas were largely in the fells and forests, and were very suitable for sheep-runs. They were managed from granges with a priest monk in charge and they received regular visits from officials of the parent abbey. Each grange was the centre of several farms, some at least of which had their origins in the Norse settlements rearing cattle, horses, sheep and pigs. These monastic settlements oversaw the production of large quantities of butter, cheese and particularly wool, together with surplus livestock. This necessitated movement of animals and goods between the granges and the monasteries, and this traffic of packhorses, farm animals and people between monastery land holdings helped to establish roads and tracks. One such example is Mastiles Lane, the green lane linking the Malham estates of Fountains Abbey with its important grange at Kilnsey.

The four centuries between the establishment and the dissolution of the monasteries saw the development of a pastoral landscape with tracks linking the farms, granges and monasteries. The monks were keen to maximise income from their estates and oversaw land improvements such as drainage of upland pastures, the elimination of scrub, and the enclosure of small fields or assarts from the 'wastes'. Enclosures were achieved by the construction of dry-stone walls. Tom Lord, who farms Lower Winskill near Settle, has reconstructed the pattern of enclosures there as they would have been in about 1300, when it was a sheep farm (bercaria) belonging to Sawley Abbey (Fig. 35). This was made possible by the recognition that medieval dry-stone walls differed in construction from those built from the sixteenth century onwards. In particular, double-skin medieval walls did not taper markedly from their bases to their tops, and were at least 1.6 metres tall and usually 0.5 metres wide (Fig. 36) whereas more modern walls typically taper from *c.*0.75 metres wide at the base to *c.*0.40 metres at the top. Top stones on medieval walls were laid flat, but projected from the outer face of the wall to form a continuous overhang designed to prevent Wolves, still a hazard to grazing animals at this period, jumping the walls.

The monks established fisheries such as at Malham Tarn and also exploited mineral resources. In the thirteenth century Fountains Abbey mined and smelted

FIG 35. The enclosed area (infield) of the medieval Sawley Abbey sheep farm (bercaria) at Lower Winskill in about AD 1300, as reconstructed by Tom Lord.

iron and lead in Nidderdale, but wool was the major source of wealth, amounting to three quarters of its income. By the late thirteenth century regular food surpluses were achieved. However, the fourteenth century saw a deteriorating climate and, possibly as a result, increasing raids from Scotland on property and livestock. In 1320 Bolton Priory's cattle numbers fell to 31, having been 503 a few years earlier, while in the same period sheep numbers fell by two-thirds. In 1348 the Black Death drastically reduced the population, resulting in a serious labour shortage for the monastic landlords as well as loss of stock. The net result was a change from direct management of much of the monasterial estates to tenanted farms, as bondmen broke free.

FIG 36. A bield wall or wind shelter on Fleet Moss (left) and Tom Lord's diagram of a medieval double dry-stone wall profile at Lower Winskill (right), combined at similar scales (Robin Lee).

THE DISSOLUTION AND ENCLOSURES

Following the dissolution of the monasteries the land was progressively sold to raise revenue for the crown. Throughout the seventeenth and early eighteenth centuries there was progressive enclosure of the village common fields, particularly in the better valley land, but common fields and woodlands still existed on the fell sides and were organised through manorial courts. These were often managed as stinted pastures, which gave villagers the right to graze specified numbers of cattle and or sheep, but ensured the system was not abused by any individual. Stints or gates/gaits were allotted according to the size of an individual's land holding, and a formula adjusted their use for different livestock – for instance, one stint equalled one ewe with lamb, but ten stints equalled one cow. These arrangements were periodically reviewed (e.g. the 1810 agreement to stint Scales Moor above Chapel-le-Dale was superseded by a new stinting schedule in 1842). The upland wastes above the stinted pastures were still commons on which the villagers had unrestricted grazing rights. However, the parliamentary enclosures between 1760 and 1830 enclosed the remaining open fields and moorland, and in the process eliminated many smallholdings in the name of better land use and farming, but marginalised the poorer villagers. The large landowners were both the petitioners for the enclosures and the beneficiaries, not least because they could afford the land-improvement and wall-building costs. Land improvement included drainage, burning and liming. These enclosures resulted in many of the straight dry-stone walls which are such a characteristic feature of the Dales today. Stone for these walls came partly from clearing the fields, but largely from small local quarries. The Enclosure Acts often specified the wall construction. One example of a specification is as follows:

> *two skin walls five to six feet high, three feet thick at the base and narrowing to one and a half feet at the top. Twenty one throughs [stones which bridge both skin walls] in two or three rows to be placed in every seven yards of wall thus tying the two skins together, and the remaining space between the skins to be filled with small stones.*

This is broadly the method employed today to rebuild walls and gaps. Although dry-stone walls are both an important land-management and landscape feature, they also provide a habitat for plants and animals, perhaps most notably for bryophytes and lichens. An important example of this is that a few old limestone walls are colonised by one of the rarest of plants, the moss *Zygodon gracilis*, which in Britain is confined to the Yorkshire Dales National Park.

Another characteristic feature of the Dales landscape is the prevalence of field barns or byres (Fig. 37). This system of farming probably dates from the seventeenth century, but may reflect the continuation of an earlier practice. The oldest barn in Swaledale and Arkengarthdale is dated 1713, but probably most existing barns in the Dales were built between 1750 and 1850. The barns were designed to provide winter shelter for cattle below, together with their food source in the form of stored hay above. Thus the animals and the hay were not concentrated in large farmsteads in winter, but dispersed in the fields, minimising the movement of cattle, hay and dung. The system only works if there is sufficient grazing for the stock outside the meadows to allow a hay crop to be taken, and this was provided by the upland pastures. Shelters were also erected for sheep in exposed areas on the fells. These were known as bields, and were little more than short lengths of wall providing shelter from the wind (Fig. 36). Most have fallen into disrepair today.

Walls were needed not only to enclose the fields but also to demarcate the old roads, drove routes and trackways as well as the new turnpikes. New walled roads also provided access to the remaining upland commons for villagers with rights for example to graze stock and to dig peat. For centuries after the woodland was cleared peat was the most important fuel used in the Dales, and retention of access to moorland for the extraction of this resource was often a feature of the enclosure awards, legal documents recording the ownership and distribution of the lands enclosed. Most farms had peat or turf houses, and peat digging was

FIG 37. Field barns and meadows near Muker, Swaledale: exemplars of a system of agriculture where animals and hay were not concentrated in large farmsteads.

a vital part of the yearly cycle which largely took place in the spring between lambing and hay time.

The enclosure awards frequently included the retention of parish quarries to provide villagers with stone for houses. They also permitted the building of lime kilns, but lime production has a long history in the Dales dating back at least to the twelfth century, when it was largely used for mortar. Lime kilns were usually sited near to limestone outcrops, where small quarries provided ready access to the heavy raw material (Fig. 38). Fuel was provided by peat and wood, but thin coal seams in the Yoredale and lower Millstone Grit strata were also important and were mined from small pits on the fells above the kilns. The lime produced was largely used to improve the newly enclosed hill pastures. Kiln siting was thus designed to minimise uphill carriage of the raw material, fuel and lime. These very numerous kilns were a feature of the landscape in the Dales, and as late as the 1960s Arthur Raistrick recorded more than 300 kilns in just the upper parts of Wharfedale, Wensleydale, Garsdale and Dentdale. Prodigious quantities of lime were used in land improvement, and Raistrick recorded that at one farm alone, Pickering End in Wharfedale, 3,088 pony loads of lime were used in 1822 in improving some rough moorland pasture.

FIG 38. Lime has long been used in the Yorkshire Dales, both for mortar and for land improvement, and lime kilns, many of which date from the late eighteenth century, are numerous. This one is at Gunnerside, Swaledale.

INDUSTRIAL INFLUENCES

Local sources of fuel and water were integral to the major industry, lead mining, which was at its zenith in the eighteenth and nineteenth centuries, but had its origins at least as far back as the Roman occupation. Early mining was very small-scale, leaving little or no detectable influence on today's landscape, but, as the demand for lead grew from the twelfth century onwards, the profound effects this caused are still clearly visible today even though a century has passed since the mines ceased operation. In 1993 English Heritage estimated that 400 square kilometres of the Dales were directly affected by lead mining and smelting operations. The main centres of lead mining were Wharfedale, particularly around Grassington, Swaledale and Arkengarthdale, with smaller-scale activities elsewhere.

Peat was a major fuel used in the smelt mills, and this involved not only extensive digging on the moors above the mills, but also large peat houses to store and dry the peat at the smelters (Fig. 39). Water was required as a source of power, for example in the operation of the smelter bellows and as part of the ore-dressing process; sometimes this led to the diversion of water courses and to the creation of dams, of which the Duke's Water Course on Grassington Moor, utilising both beck water and water stored in dams, is one of the best examples. The dams provided a reliable source of water in dry weather, but in wet weather they could be short-circuited and the beck water used directly, thus ensuring that activities were less affected by any vagaries of the weather. Water was also used both in the location and working of surface lead veins, and this resulted in local but large effects on the vegetation and soils. The process was called hushing, and

FIG 39. Remains of an early nineteenth-century peat house for lead smelting, Gunnerside Gill, Swaledale.

involved impounding water in dams above steep hillsides in which lead veins were expected. Two forms of hushing were used. In exploration hushing, the sudden release of the water from the dam carried away the vegetation, soil and loose rock onto the valley floor, hopefully revealing any lead veins on the hillside. Once the veins were identified, the miners could loosen the mineral ore in the vein with chisels, hammers and crowbars. Extraction hushing involved a second sudden release of water from the dam to wash the broken ore and rock to the valley floor, helping to sort the heavy lead ore from the lighter rock. Thus the fell-side and valley-floor vegetation were greatly modified, and much gravel and debris entered the rivers (Fig. 40). The scale of the operation can be appreciated from Arthur Raistrick's observation in 1955 (nearly 80 years after the last mining operations) that the Swale below the Old Field Hush close to the Beldi Hill mines near Keld contained several miles of banks of gravel and other debris from hushing. Today, the scars from hushing are still clearly visible on hillsides in this area, as well as elsewhere in the mining districts.

Smelting the lead ore also had both direct and indirect effects on the landscape. The need for timber and peat for fuel helped denude the remaining woods and disturb the blanket peats. Early smelting was carried out on bail or bole hills in an open hearth surrounded by a low wall of stones with openings in the direction of the prevailing wind. Layers of peat and brushwood were topped with crushed ore, and the fire lit when the wind was strong and steady enough to provide the appropriate draught. A channel cut in the base of the hearth to the outside received the molten lead, which flowed into a hollow from which it could be scooped. The process could be kept going by the regular addition of fuel and ore. These crude open hearths had a number of disadvantages, including danger to the

FIG 40. Stoddart Hush near Langthwaite in Arkengarthdale, one of many examples of the devastation caused by the lead-mining process known as hushing, still clearly visible today.

workmen from the fumes, a considerable loss of lead in vapour, and damage to the surrounding ecosystems partly from lead poisoning, but probably particularly from sulphur dioxide pollution released from the galena ore. Damage by fumes to ecosystems occurred not just immediately around the smelt mills but much further afield, as can be attested by a 1770 report recorded by Raistrick & Jennings (1965):

> *... the reek of Smoak of a Lead Mill is of such a Nature as not very readily to mix with the air, and frequently is driven in an unbroken Current upon the Earth's surface to a Miles Distance, nay we have ourselves seen the Smoak of Lead Mills at the Distance of 6 or 7 miles; it seems therefore that the Mill Reek is capable of affecting or having the appearance of affecting so large a surface that Mr Falls complaint was ever so well founded.*

By the late eighteenth and early nineteenth centuries reverberatory furnaces had replaced the open hearths, and recovery of the lead was much improved by ground-level flues joining the furnace to chimneys several hundred yards away up the hillside (Fig. 41). Condensation of lead in these flues allowed it to be scraped or washed off the internal walls and recovered, a task both unpleasant and dangerous. Thus in the centres of mining and smelting such as Grinton in Swaledale not only was there considerable despoilation associated with fuel

FIG 41. A partially restored early nineteenth-century ground-level flue used to carry smelter fumes up the hillside to a chimney on Grassington Moor. Lead condensing in the flues was recovered from condenser houses built into the flue system.

supply, ore winning and preparation, but also flues and chimneys became prominent features in the landscape. The noxious emissions from these would have influenced surrounding ecosystems as can be attested in the very high concentrations of lead in near-surface peat from surrounding blanket bogs such as on Grassington Moor (Fig. 42). Peat dated to the second half of the nineteenth century has been shown to contain up to 0.8 per cent of the metal, peaking at the time of maximum lead production from the moor.

With the demise of the lead industry at the end of the nineteenth century some of the parishes in Swaledale lost more than two-thirds of their populations, and 'a melancholy array of deserted Hamlets in Swaledale' was recorded by Joseph Morris in 1901. The population of Muker, for example, was 1,321 in 1851, but by 1951 this had fallen to 416 (Hartley & Ingilby, 1956). Many of the mine buildings quickly fell into ruin, and the associated atmospheric pollution problems largely disappeared. However, effects of the industry on the landscape, and on both aquatic and terrestrial ecosystems, can still be observed.

Lead mining was a precarious activity, and many miners ran smallholdings to bolster their livelihoods. These often involved making intakes from the fell which they improved by liming. Some of these improved pastures today still provide a stark contrast to the surrounding moorland.

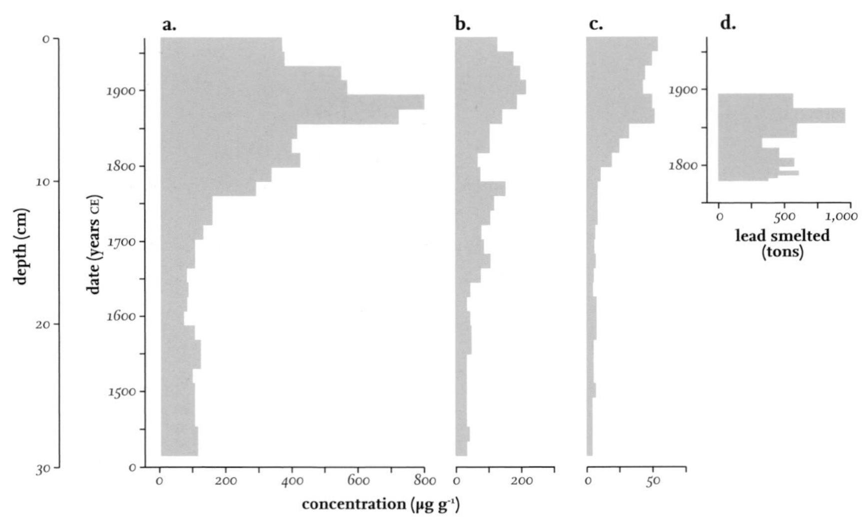

FIG 42. Concentrations of (a) lead, (b) zinc and (c) copper in the peat profile from Grassington Moor, plotted on a pollen-analytically determined time-scale, and (d) the amount of lead smelted at Grassington Moor. Data of Raistrick (1953), from Livett *et al.* (1979).

Other mining operations, for chert, copper, fluorite, zinc and particularly for coal, have also left their mark locally in the Dales, but their effects have been much less extensive than those of the lead industry. As many as 19 coal mines have been recorded in or close to the National Park. The Tan Hill mines were operational as early as 1296 and as late as 1934 and, during the eighteenth and nineteenth centuries, provided coke from primitive beehive ovens for the Swaledale lead industry. A colliery on Fountains Fell also provided coal and coke for a smelt mill on Malham Moor. The last working pit on the edge of the Dales was the New Colliery in Ingleton, which was established in 1913 and replaced earlier nineteenth-century pits in the area. This remained operational until 1937, and the 120 houses built in the village to house the miners are a lasting legacy. In the first half of the twentieth century, chert extraction in some old lead mining areas of Arkengarthdale occurred for use in porcelain manufacture. The main mining sites were Fremington Edge and the Hungry Hushes. At the latter site extraction began in 1932 and continued for almost 20 years, ending in 1950 (Brennan & Brennan, 2013).

Stone was vital for building from earliest times, and small quarries were established for this purpose around settlements, parishes and townships. Although these quarries, like those established to supply the lime kilns, have left little mark on the landscape today, and are often almost indistinguishable from natural scars, they have provided one of the glories of the Dales in the form of old stone buildings made of grit, limestone and flagstones. Few of the old stone farmhouses date from before 1600, from when they began to replace old 'crucked' timber and thatch dwellings (Raistrick, 1967), and the field barns or byres are later still, but both are striking landscape features of the Dales today. Some of this quarrying for building materials, such as for the Burtersett flags in Wensleydale, was underground, leaving almost no visual impact above ground apart from 16 quarrymen's cottages and stone-flagged paths across the fields.

Quarrying became more industrialised in the nineteenth century. The increased demand for lime led to the construction of a Hoffman kiln at Langcliffe Quarry in 1872 (Fig. 43). This had 22 chambers in which heat from the burning chamber was vented to the next, thus allowing for continuous operation with none of the cooling delays of a single kiln. The fires took six weeks to make a complete circuit through the chambers. The kiln is now preserved, and its old quarry face above forms a weathered cliff on Stainforth Scar. The largest quarry working today is Horton Quarry, which was started in 1888 following the building of the railway line up Ribblesdale. A large extension to the operation was granted in the 1940s to exploit the Great Scar Limestone, which is used today for concrete aggregate. The quarry abuts closely on the Ingleborough National Nature Reserve, providing a stark illustration of two potentially conflicting interests. However,

FIG 43. The Hoffman kiln at Langcliffe in Ribblesdale, built in 1872, had 22 chambers, allowing for continuous operation without the cooling delays associated with single lime kilns.

this huge quarry is probably destined to be the last operational in the National Park, not least because beneath the Great Scar Limestone lies a large reserve of unexploited top-quality road stone in the form of Silurian greywackes. These latter rocks are currently being extracted in quarries in places such as Ingleton and Dry Rigg (Fig. 44). Even with modern best-practice restoration techniques, the large quarries, as they come out of production, are unlikely to blend as easily into the landscape as the old, small quarries used to build the Dales villages or to feed the lime kilns. Nevertheless they will probably supply important wildlife habitats for the future, as evidenced by Ribblehead quarry, last used in 1958 but already of conservation interest today.

One of the major effects on the landscape of the Dales came from the building of the Settle-to-Carlisle railway by the Midland Railway between 1864 and 1875 to provide a route to Scotland over their own tracks. Ribblehead became the site of a construction camp for some 2,000 people, involving considerable modification of the landscape and the building of wooden houses, a hospital, schools, shops and a library. An engineering camp called Sebastapol, nearer the viaduct itself, included a brickworks. The remains of the camps, including the brickworks, are still discernable today. The current view at Ribblehead is dominated by the railway viaduct, which is over 400 metres long and 32 metres high, composed of massive piers of dark limestone and capped by 24 brick arches (Fig. 45). This viaduct crosses Batty Moss at the head of Chapel-le-Dale and is a remarkable landscape feature; but there are also three other large viaducts in the Dales, two in Dentdale at Dent Head and Artengill, and one in Garsdale at Dandrymire. The stone for all these was provided by local quarries, not least because of the difficulty and cost of transporting strong stone from any distance.

FIG 44. Dry Rigg Quarry near Helwith Bridge, Ribblesdale. Steeply bedded Silurian greywackes are exploited as roadstone. The greywackes are overlain by near horizontally bedded Carboniferous limestone.

The use of water power was not confined to the lead industry, but has a long history in the Dales. Most medieval villages had mills for grinding corn, and some had fulling mills for cleaning woollen cloth. Both involved the construction of dams, leats or goits and tail races. Dams in rivers increased the power of the

FIG 45. The Ribblehead viaduct carrying the Settle-to-Carlisle railway across Batty Moss.

mills and reduced the effect of droughts, but were sometimes a cause of disputes where the river marked the boundary between different manors (Raistrick, 1967). Altitude and climate meant that cereal growing was always marginal in the Dales and, by the eighteenth century, small village mills became increasingly uneconomic as larger mills were established near growing centres of population. During this period some small cereal mills were adapted and enlarged for other purposes as cotton and woollen mills, and some new mills were constructed, such as Yore Mill at Aysgarth, opened in 1784. By the middle of the nineteenth century, however, most of these textile mills were redundant, and had been either converted to other uses such as saw mills or left to become derelict.

CONCLUDING REMARKS

Today the Yorkshire Dales can be said, at least in part, to be a post-industrial landscape, and one, even away from old mining and quarrying centres, which has been largely shaped by human activities. The woodlands which in the Post-glacial period covered all but perhaps the scars and summits of the highest hills have been largely replaced by grassland and moorland, much of the latter on large estates, which are currently managed for grouse shooting. The present-day woodland has been largely planted in the last two centuries, and little, if any, truly ancient woodland survives. Human populations and their grazing animals have ruled the landscape, but in the process have helped to create a region of great beauty and interest, beloved by many. The stone-built villages with their often ancient churches, the farmsteads and field byres, and dry-stone walls running over the fells and dales all help to define the present landscape for the visitor. However, it should not be forgotten that human activities have also appreciably influenced the biological diversity and natural history of the region, and indeed continue to do so. Indeed it might be said that even farming in the National Park is entering a post-industrial era, as many farms enter agri-environment schemes designed at least in part to encourage wildlife, often associated with a reduction in stocking. Management designed to increase natural history interest, such as schemes to re-create the species-rich hay meadows which were a major landscape and wildlife feature of the Dales before the Second World War, has also increased in recent years. And last, but not least, the area of land in the Dales managed as nature reserves, both local and national, has increased considerably in the last fifty years. The Yorkshire Dales National Park is a living landscape, and today managed more than at any time in the past to encourage biological diversity.

CHAPTER 4

Woodlands

Woodlands today cover less than 5 per cent of the land surface in the Dales. Much of these have been planted within the last two centuries, and little, if anything, of what was probably the near-complete ancient forest cover remains. The reasons for this are not hard to find, in that humans were dependent for millennia on wood for building, cooking and heating. Fire was probably an important early aid to hunting, and forest clearance was essential for pastoral farming, which also effectively eliminated forest regeneration. In addition, the subsequent demands of the lead industry on timber as a fuel were very substantial. It is though instructive to understand the nature of the ancient forest, how it developed and to what extent, if at all, its characteristics are observable today in some at least of the remaining woodland cover. In the Dales this can best be demonstrated from the pollen record.

THE ANCIENT FOREST

The development of forest cover and its nature can be discerned from the pollen record preserved in peat and lake sediments. These stratified deposits can be aged by radiocarbon dating and give a representation of the vegetation cover in the area of the deposit. They do not reproduce the vegetation in its entirety, for a number of reasons: species differ in the amounts of pollen they produce, wind-pollinated plants are better represented than insect-pollinated ones, and some pollen grains are better preserved in these deposits than others. However, they allow a good approximation to the development of forest cover since the Last, or Devensian glaciation, and how the species composition has changed over time.

Our knowledge of the vegetation history of the Yorkshire Dales depends heavily on the early work of Arthur Raistrick and Kathleen Blackburn (1938) at Linton Mires and Donald and Margaret Pigott (1959, 1963) at Malham Tarn. These studies did not have the advantage of radiocarbon dating, but later studies by David Bartley and his research students at the University of Leeds, employing this technique, have added considerably to our knowledge. These workers have investigated a range of sites, including in lowland Craven (Bartley *et al.*, 1990), on the Ingleborough massif (Swales, 1987) and in Wensleydale (Honeyman, 1985), thus expanding considerably the geographical coverage of the Dales.

Figure 46 shows the tree pollen diagram from Malham (Pigott & Pigott, 1959). This suggests that Juniper scrub occupied the limestone uplands in the Late-glacial. In the earliest peat deposit examined on Ingleborough, Susan Swales dated an open countryside with Juniper (*Juniperus communis*) and birch (*Betula* species) to 9240 years before the present (BP). David Bartley and his co-workers showed that the basal deposits in lowland Craven demonstrated a treeless landscape before 9430 BP, again with Juniper and other shrubs including willow (*Salix* species). Juniper scrub today is one of the rarest habitats in the Dales, being largely confined to two examples: Moughton Fell on Ingleborough and Thwaitestones in Swaledale.

At the end of the Late-glacial temperatures began to rise, marking the start of the Holocene epoch around 10,300 BP. The period of gradual climatic amelioration which followed is divided into the Pre-boreal, to 9000 BP, and the Boreal, to 7500 BP. In the earliest part of the Pre-boreal most of lowland Craven at least was covered by birch woodland, but this was replaced by Hazel (*Corylus avellana*) and Scots Pine (*Pinus sylvestris*), a phase also represented in upland Craven. Hazel became a major component of the Ingleborough vegetation by 8730 BP, early in the Boreal. However, the initial expansion of Hazel in lowland Craven was followed by a gradual decline throughout the Boreal period to a minimum at 7600 BP, when Scots Pine was near a maximum at some sites. At Malham the well-marked pine–hazel phase was replaced by elm (*Ulmus* species) and oak (*Quercus* species), a process mirrored elsewhere in the Dales. Pine fell to a minimum in lowland Craven between 6080 and 6400 BP, as Alder (*Alnus glutinosa*) rose to a maximum after the Boreal–Atlantic transition when the climate became wetter and warmer than in the immediate past. The mixed deciduous forest in which Alder was prominent probably extended over the whole altitudinal range in the Dales. Judy Turner showed this to be the case for the northern Pennines for the range from 200 to 750 metres, although with differences between sites; for example, Hazel and elm were more abundant at higher altitudes (Turner & Hodgson, 1979). There is little evidence to support what Oliver Rackham (2006)

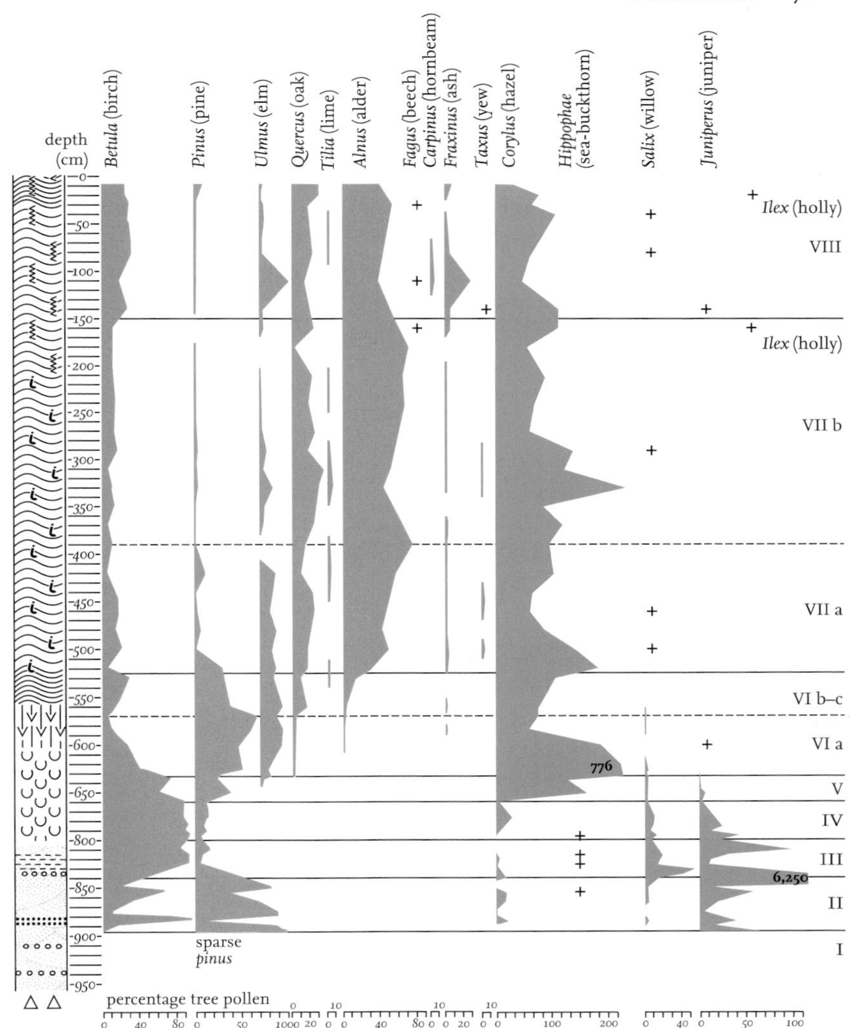

FIG 46. Tree pollen diagram for Tarn Moss, Malham, from Pigott & Pigott (1959). The vertical axis shows the depth of the peat from the surface, with the oldest at the bottom. The horizontal axis shows the percentage of total tree pollen for each tree type. Roman numerals indicate different pollen zones.

termed the 'savanna' model of ancient forests in the Dales, with groves of trees interspersed with large areas of grassland maintained by grazing of wild animals as proposed by Vera (2000). But undoubtedly some clearings will have persisted as the result of herbivore activity, and on the scars and summits of the highest hills forest cover is likely to have been much more open.

Between 6000 and 5000 BP the mixed deciduous forest cover in and around the Dales may have remained relatively stable, with lime (*Tilia* species) as a minor component. However, a major change occurred *c.*5000 BP with a marked decline in elm, a phenomenon mirrored elsewhere in Britain and mainland Europe. The cause of this decline has been attributed to the activity of Neolithic farmers, but its near synchronicity (thought now to be at most a four-year period) over such a large geographic area suggests either a climatic cause or the involvement of disease such as that caused by *Ceratocystis* fungi which was responsible for elm disease in the UK from 1965. The fact that the decline affected elm only, and throughout its range, points to disease as the most likely cause.

Another interesting feature at the time of, or soon after, the elm decline is the appearance of weed pollen such as Ribwort Plantain (*Plantago lanceolata*) and also cereal grains, of which the latter at least must mark human impact. In lowland Craven, a continuous curve in the Ash pollen record is established at around this time. One of the more remarkable features to anyone familiar with the Dales today is the paucity of Ash (*Fraxinus excelsior*) in the pollen record. To some extent this reflects the fact that Ash produces less pollen than other trees such as birch, pine and oak, and it is therefore probably under-represented in the deposits. Nevertheless, at the time of the elm decline, Ash was undoubtedly a much less important component of Dales woodlands than it is today.

On Ingleborough, Susan Swales determined that small-scale and short-lived decrease in the extent of mixed oak woodland due to human interference began in the late Mesolithic or early Neolithic period, *c.*5700 BP, and this provided evidence for pastoral and perhaps arable farming being undertaken on the shallow well-drained limestone soils. However, most evidence for forest clearance comes from the late Neolithic or early Bronze Age with cereal production in the Craven lowlands after *c.*4500 BP. Anne Honeyman showed a major clearance phase at three sites in Wensleydale dated at 4550, 3930 and 3850 BP, but concluded that the woodlands in the dale were coming under increasing human pressure from 5000 BP. In lowland Craven the first major increase in plantain and grass pollen in a profile from Eshton Tarn, midway between Malham and Gargrave, is dated to the early Bronze Age at 3600 BP, with increases in cereal pollen at 3160 BP. This profile also reveals an almost continuous curve for Salad Burnet (*Poterium sanguisorba*) pollen *c.*3100 BP, indicating the establishment of limestone grassland. But the work in lowland Craven also demonstrates that the forest clearance on shallow limestone soils occurred much earlier than that on the deeper, clay-rich glacial drift, with its much less easily worked soils. Thus in the White Moss region,

8 kilometres south of Settle, there is no evidence of major forest clearance until about 600 CE, two thousand years later than on the limestone around Eshton Tarn.

Although the mixed deciduous forest covered the whole of the Dales, the relative composition of the woodland would have differed from place to place. For example, on the less well-drained areas throughout the Dales, Alder would have been more prominent than on the shallow limestone soils, and there is some evidence that Hazel was more abundant in Wensleydale than in other areas throughout the Holocene. The more or less continuous woodland landscape of the Dales was gradually denuded as agriculture grew in importance, more quickly perhaps on the shallow limestone soils, and more slowly on the clay-rich glacial drift. This was certainly not a continuous process, and periods of forest regeneration occurred at times when the human population declined. However, it was not just the forest cover, but also its composition, which was affected by human activity. The preferential exploitation of species for agricultural and domestic purposes must have played a part in this. Harvesting tree foliage for feeding livestock is but one example. Elm was perhaps the preferred tree source, and this would have affected flowering at least to some extent, but Ash foliage, dried like hay, was also used to feed cattle – as it still is today in parts of Europe. Certainly one of the most remarkable features of the pollen record is the scarcity of Ash before the rise of agriculture, which suggests that this species was able to benefit from human activity by rapidly colonising abandoned clearings, and was certainly not being overexploited. Ash has some of the characteristics of a pioneer species, producing seeds that are fairly readily dispersed by wind and capable of germination in forest clearings or in the open. It has the further advantage that its seedlings can survive browse damage. Thus human activities may have inadvertently helped Ash rise to prominence.

The peat and lake deposits have so far told us little of the woodland fauna. However, cave artefacts reveal both a long human presence in the Dales and something of the fauna which was hunted by them. Radiocarbon dating by accelerator mass spectrometry has been used recently to date artefacts from the Victoria and Kinsey Caves. This has revealed that people were present in Craven before 12,000 BCE, hunting amongst other species Brown Bears (*Ursus arctos*), Mountain Hares (*Lepus timidus*), Reindeer (*Rangifer tarandus*), Wild Horses (*Equus ferus*) and Wild Cattle (Aurochs, *Bos primigenius*). This is long before any human influence can be detected in the pollen record. Cave artefacts by their nature cannot easily provide a continuous record through time, but rather occasional insights. For example recent dated finds of Lynx (*Lynx lynx*) bones suggest that large enough areas of woodland must have survived up to medieval times to provide a habitat for this predator.

PRESENT-DAY WOODLANDS

Ash is the predominant tree of deciduous woodland in the Dales today. In this regard alone the present semi-natural woodlands do not resemble the forest cover at the time of the elm decline and before human impact became appreciable. Oak is much less prominent now, as are elm and lime. This should really come as no surprise, even if some at least of the small area of present-day woodland has been continuously forested throughout the Holocene. The present-day woodlands must reflect their importance to the Dales people over many generations as a source of fuel, building, furniture and tool-making materials, as well as their uses in the lead and agricultural industries. It can readily be appreciated that the importance of oak as a timber tree might lead to demand exceeding supply and, if not carefully managed, provide opportunities for Ash and birch to replace oak. The ability of Ash seedlings to survive periods of browsing would also have been an important property in woodlands subjected to seasonal or occasional grazing.

Wood and timber were too important to communities to be left unmanaged. Management involved attempts to achieve a sustainable supply. In many parts of Britain this involved a system of coppice with standards. The coppice involved the repeated cutting of trees near the base of the trunk on a regular cycle of between 7 and 25 years, depending on the species, in order to supply wood for fuel, tools and many other uses. The standards provided large timber for building on a much longer cycle of about a hundred years. Coppiced trees produce many stems from each stool which are easily thinned as necessary and harvested. Pollarding, cutting the trees between 2 and 3 metres from the ground, also produces a regular supply of wood. It is harder work than coppicing, but it has the advantage where it is difficult or impossible to remove grazing animals, whereas successful regeneration of both coppiced stools and standards requires the exclusion of grazing animals for several years. Over time the composition of the woodlands might change, particularly if the timber trees were extracted and not given a sufficient period of grazing relief to allow successful regeneration.

The ancient semi-natural Dales woodlands are not uniform. They differ to some extent from dale to dale and also reflect differences in soils within a dale. Thus wetter or periodically waterlogged soils in the valley bottoms support Alder with associated willow species; the more freely drained acidic soils (although relatively rare in the predominantly limestone Dales) support Sessile Oak (*Quercus petraea*) woodland with birch and Holly (*Ilex aquifolium*); the shallow limestone soils support predominantly Ash with birch and some oak. Hazel is more abundant in Wensleydale woodlands than in other dales, and oak is largely absent from Swaledale woodlands. These ancient semi-natural woodlands represent a minute proportion of the National Park land cover (0.84 per cent), and less than a fifth of the total woodland cover (which was 4.45 per cent of the total land area in 2006); however, they are of great conservation value and most are National Nature Reserves, Yorkshire Wildlife Trust or Woodland Trust reserves or Sites of Special Scientific Interest.

Ash woods make up about 80 per cent of semi-natural Dales woodlands and mostly conform to the *Fraxinus excelsior – Sorbus aucuparia – Mercurialis perennis* woodland (W9) of the National Vegetation Classification (NVC) (Rodwell, 1991a, 1991b, 1992, 1995, 2000). This is the upland Ash wood community in Britain in which Ash and Hazel are ever-present and frequently dominate the woodland cover. Downy Birch (*Betula pubescens*) is common, and Rowan (*Sorbus aucuparia*) is also prominent, particularly in ungrazed woodlands. Wych Elm (*Ulmus glabra*), oak (usually Sessile Oak) and Sycamore (*Acer pseudoplatanus*) are also common, but Wych Elm has declined following the arrival of Dutch elm disease in the 1970s, and Sycamore will have become more common. Sycamore was introduced into Britain in the fifteenth or sixteenth century from central Europe and is not a native species (defined as a species present before the land bridge to the Continent was broken *c.*5000 BCE). It has become widely naturalised, and its presence is a certain marker that tree cover does not resemble closely the original Dales woodland.

Very locally in the lower dales there are small fragments of Ash woods more typical of southern England containing Field Maple (*Acer campestre*) and corresponding to the *Fraxinus excelsior – Acer campestre – Mercurialis perennis* (W8) woodlands in which birch and Rowan are less abundant than in upland Ash woods.

Most of the surviving Ash woodlands in the Dales are on steep slopes, for example the Woodland Trust's Hebblethwaite Hall Wood near Sedbergh in the Rawthey Valley, or in areas with irregular topography which leads to a mosaic, not only of the tree cover, but also of the shrubs and ground vegetation. The presence or absence of grazing also has a marked effect on the latter. In this mosaic, particularly where water seeps to the surface, flushing the slopes, Alder is frequently present. Alder is also found in woods where it is the dominant tree, conforming to the *Alnus glutinosa – Fraxinus excelsior – Lysimachia nemorum* (W7) community. These woods occur typically as often very small areas in wet gills or in strips fringing becks and rivers throughout the Dales. Other trees in this community include Ash, Downy Birch and Goat Willow (*Salix caprea*), with Sycamore often occurring on the slightly drier soils.

RIBBLEHEAD WOODLANDS

Two National Nature Reserves, Colt Park and Ling Gill Woods, both near Ribblehead, are thought to be fragments of the sub-alpine Ash forest which was once much more extensive in the Dales. Neither is currently grazed by domestic livestock. Colt Park is on limestone pavement and has been largely ungrazed since at least the 1930s, and probably only lightly grazed for much longer (Fig. 47). Ling Gill is in a steep-sided ravine cut into the Great Scar Limestone by the Cam Beck and flanked by moorland over glacial drift (Fig. 48). Woodland on the scars would have been free from grazing, but livestock was excluded from the gill in 1958, leading to strong woodland regeneration in places by the 1990s.

Both woodlands have an open Ash canopy corresponding to NVC W9 with other tree species scattered through including Wych Elm, Downy Birch and Aspen (*Populus tremula*) (in Ling Gill only). In addition, on the acidic soils on glacial drift above the southern side of Ling Gill gorge, there is the only example in the Dales of birch woodland over *Molinia*, corresponding to NVC community 4b, *Betula pubescens – Molinia caerulea* woodland, *Juncus effusus* sub-community.

FIG 47. Colt Park wood, Ribblesdale, an example of W9 *Fraxinus excelsior – Sorbus aucuparia – Mercurialis perennis* sub-alpine Ash woodland on limestone pavement, in which Ash and Hazel are ever present and frequently dominate the woodland cover.

FIG 48. Ling Gill, W9 sub-alpine Ash woodland in a steep-sided ravine cut into the Great Scar Limestone by the Cam Beck, looking across Ribblesdale towards Colt Park and Park Fell in the distance.

This community must have been much more extensive on soils over glacial drift in Craven in the past. The shrub layer of the Ash woods consists of Hazel, Hawthorn (*Crataegus monogyna*), Rowan and Bird Cherry (*Prunus padus*) (Fig. 49).

FIG 49. Bird Cherry (*Prunus padus*) flowering in Colt Park Wood, one of the commonest shrubs of Ash woodland and hedgerows in the Dales.

Mezereon (*Daphne mezereum*) is an uncommon component of the shrub layer in Ling Gill (Fig. 50). The lack of grazing has resulted in woodland with a tall herb field layer characteristic of the *Crepis paludosa* sub-community of NVC W9. This contains widely distributed species which favour cool, moist calcareous soils such as Meadowsweet (*Filipendula ulmaria*), Water Avens (*Geum rivale*), Giant Bellflower (*Campanula latifolia*), Wild Angelica (*Angelica sylvestris*) and Marsh Hawk's-beard (*Crepis paludosa*), which gives its name to the sub-community.

These woods contain important species of northern distribution in Europe: Globeflower (*Trollius europaeus*) and Wood Crane's-bill (*Geranium sylvaticum*), which form a characteristic plant community in Scandinavian birch woodlands on calcareous soils up to and well beyond the Arctic circle (Figs. 51 & 52). Other northern elements include Baneberry (*Actaea spicata*), Melancholy Thistle (*Cirsium heterophyllum*) and Northern Hawk's-beard (*Crepis mollis*), which is a rare plant in these woodlands. Local or rare plants also include Herb Paris (*Paris quadrifolia*), Yellow Star-of-Bethlehem (*Gagea lutea*), Angular Solomon's-seal (*Polygonatum odoratum*), and Prickly Sedge (*Carex muricata* ssp. *muricata*). Since grazing was excluded in Ling Gill, ferns such as the Male-fern (*Dryopteris filix-mas*) and the Lady-fern (*Athyrium filix-femina*) have increased, while the herb-rich pasture has become more species-poor. Holly-fern (*Polystichum lonchitis*) is another rare plant in Ling Gill. Ferns also abound in Colt Park, where the Hart's-tongue Fern (*Asplenium scolopendrium*) is common in the grykes, but more local species such as Limestone Fern (*Gymnocarpium robertianum*) also occur.

The large number of rain days at Ribblehead (225 per year) and high mean rainfall (1,920 mm per year) result in year-round humid conditions in Ling Gill and in the large deep grykes of Colt Park wood. The result is a rich bryophyte flora. This includes common moss species of calcareous woodland such as *Ctenidium molluscum*, *Plagiomnium undulatum* and *Rhytidiadelphus triquetrus*, but also less common species of northern or western distribution in Britain such as *Seligeria trifaria* and the leafy liverworts *Pedinophyllum interruptum* and *Plagiochila spinulosa*.

Both woods are now managed with minimum intervention to encourage natural woodland cover. Shortly after livestock was excluded some tree planting was attempted in Ling Gill, but this was largely unsuccessful except in the case of Aspen. Dutch elm disease killed a large proportion of the Wych Elms in the 1970s, creating gaps which have been left to colonise naturally. This minimum-intervention strategy is also designed to encourage and protect rare species including the woodlouse *Armadillium pictum* and the Red Data Book cranefly *Tipula cheethami*. Some grazing and browsing by Brown Hares (*Lepus europaeus*), Rabbits (*Oryctolagus cuniculus*) and Roe Deer (*Capreolus capreolus*) does occur.

FIG 50. Mezereon (*Daphne mezerium*), a rare shrub of sub-alpine Ash woodland.

FIG 51. Globeflower (*Trollius europaeus*), one of the most attractive tall herbs of damp limestone woodlands and meadows, in Globe Flower Wood, Malham.

FIG 52. Wood Crane's-bill (*Geranium sylvaticum*), a prominent component of the tall herb community in sub-alpine Ash woods.

In addition, English Nature established several small exclosures in the pasture immediately to the east of Colt Park Wood in the late 1990s (Fig. 53). Ash saplings grown from local seed sources were established in the exclosures, and these can be seen as small plantations effectively extending the wood into the surrounding pasture.

A rare example of Juniper scrub occurs further down Ribblesdale, at Moughton Scar on Ingleborough (Fig. 54). This corresponds to the *Juniperus communis* ssp. *communis – Oxalis acetosella* woodland community (W19). Before the establishment of the Ingleborough National Nature Reserve, this Juniper scrub had become moribund, in common with many other examples in the north of England. Juniper scrub is very susceptible to fire, and heavy grazing eliminates establishment from seed, although mature plants are largely avoided by browsing animals. In Teesdale, and probably in other Pennine areas, Juniper was cut for firewood, and large boughs were used as a base for haystacks (Gilbert, 1980). Juniper wood burns with little smoke, making it ideal for illicit uses such as alcohol distillation, and Juniper charcoal was also used in gunpowder production.

FIG 53. Small Ash woodland plantations, established in the late 1990s, in pasture below Colt Park Wood (top left of picture).

FIG 54. Juniper scrub at Moughton, Ingleborough NNR photographed in 2011 before it became moribund as the result of infection by the oomycete *Phytophthora austrocedrae*.

FIG 55. Hard Shield-fern (*Polystichum aculeatum*), a prominent fern at Moughton and common in limestone pavements and woodlands in the Dales.

Oliver Gilbert suggested that the survival of Juniper scrub in the Pennines resulted from the combination in the past of lead mining and farming, which often resulted in erratic pasture management and might allow regeneration if the grazing pressure was relieved long enough for seedlings to become established. Since the establishment of the reserve, livestock has been excluded from Moughton Scar, and the condition of the scrub had improved markedly, with young plants appearing. However, recently the scrub has become moribund again as the result of infection by the oomycete *Phytophthora austrocedrae*.

The scrub is notable for a rich fern flora which includes Hard Shield-fern (*Polystichum aculeatum*) (Fig. 55), Lady-fern, Scaly Male-ferns (*Dryopteris affinis* ssp. *affinis* and ssp. *borreri*), Polypody (*Polypodium vulgare*), Intermediate Polypody (*P. interjectum*), Rigid Buckler-fern (*Dryopteris submontana*), Limestone Fern (Fig. 56) and, most notably, Holly-fern (Fig. 57).

FIG 56. Limestone Fern (*Gymnocarpium robertianum*), a member of the rich fern flora at Moughton, a plant of screes, rocky outcrops and limestone pavements in the Dales.

FIG 57. Holly-fern (*Polystichum lonchitis*), a rare fern found at a few sites in the Dales.

LITTONDALE WOODLANDS

Hawkswick Wood and Scoska Wood are contrasting National Nature Reserves in Littondale. The former is southwest-facing on a steep slope below the Carboniferous limestone scar. The latter lies on a northeast-facing slope with the wood on the scar and upper slopes of the dale grading into herb-rich pastures below where springs with their associated flush communities emerge (Fig. 58). The difference in aspect is reflected in the fact that Scoska Wood has a cool, moist microclimate whereas Hawkswick Wood receives more insolation (solar radiation) and is drier (Fig. 59).

There is some doubt as to whether Scoska Wood is semi-natural, given the presence of strip lynchets. However it has certainly been a wood for several centuries at least, and the 1843 tithe map shows it occupied the same area then as it does today. The grazing history of these two woodlands also differed, at least in the years following the Second World War, with Scoska Wood being the more heavily grazed. In 1991 the grazing pressure was removed from Scoska Wood when it was fenced to prevent sheep and Rabbit grazing.

FIG 58. The edge of the northeast-facing Scoska Wood NNR in Littondale. The presence of strip lynchets within the wood suggests that it may not be semi-natural, but woodland has occupied the site since at least 1843, as shown on the tithe map of that date.

FIG 59. The view across Littondale to the south-facing Hawkswick Wood NNR.

These woodlands again conform to community W9 of the NVC, with Ash as the dominant tree with some Downy Birch and Sycamore while Yew (*Taxus baccata*) is only on the scars. The scattered shrub layer consists of Hazel, Hawthorn and Bird Cherry, but in Hawkswick some shrubs such as Rock Whitebeam (*Sorbus rupicola*) and Spindle (*Euonymous europaeus*) are present but confined to the scars.

Well-developed tall herb stands conforming to the W9 *Crepis paludosa* sub-community are confined to Scoska Wood, and are found at the woodland edge. These include Wood Crane's-bill, Meadowsweet and Melancholy Thistle. Tufted Hair-grass (*Deschampsia cespitosa*) is locally dominant in the field layer, which contains Dog's Mercury (*Mercurialis perennis*), Primrose (*Primula vulgaris*), Herb Paris, Ramsons (*Allium ursinum*) and Sanicle (*Sanicula europaea*). In Scoska Wood the scar and scree occur within the wood, supporting Baneberry, as well as several fern species including Maidenhair Spleenwort (*Asplenium trichomanes*) and Hard Shield-fern. Hawkswick Wood also supports a range of fern species including Maidenhair Spleenwort, Hard Shield-fern, Wall-rue (*Asplenium ruta-muraria*) and Green Spleenwort (*Asplenium viride*).

Hawkswick Wood's field layer contains Bracken (*Pteridium aquilinum*), False Brome (*Brachypodium sylvaticum*), Wood Anemone (*Anemone nemorosa*),

Bluebell (*Hyacinthoides non-scripta*), Ramsons and Dog's Mercury as prominent components. Near the scree a range of woodland herbs occur, including Herb Paris, Primrose and Lily-of-the-valley (*Convallaria majalis*). Wood Sage (*Teucrium scorodonia*) and Herb-Robert (*Geranium robertianum*) are also prominent on the scree. The damper nature of Scoska Wood is exemplified by flush communities at the woodland boundary containing Bird's-eye Primrose (*Primula farinosa*), Grass-of-Parnassus (*Parnassia palustris*), Marsh Valerian (*Valeriana dioica*), Fragrant Orchid (*Gymnadenia conopsea*) and Broad-leaved Cottongrass (*Eriophorum latifolium*). Scoska is also noted for a small colony of the Northern Brown Argus butterfly (*Articia artaxerxes*), and in nearby Scoska Cave there is a hibernation site of the Herald (*Scoliopteryx libatrix*) and Tissue (*Triphosa dubitata*) moths.

WHARFEDALE WOODLANDS

Grass Wood in upper Wharfedale, 2 kilometres upstream of Grassington, is managed as a nature reserve by the Yorkshire Wildlife Trust. It has been known for many years for its rich field- and ground-layer flora, which has been taken to indicate ancient woodland. However, the tree cover has been much altered from what is thought to have been W9 Ash woodland with Wych Elm and Oak until the nineteenth century. The wood occupies south- and west-facing slopes on Carboniferous limestone which outcrops as scars, screes and pavement areas. In the nineteenth century Beech (*Fagus sylvatica*) and Sycamore were introduced to the lower slopes, and in the 1960s the northeastern part of the wood was replanted with stands of Beech, Larch (*Larix decidua*), Scots Pine and Norway Spruce (*Picea abies*). In recent years the Wildlife Trust has been removing the introduced species, notably the conifers, to make a canopy that more closely resembles the presumed semi-natural woodland cover, and creating glades to encourage flowering plants and insects (Fig. 60). The wood contains both common field-layer species such as Bluebell, Primrose and Dog's Mercury, and also rarer species including Lily-of-the valley, Stone Bramble (*Rubus saxatilis*), Angular Solomon's-seal and Mountain Melick (*Melica nutans*) (Fig. 61). Although the vegetation is largely composed of calcicole (lime-loving) species, on the deeper soils Bracken and some calcifuge (lime-hating) species occur, and local seepage through the limestone leads to damp soils supporting Common Valerian (*Valeriana officinalis*) and Wild Angelica. More open areas in the rides support tall herb communities, and, on shallow soils, grassland calcicoles such as Bloody Crane's-bill (*Geranium sanguineum*), Common Rock-rose (*Helianthemum nummularium*) and Salad Burnet occur.

FIG 60. A Yorkshire Wildlife Trust working party creating a glade in Grass Wood, Wharfedale, renowned for many years for its rich flora.

FIG 61. Mountain Melick (*Melica nutans*), a grass of woodland, scrub and limestone pavements.

FIG 62. Dark-red Helleborine (*Epipactis atrorubens*), a plant of open limestone woodland, grassland, scrub and pavements, and a member of the rich field layer in Bastow Wood.

Bastow Wood adjoins Grass Wood to the northeast. It overlies a Celtic field system, suggesting that it is more recent in origin than the latter wood. The canopy is open, resembling that of wood pasture, containing scattered trees of Ash, birch, Sycamore and Rowan with a Hazel understorey. Other shrubs present include Hawthorn, Blackthorn (*Prunus spinosa*), Bird Cherry and Guelder-rose (*Viburnum opulus*), but the wood is best known for the rich field layer which includes uncommon species such as Dwarf Milkwort (*Polygala amarella*), Dark-red Helleborine (*Epipactis atrorubens*) (Fig. 62) and Jacob's-ladder (*Polemonium caeruleum*).

Lower down Wharfedale, above Bolton Abbey, is Strid Wood. This wood, in contrast to Grass and Bastow Woods, is on Millstone Grit. The wood lies on both sides of the river (Fig. 63). The northeast side provides the largest area of Sessile Oak woodland in the National Park, with an understorey in which Bilberry (*Vaccinium myrtillus*), Wavy Hair-grass (*Deschampsia flexuosa*) and Great Wood-rush (*Luzula sylvatica*) are prominent. Base-rich flushes occur locally within the wood. These give rise to Alder and Wych Elm as the canopy trees, and support a contrasting field layer with Opposite-leaved Golden-saxifrage (*Chrysosplenium oppositifolium*), Wood Melick (*Melica uniflora*) and Mountain Melick. There is also remnant oak wood-pasture with pollarded Sessile Oak, Holly and Downy Birch amidst acidic grassland and Bracken. The southwest side supports much altered oak and Ash woodland into which Beech, Sycamore, Larch and Douglas Fir have been introduced, but the soil is less acidic and supports a field layer in which Dog's Mercury, Ransoms, Sanicle and Sweet Woodruff (*Galium odoratum*) are prominent. Yellow Star-of-Bethlehem is a notable plant in this part of the wood.

FIG 63. Strid Wood, Wharfedale, looking southwest through remnant Sessile Oak woodland to the River Wharfe and the much-altered woodland beyond.

The ferns growing on the damp shaded slopes include Beech Fern (*Phegopteris connectilis*), Oak Fern (*Gymnocarpium dryopteris*) and Lemon-scented Fern (*Oreopteris limbosperma*). The bryophyte flora is rich, containing many common woodland species and less common ones such as *Amphidium mougeotii, Calypogea integristipula, Distichium capillaceum, Fissidens rufulus* and *Nowellia curvifolia*. The wood also has a rich lichen flora, possibly the result of woodland management by selective felling rather than by clear felling. Rarer species present include *Arthonia didyma, Cladonia parasitica, Endocarpon pusillum* and *Thelotrema lepadinum*, and the wood contains a rich fungus flora. The wood is also known for two uncommon minute land snails, *Acanthinula lamellata* and *Leiostyla anglica*.

AUSTWICK AND INGLETON WOODLANDS

Oxenber and Wharfe Woods near Austwick largely contain Ash woods and wood-pasture on shallow limestone soils with Hazel coppice (Fig. 64) and Hawthorn in

FIG 64. Old Hazel coppice on shallow limestone soil, Austwick.

the understorey. They have been grazed, and some shrubs such as Spindle and Dogwood (*Cornus sanguinea*) are more or less confined to the scars. Spurge Laurel (*Daphne laureola*) is also present. Field-layer species include Dog's Mercury, Wood-sorrel (*Oxalis acetosella*) and Primrose. At the northern end of Wharfe Wood, on more acidic soils, Downy Birch, Rowan, Holly and Hazel form the canopy, and the field layer consists of a mixture of calcifuge species such as Bilberry and Heath Bedstraw (*Galium saxatile*) with herbs of more neutral or calcareous soils such as Wood Anemone and Primrose.

Thornton and Twisleton Glens at Ingleton provide two deep-cut valleys with contrasting vegetation. Thornton Glen is cut into the Carboniferous limestone whereas Twistleton Glen is on the Silurian slate. The former supports Ash woodland with Wych Elm by the river, and Yew on the scars. Hazel is the most prominent understorey shrub. The field layer is dominated by Dog's Mercury, Ramsons and Tufted Hair-grass, but also contains a range of other common woodland species. Helks Wood in Thornton Glen was once known for containing the Lady's Slipper Orchid. Twistleton Glen supports oak–birch woodland with Pedunculate Oak (*Quercus robur*) and Silver Birch (*Betula pendula*) as the canopy trees. Small-leaved Lime (*Tilia cordata*) is also present close to the river. The field layer is typical of Pennine acid oak woods with Wavy Hair-grass and Bilberry as prominent components together with the Great Wood-rush. The woods are also known for their rich bryophyte and lichen floras. The former contains a number of Atlantic species near their eastern and southern limits, and the latter includes a number of rare species of old forests, including *Lobaria virens, Normandina pulchella, Opegrapha rufescens* and *Thelotrema lepadinum.*

SWALEDALE AND WENSLEYDALE WOODLANDS

Kisdon Force Wood borders the River Swale. It is predominantly Ash woodland on Carboniferous limestone conforming to W9 *Fraxinus excelsior – Sorbus aucuparia – Mercurialis perennis* woodland (Fig. 65). Wych Elm is an important contributor to the canopy near the river, and Downy Birch is prominent on the more acidic shale-capped spur towards the woodland margins. The understorey includes Bird Cherry, Blackthorn, Hawthorn and Rowan. The field layer includes Bluebell, Dog's Mercury, False Brome, Primrose, Ramsons and Sanicle, while there is good range of bryophyte communities.

Thwaitestones, on the southwest slopes of Kisdon Hill, is another rare example of semi-natural Juniper woodland. It contains mature Juniper plants with an understorey of Bilberry, Heather, Wavy Hair-grass and bryophytes on shallow soils with bare rock and screes and containing scattered groups of broadleaved trees, notably of Downy Birch and Rowan. It is owned by the Woodland Trust, who in the period 2005–07 attempted to establish young Juniper plants in areas adjacent to the mature stands. These attempts failed owing to sheep and Rabbit grazing, drought and vandalism. Laurie (2012) records that Juniper is widely distributed across the whole of the Swale catchment upstream from Ellerton Scar, but at many sites only a few isolated bushes survive, and these are often old plants with some bare branches and/or browned foliage. Juniper is absent from neighbouring Wensleydale (Millward, 1988).

FIG 65. W9 *Fraxinus excelsior – Sorbus aucuparia – Mercurialis perennis* woodland near Kisdon Force, Swaledale with Yew (*Taxus baccata*) colonising the limestone cliff edge.

Small fragments of semi-natural woodland occur elsewhere in Swaledale, notably in Rowleth Wood and in Birbeck Wood in Gunnerside Gill, the latter wood now extended by recent plantation of native broadleaved trees. Such woodland as remains in Arkengarthdale has mostly been affected by planting non-native trees, but a small Birch wood on a steep slope above the Arkle Beck at Eskelleth is unusual in the Dales in having a luxuriant field layer of calcifuge plants established on a rocky gritstone talus including Great Wood-rush, Bilberry and Wavy Hair-grass, perhaps indicative of former Sessile Oak woodland (Fig. 66). Many of these woodland fragments are very small and confined to steep cliffs and waterfall ravines where they are both largely inaccessible to livestock and Rabbits, and difficult to exploit (Laurie, 2012). On limestone cliffs Yew is often prominent, with Wych Elm, Rowan and Hazel, while in some ravines and cliffs Aspen is present, sometimes as small stunted trees. The Swaledale Woodland Project, led by Tim Laurie for the Swaledale and Arkengarthdale Archaeology Group, is producing detailed tree-site and individual tree records in these dales but also extending into Wensleydale.

FIG 66. Birch woodland on a rocky gritstone tallus at Eskelleth, Arkengarthdale.

Freeholders' Wood is an ancient woodland in Wensleydale extending to nearly 15 hectares in which the villagers of Carperby have estover rights, entitling them to take limbs of timber for minor building works and making farm implements, and to take dead wood for fuel (Fig. 67). It is a mixed deciduous woodland with Ash, Wych Elm, Pedunculate Oak and Rowan, but Hazel dominates over much of the area, providing as much as 80 per cent of the tree cover. It has been managed historically as Hazel coppice, a practice which has been revived recently using a 15-year rotation. The coppice is cut leaving a buffer zone of uncut Hazel around each compartment. The field layer contains many common deciduous woodland herbs including Wood Anemone, Bluebell, Dog's Mercury, Dog Violets (*Viola reichenbachiana* and *V. riviniana*) and Primrose. Herb Paris is also present. The Common or Hazel Dormouse (*Muscardinus avellanarius*) was reintroduced to this wood in the spring of 2008 (White & Court, 2012). Dormice nest boxes were set up, and 35 captive-bred Dormice were introduced initially in soft-release cages (Fig. 68). The nest boxes also allowed for standardised monitoring of the population. In September 2008, 58 Dormice were found in a total of 19 nest boxes, of which only 15 were the originally released animals. The largest litter observed was of eight animals. Population monitoring in the following three Septembers gave 40 animals in 2009, 17 in 2010 and 39 in 2011, suggesting that the reintroduction has been successful, a fact confirmed by continued annual monitoring, which for example gave 55 Dormice in October 2014 (Court & White, 2015).

FIG 67. A recently coppiced area of Freeholders' Wood, Wensleydale, with fencing to protect against browsing. The wood was historically managed as a Hazel coppice, and the coppicing has recently been revived.

FIG 68. A Dormouse box in a recently coppiced area of Freeholders' Wood. Dormice were introduced into the wood in 2008 and have become successfully established.

Ox Close Special Area of Conservation near Carperby is primarily designated for its grasslands in an old area of lead mining. However, it also has small areas of Ash woodland with a Hazel understorey on rocky slopes which contain the native Small-leaved Lime and a hybrid between it and the other native species, Large-leaved Lime (*Tilia platyphyllos*) (Donald Pigott, personal communication). This woodland has affinities to the *Tilio–Acerion* ravine forests in mainland Europe. Large-leaved Limes, often as multi-stemmed trees, are today to be found on the steep banks of the River Cover in lower Coverdale, and its northern limit in Britain is in Swaledale, where it is found clinging to cliffs on both sides of the Swale from Applegarth down to Richmond (Laurie, 2012; Pigott, 2012). In both these situations Large-leaved Lime cannot have been deliberately planted, but unlike the Small-leaved Lime it sets fertile seed in northern England, allowing natural colonisation of, for example, rock crevices. There remains some doubt as to whether this natural colonisation has been aided by human activities in the past. Several naturally colonised sites at least lie close to old monasteries where the tree may once have been planted by monks (Donald Pigott, personal communication).

PLANTATIONS

Three-quarters of all Dales woodland has been planted by humans, and mostly within the last two hundred years. Much of this woodland has been planted with non-native trees, broadleaved species as well as conifers. Sycamore, a species first introduced into Britain in the fifteenth or sixteenth century, and Beech, thought only to be native in southern Britain, have been planted widely. These species have commonly been planted to provide shelter belts, while mixed woodlands of Sycamore and Larch, both European and Japanese (*Larix kaempferi*), and the hybrid between them, have also been planted in gills and along river banks. In some parts of the Dales much of the woodland cover is confined to these latter habitats. Non-native species have also been planted into semi-natural woodlands, as for example in Grass Wood, and on river banks where they commonly occur with Alder and willow species, which were formerly major components of the wildwood in this situation.

The establishment of large conifer plantations in Britain began after the First World War and was particularly a feature of the second half of the twentieth century when for a period tax concessions encouraged landowners to invest in forestry. Among the trees planted in the Dales were several pine species including Lodgepole Pine (*Pinus contorta*), and Norway and Sitka Spruce (*Picea abies* and *P. sitchensis*). Sitka Spruce, a native of northwest America, was the main species planted in large blocks, not least because of its ability to grow well on poor soils in cool oceanic climates. Examples of these plantations can be seen in upper Nidderdale, upper Ribblesdale and Widdale, and it was also the practice to establish plantations around reservoirs, such as in the Washburn valley. The largest conifer woodland is Greenfield Plantation in Langstrothdale, which covers *c.*1,200 hectares.

Plantations of both deciduous trees and conifers have added to the biodiversity interest in at least one particular way. Many temperate forest tree species form a symbiosis with soil fungi called a mycorrhiza, literally a fungus root. In this symbiosis, the tree gains soil nutrients via the fungus in exchange for a carbon supply to the latter. The predominant form of mycorrhiza found in temperate forest trees is the ectotrophic mycorrhiza, in which the fungus forms a sheath around the tree roots. Many of the fungi involved in this form of mycorrhiza are toadstools or other members of the Basidiomycetes whose large fruiting bodies can be abundant in plantations in the autumn. In contrast, Ash, the predominant native tree of most surviving semi-natural woodlands in the Dales, forms vesicular–arbuscular endotrophic mycorrhizas. The fungi involved in these mycorrhizas do not produce large fruiting bodies, and as a consequence these woodlands generally lack a rich assemblage of toadstools except where subordinate ectomycorrhizal species such as Downy Birch occur. The mycorrhizal fungus most often linked by naturalists with the latter species is the Fly Agaric (*Amanita muscaria*) with its large red cap bearing white scales, but there is also a range of other species including several boletes such as *Leccinum versipelle* and the Coconut-scented Milk Cap *Lactarius glyciosmus*. Although most commercially planted species are ectomycorrhizal, one notable exception is Sycamore.

Robin Sutton has been recording the larger fungi on the Malham Tarn estate for a number of years, and by 2011 he had recorded 224 species (Shorrock & Sutton, 2012), many from the Tarn Woods plantation, and, of these, many species associated with Beech trees. These include species from known mycorrhizal genera such as Wood Hedgehog (*Hydnum repandum*), Orange Milkcap (*Lactarius aurantiacus*) and White Fibrecap (*Inocybe geophylla*).

The conservation interest in large, dense conifer plantations can be very limited, particularly from a botanical viewpoint, but from the zoological perspective this rises somewhat if they contain significant amounts of open grassland, which can attract owls and other birds of prey. However, in some areas in the Dales, conifers may play a key role in attempts to conserve Red Squirrels (*Sciurus vulgaris*) (Fig. 69). Populations of this species have declined for many decades as a result of habitat loss and fragmentation together with competition for food from the introduced Grey Squirrel (*S. carolinensis*). The latter also carry the squirrel pox virus, to which the Reds are particularly susceptible. The major centre of Red Squirrels is in the northwest of the National Park, notably in

FIG 69. Red Squirrel (*Sciurus vulgaris*). The major centre for these squirrels is in the northwest of the National Park, notably in Garsdale and Widdale. (Andrew Mason)

Cumbria. Stephen Rushton and his co-workers (2006) analysed the incidence of the disease and changes in the distribution of Red and Grey Squirrels in Cumbria over a 10-year period from 1993. They found that Greys increased while Reds declined. Not all populations of Grey Squirrels carry the squirrel pox virus, and these workers showed that the decline in Red Squirrel numbers was 17–25 times higher in regions where the virus was present in Grey Squirrel populations than when it was not. Using a modelling approach, they predicted that that Grey and Red Squirrel populations would overlap for 3–4 years before the Reds were lost, which was similar to what they observed in the field. The model also predicted that a Grey Squirrel control of greater than 60 per cent kill was needed to stop the decline in Cumbrian Red Squirrel populations.

The distribution of Red Squirrels in the Dales was summarised by Court & Fawcett (2008). They showed that in the period 1990–99, Red Squirrels were recorded in 83 one-kilometre squares, of which 79 were in the Cumbrian area and 4 in the Richmondshire area of the National Park. This compares with records from 87 squares in 2000–06, of which 65 were in the Cumbrian area, 21 in Richmondshire and one in Craven. These data suggest that the distribution of Red Squirrels in the Dales has shown some increase since the 1990s, perhaps as a result of more conifer plantations beginning to produce cones in quantity. Interestingly Lurz & South (1998) demonstrated another food source for squirrels in recent conifer plantations. In the Kielder Forest, they showed that Red Squirrels were caching fungal fruiting bodies in trees as a food source, of which the most abundant species was *Russula ochroleuca*. But whether this source of food is important to Red Squirrels in the Dales is unknown. Although the distribution data do suggest some increase in Red Squirrels in recent years, caution is necessary in the interpretation, given possible complications caused by increased survey effort, observer awareness and record submission. Nevertheless it would appear that some increase in Red Squirrel populations had occurred between the two survey periods, a fact supported by a later hair tube survey (Court & Bentley, 2011). Hair tube surveys involve strapping small PVC tubes (typically 300 millimetres long and 75 millimetres in diameter) to tree branches. Double-sided sticky tape is placed inside the top of the tubes together with sunflower seed and maize on the bottom. As the animals enter the tubes for the food they leave some hairs on the tapes. Using this method, Red Squirrel hairs were even recorded from tubes at Freeholders' Wood, 14 kilometres distant from the nearest known population.

The need for active conservation measures to conserve the Reds in northern England was recognised in the 1990s. The Yorkshire Dales National Park Authority produced its Red Squirrel Species Action Plan, which involved determining the distribution of the species, trying to ensure that appropriate woodlands were being managed to encourage the squirrels, and raising the awareness of its conservation requirements as well as of the need to control Grey Squirrel numbers. More widely across the North of England the Red Alert Partnership was formed which included wildlife trusts, the Forestry Commission, landowners, businesses and local community representatives. In 2005 this launched the Red Squirrels Northern England (RSNE) strategy, which designated 16 carefully selected Red Squirrel reserves across the region. These include areas within and adjacent to the National Park in Widdale, Garsdale and Mallerstang. Each reserve has a 5-kilometre buffer zone around it in which Grey Squirrels are controlled, and the planting of large-seeded broadleaved species such as Hazel and Sessile Oak, favoured by the Greys, is discouraged. In 2008 Greenfield Plantation was also designated as a Red Squirrel refuge.

OTHER WOODLAND MANAGEMENT

Management to encourage Red Squirrels is not appropriate everywhere. In some parts of the Dales conifer plantations have been removed. On Darnbrook Fell on the Malham estate this has been done to allow reversion to blanket bog where trees have been inappropriately planted in the past. At other sites, conifers have been or are being replaced by native broadleaved trees to improve the overall biodiversity interest, as for example in Grass Wood. This is encouraged by the National Park Authority, which also provides incentives for the planting and management of broadleaved and mixed woodland. The Yorkshire Dales Millenium Trust (YDMT), formed in 1996, is a charity with a mission 'to support the environmental, social and economic well-being of the Yorkshire Dales'. It carries out a range of environmental activities including the establishment of woodland. A good example of the Trust's work is the establishment of 4.5 hectares of new woodland at a site on the Bolton Abbey estate in Wharfedale including Posworth Gill and around the 700-year-old Laund Oak. This new woodland extends and links to Strid Wood. The planting site was made stock- and Rabbit-proof before being planted with Blackthorn, Hawthorn, Holly, Rowan, Crab Apple (*Malus sylvestris*) and Juniper as understorey species with the hope that the surviving oak trees would provide seed sources leading eventually to oak woodland. The Trust also has established new woodland plantations of native species on open fields at several sites, and by 2008 it had already been involved in hundreds of tree-planting and woodland restoration schemes in the National Park and surrounding areas (Speakman, 2014).

There is so little woodland in the Dales today that the renewed interest of the last few decades in its conservation and its modest expansion is greatly to be welcomed. Even some of the often despised larger twentieth-century conifer plantations may have considerable value in terms of the conservation of certain animal species, including the Red Squirrel, and possibly also of some birds of prey. However, it is unlikely that new large blocks of woodland covering the dale sides, which have been strongly opposed in the past (see e.g. Speakman, 2014), would be welcomed by residents and visitors who love the open Dales landscape or, for that matter, be approved of by the National Park Authority. New woodland of native species helping to provide corridors between the existing fragments, thus aiding species movement through the landscape, is probably the best conservation strategy at the present time.

THE THREAT OF DISEASE

A considerable threat to both old established and new woodlands is provided by tree diseases. The rare Juniper woodlands are already threatened by the fungus *Phytophthora austrocedrae*, a South American species until recently unknown in Britain, which has attacked and killed trees in neighbouring areas of Teesdale. By 2013, infection had also been reported at 11 sites in Cumbria (Douglas, 2013) as well as at Moughton, where in November 2013 Terry Whitaker (personal communication) estimated that over 70 per cent of the plants in over 14 hectares were already dead or moribund.

But much more important in landscape terms is Ash-dieback. The disease was first reported in Polish forests in the early 1990s as leaf loss, dieback of the crown of the tree and tree death, but the fungus responsible, *Chalara fraxinea*, was not identified until 2006. It was described as an imperfect fungus, that is a fungus for which only its asexual method of reproduction is known. It was shown to produce asexual spores (conidiospores) in sticky masses on ash leaves in summer. These spores disperse locally to create new infections on the tree and its neighbours. The sexual stage was not described until 2010, when it became clear that the fungus involved is the ascomycete or cup fungus *Hymenoscyphus pseudoalbidus*. The small white cups, about 3 mm in diameter, are produced on leaf midribs in the autumn. These shoot off ascospores, the sexual spores, which can be carried on the wind to infect more distant trees and spread the infection. Despite the identification of the sexual stage of the fungus, the disease is still most often known as *Chalara* Ash-dieback. The fungus is an invasive species from East Asia which since 2000 has spread to most European countries and infected a high proportion of Ash trees, including approximately 90 per cent of those in Denmark. Its first recognition in Britain in 2012 is a cause for considerable concern, not least because it is spread by wind-borne spores that make it impossible to contain by phytosanitation measures. Although it was first thought to have been introduced into the United Kingdom on recently imported young Ash saplings, raising the possibility that eradication in new plantations might be achievable, it has also been detected in mature trees in East Anglia. This suggests that the disease may also have arrived via wind-borne spores from the Continent, and if so, eradication may be impossible. The disease rapidly kills young trees, and may kill older trees quickly if Honey Fungus (*Armillaria mellea*) is also present, which it is in many woodlands.

Ash is the major forest tree in the Dales. Although no cases of Ash-dieback had been reported in the Dales by December 2013, infected trees had been recorded fairly close to the National Park, notably in the Forest of Bowland, and it seemed only a matter of time before it spread to the Dales. Sure enough, by summer 2014 outbreaks were reported at Malham Tarn and just north of Stainforth, little more than 10 kilometres south of the important Ribblehead woods of Colt Park and Ling Gill. If, as seems likely, the Ash-dieback becomes established widely in the Dales, the woodlands will become drastically altered. Because Ash is such an abundant and dominant plant in the remaining semi-natural woodlands, the disease probably would have proportionately a much greater effect on their ecology and structure here than for example Dutch elm disease has had on British woodlands in general.

A detailed study of the impacts of Ash-dieback on British woodlands has been made by Mitchell and coleagues (2014a, 2014b). As well as an assessment for the UK as a whole, these researchers also undertook assessments of the potential impacts of the disease on a number of important Ash woodlands, though unfortunately none of these were in the Yorkshire Dales. For the UK as a whole they found that 955 species were particularly associated with Ash woodlands and thus potentially at risk. They also found that many of these species could be supported by other trees: for example, oaks support 640 of the 955 species, suggesting that this lessens the threat to biodiversity from the disease. However, some epiphytic lichens and bryophytes of Ash trees, together with some specialist invertebrates, are most at risk. We might speculate that if Ash does succumb, Downy Birch and Sycamore would become much more prominent in Dales woodlands and, as these species are also able to support many Ash-associated species, there might be minimal loss of biodiversity, but the ecological character of the woodlands would change to some degree at the very least.

CHAPTER 5

The Lady's Slipper Orchid

The Lady's Slipper Orchid (*Cypripedium calceolus*) has a widespread distribution across northern Europe and Asia, and throughout much of its range this beautiful plant is not threatened. For example, it has been estimated that there are over one million individuals in Sweden. At the western extreme of its range in northern England, however, where most old records are from open woodland on limestone, it is extremely rare, and has been so since at least the beginning of the twentieth century. Indeed, by the middle of that century the orchid was regarded as the holy grail for many botanists and plant lovers in Britain. Most of the botanical community had thought that the plant was probably extinct in England by the time of the First World War. Rumours persisted that it might still be found somewhere in the Yorkshire Dales – but where? Many searches of likely places were undertaken over several decades, but any locations, if they existed at all, remained closely guarded secrets.

Old records show that this orchid was at one time distributed in a belt across northern England, from Lancashire and Westmorland in the west to Yorkshire and Durham in the east, with an outlying site on the Derbyshire Carboniferous limestone. The plant was probably never particularly common, but, for example, Curtis (1777–87) reported that 'it was in considerable plenty in the neighbourhood of Kilnsey'. However, its large and very attractive flowers would have made the plants both conspicuous in many habitats and desirable to gardeners. The net result was that it was dug up and sold. There are records of the plant being sold in Skipton market in the eighteenth century, and doubtless this would have occurred in other local markets in northern England. In his *Wild Orchids of Britain*, V. S. Summerhayes records the demise of the plant in the Ingleton area (Fig. 70):

FIG 70. Thornton Glen, part of the Ingleton Waterfalls Walk and the site of Helks Wood, where the Lady's Slipper Orchid once abounded.

> *It was first recorded in 1640 from 'a wood called the Helkes in Lancashire neere the border of Yorkshire' by Parkinson, a London apothecary, in his* Theatrum Botanicum, *an account of all the plants then known. The species was no longer to be found in Helks Wood, which is near Ingleborough, in 1796, it having been eradicated by a gardener at Ingleton who apparently had a ready sale for it.*

Reginald Farrer, who lived near Ingleborough, elaborates this story in his book *My Rock Garden* (1908):

> *Parkinson tells how the* 'Calceolus Mariae' *abounded in the 'Helks Wood by Ingleton, under Ingleborough, the highest hill in England', and had often (Oh shame!) been sent up to him, root and all, by Mistress Tomasin Tunstall, 'a worthy Gentlewoman, and a great lover of these delights, who dwelleth at Bull Bank, nigh unto Hornby Castle in those parts.' A worthy gentlewoman, indeed! O Mistress Tomasin, if only you had loved these delights a little less ruinously for future generations!*

The Lady's Slipper continued to be found at other localities in the Ingleborough district, but was 'rarely met with' in 1838, and by 1888 was said to be 'very rare'. Lees, in his *Flora of West Yorkshire* (1888), lists about ten old locations for the plant, but records that there were only two extant in 1887. Farrer also records:

> *In the Arncliffe valley the history of the Lady's Slipper has been even darker ... Here, in these mountain copses, ever since the time of Withering, the* Cypripedium *has been known. And one old vicar [Farrer is probably referring to Archdeacon William Boyd] kept careful watch over it, and went every year to pluck the flowers and so keep the plant safe, for without the flower you might, if uninstructed, take the plant for Lily of the Valley. Then one year he fell ill. The plant was allowed to blossom; was discovered and uprooted without mercy, and that was an end of him. And worse was to follow: a professor from the north [Edinburgh] ... put a price on the head of* Cypripedium, *and offered the inhabitants so much for every rooted plant they sent to him (one guinea). The valley accordingly was swept bare, and until the patient plant was rediscovered last year [Farrer records its rediscovery in Arncliffe in 1907], there was nothing left to tell of the glen's ancient glory except one clump of* Cypripedium *which, to keep it holy, had been removed to the vicarage garden, there to maintain, in a mournful but secure isolation, the bygone traditions of Arncliffe.*

Doubtless some nineteenth-century botanists and plant hunters added to the orchid's depredation across its range in northern England, and perhaps changes in management and grazing pressure contributed to its demise in at least one or two sites into the twentieth century, including at Arncliffe. But perhaps before we consider the recent history of the plant in the Dales further, we should consider the orchid's biology in more detail.

PLANT DESCRIPTION

The Lady's Slipper Orchid is a herb with creeping underground stems or rhizomes and erect flowering shoots up to 30 cm in height bearing three or four ovate pubescent leaves and usually a single terminal flower. It is capable of clonal growth, producing shoots as its rhizome slowly extends through the soil. The common name of the orchid comes from the shape of the mainly yellow lip or labellum of the flower, which is a deeply concave bowl said to resemble a lady's slipper. The flower is the largest of any British orchid, with the lip being *c.*3 cm in length and the maroon tepals 3–5 cm long (Fig. 71). The lip has an opening on its upper side that is partially blocked by the column bearing the reproductive organs. The column is terminated in a large shield-shaped plate or staminode, white with red spots with two lateral fertile anthers below and behind it. The result is that the lip opening is divided into three: a larger opening in front of the staminode with two smaller lateral ones adjacent to the anthers. The stigmas lie beneath the staminode and inside the slipper, and are covered in small stiff projections. The lip attracts insects, which enter via the larger opening but are unable to escape by that route owing to its incurved edges; but the insects do escape by crawling up the rough surfaces of the stigmas and past the anthers, carrying away pollen grains to fertilise other flowers. Unlike other British orchids, *Cypripedium* disperses separate pollen grains rather than in large masses or pollinia. However, grains are not dispersed dry, but in a substance that sticks to the insects. Observations on European populations have shown that the flowers lack nectar but attract pollinators by deception, in that insects still visit expecting nectar. Medium-sized female solitary bees of the genera *Andrena, Lasioglossum* and *Halictus* are the most frequent pollinators in Swedish populations, but the flowers also attract and trap small Coleoptera and Diptera species, some of which may act as facultative pollinators. The fruit is a capsule 3 cm long and nearly 1 cm in diameter containing at maturity between 6,000 and 17,000 dust-like oblong seeds that are probably wind-dispersed.

FIG 71. The Lady's Slipper Orchid (*Cypripedium calceolus*), the rarest flowering plant in the Yorkshire Dales, and one of the most sought-after in the whole of Britain.

All orchid seeds require infection by specific fungi to stimulate germination, and on these the seedlings are completely dependent for their early growth. Germination most probably occurs in spring, and a protocorm develops during the first year. In the second year the protocorm produces a scale leaf enclosing the stem and two roots. In year three the stem elongates, producing a large apical bud, and one or more new roots are sent out. It is not until year four that an aerial leaf emerges. Thus the orchid is completely dependent on fungal sugars for the first three years of growth. This raises the prospect that, if *Cypripedium* specialises on particular mycorrhizal fungi, the distribution of the latter may limit that of the orchid. The fungi involved could be acquiring carbon by saprotrophic decomposition of soil organic matter or by a mycorrhizal association with another plant in the community. This raises the prospect of a further restriction on the orchid's distribution. Studies of Estonian populations of *Cypripedium* have demonstrated that the fungi involved belong to the Tulasnellaceae family, to which many known orchid mycorrhizal fungi belong. The current consensus is that *Cypripedium* species are infected by specialist fungi belonging to this family, but much further work is required to identify the individual fungi, their distribution, and whether or not they are co-associates with other green plants in the community and, if so, with which species. What is certain is that a considerable time elapses between seed germination and flowering of the established plant. In the closely related North American species, *Cypripedium parviflorum*, the average time from germination to flowering is 12 years, and it is probable that the vegetative period in *C. calceolus* lasts for at least 6–10 years. *Cypripedium calceolus* is certainly long-lived, with many plants living in excess of 30 and some to more than 100 years.

THE HABITAT

Evidence for this comes from old records in England and the existing distribution in northern Europe. Most evidence supports the view that the Lady's Slipper Orchid occurs in relatively open woodland on lime-rich soils. In England all the old records were from soils formed either on Carboniferous or Oolitic or Magnesian limestone. Many of these records were from ungrazed or lightly grazed sites such as Castle Eden Dene in Durham, and on steep slopes with the soils containing perhaps little organic matter, but abundant limestone fragments. Although these soils might be expected to be freely draining, they probably also remain moist throughout the year as the result of seepage of water down slope, particularly on north-facing slopes with low evaporation. In northern Europe the range of habitats in which the plant is found is wider, including coniferous woodlands, alpine meadows and drained peatlands, but usually on soils with at least some calcareous influence. In the English sites, the open deciduous woodland is or was mixed stands of oak, Ash, Hazel and birch and a field layer containing species such as Wood Anemone (*Anemone nemoralis*), Lily-of-the-valley (*Convallaria majalis*), Wild Strawberry (*Fragaria vesca*), Herb Paris (*Paris quadrifolia*) and Stone Bramble (*Rubus saxatilis*). Establishment from seed is probably aided by some form of disturbance creating patches of bare ground. Seedlings and mature plants do not persist well under dense woodland cover.

THE REDISCOVERY

In the period immediately after the First World War, many naturalists thought the orchid was probably extinct in Britain, but a location near Grassington was accidentally rediscovered by two walkers. It is fairly certain that these were the Jarman brothers, cotton weavers from Silsden, and the date was 6 June 1930; although a Jack Smith, visiting the site in 1977, told the then warden that he had discovered the plant in 1928. What is certain is that one of the brothers, Willie Jarman, recorded the performance of the plant in 1930 when it had 14 shoots, one of which was in flower, and that he, and later his son Bob Jarman, continued to do so annually up to 1967. The discovery was kept a closely guarded secret to avoid the orchid's destruction by plant hunters. The discoverers shared their knowledge with a few trusted individuals, but exactly who these individuals were is not known.

A few years earlier, sometime in the 1920s, a group of prominent Dales naturalists met at Arthur Raistrick's house in Linton. What prompted this gathering is uncertain, but it may have been the discovery of the plant in one or more other locations. The membership of the group included John Crowther, Norman Frankland and Arthur Waters; and they continued to meet annually, forming a secret society sworn not to reveal either sites or that they had any knowledge of sites supporting the orchid. Norman Frankland records in *A Flora of Craven*: 'One specimen [of *Cypripedium*] found in a wood near Kettlewell 1927 by a youth named Raw of Kettlewell – root not taken', and perhaps this had been the catalyst for the secret society to form. At that time members may have also been aware of a site in Wensleydale, which Deborah Millward (1988) lists as being lost in the late 1950s or early 1960s.

Norman Frankland also provides evidence that the Jarmans' find was not immediately known to the members of the society. In a letter to the Settle naturalists Elizabeth and Brian Shorrock dated 19 December 1975, Frankland wrote:

> *L.S. was found ... in 1930 by Willie Jarman and his brother ... They were both spinners at Green's mill at Bradley. Green's wife told me several times to approach them about it. However I didn't believe it so I never did. Consequently I had to wait many years before I did see it there. It is really marvellous that it has persisted there so long.*

Thus for some years at least after 1930, there were two groups working secretly to conserve the Lady's Slipper in the Dales. Exactly when the interests of both groups coalesced around the one site near Grassington discovered by the Jarman brothers is unknown.

It is probably now impossible to discern who was party to the secret. The journalist and naturalist Eric Hardy is one for whom there is documentary evidence. In a letter to Ben Mercer of the Nature Conservancy Council in 1992, he stated that just eight people knew the secret. He had known about the site since 1930, and for many years had been working with his colleague E. Lloyd Jones on the fertilisation of the plant by *Andrena* bees.

In the early post-war years one or two others were let into the secret. Philip Oswald recalls that, in the summer of 1953, he and Peter Sell were invited to join John Raven (one of the authors of the New Naturalist *Mountain Flowers*) and his friend Dick Burges (a Birmingham general practitoner) on a botanical tour in Wales and northwest England:

> *We visited Grassington on 30 June, seeing,* inter alia, Polemonium caeruleum *but not* Cypripedium calceolus. *On one of the days around that time John related how, on a previous visit to the Yorkshire Dales with Dick Burges, a year or two earlier (I think), he was collected by car (I'm not sure he told us by whom) in order to paint* Cypripedium *in situ, but Dick was not permitted to accompany him; feeling rather guilty about this, the following day John said that Dick must decide what they did and at the end of it – despite his oath of secrecy – he couldn't resist telling Dick that he (Dick) had led him within 50 yards of the orchid plant! I think I realised only later that it had appealed to John's sense of humour that once again in 1953 he had taken us within a short distance of the plant; what I'm not sure about is whether we parted company long enough for him to sneak a look at it!*

One might have expected that more leading field botanists of the day would have been told, but this was probably not the case. For example, Ted Lousley appears to have been kept in the dark – for in his Wild *Flowers of Chalk and Limestone*, published in 1950, he wrote of the orchid, 'To-day it is one of the rarest and most elusive of British plants and one of the few I have not seen wild myself.'

In the early years after the Second World War news that the plant was possibly still present came from an article in *The Dalesman* in 1949 entitled 'The lost slipper of the Dales' by T. Hey, another possible member of the secret society. He recounted:

> *There have been occasional reports in more recent years [than 1909] that the Lady Slipper still survived in these hills. Whether by some miracle an odd plant still remains it is impossible to say, for the botanists who may know wisely keep silent … I was at my desk in Bradford one June evening in 1933 when an Airedale countryman [presumably Willie Jarman] called in to describe some episodes concerning foxes, Cononley way. But I soon discovered that he had brought far more interesting news than that – he had chapter and verse for the existence of* Cypripedium calceolus *in the Grassington neighbourhood. I will not disclose the spot, but he left me with notes of the history of those few plants over three years – how many had flowered, how cattle had nibbled back two of them, and how he was certain they still survived. If his story was true, and if those particular plants have escaped the collector's grasp in the intervening years, then assuredly the Lady's Slipper is still there. But I must say that I couldn't find it when I searched.*

Another person who certainly knew the secret by the 1950s, at least, was Dr Arthur Sledge of the University of Leeds. Dr Sledge was prominent in the Botanical Society of the British Isles and in the Yorkshire Naturalists' Union, being the vice-county recorder for the former body. But he was certainly a man who could keep a secret, as evidenced by a letter from his younger and close colleague in the University of Leeds Botany department, Dr (now Professor) John Lovis, which relates to the time immediately after the existence of the plant was made more widely known: 'Sledge never told me the location, but explained why, disclosing the existence of the secret society and its code of conduct.' John Lovis's understanding is that new members of the secret society 'had to agree never to disclose the site and never to admit they knew its location. Probably, also never to admit they had any knowledge of the group in the know. I think they were told the identity of other members, but discouraged from discussing the subject with any of them.'

Although the Jarmans kept the site secret, and shared the knowledge with very few folk, in later years they did inform local naturalists of the plant's existence. Evidence for this comes in a letter dated 15 June 1962 from Bob Jarman to Mrs Joan Duncan, Secretary of the Wharfedale Naturalists Society:

Dear Mrs Duncan,

I am thrilled to be able to inform you that my brother and myself visited the site of our lovely orchid 4 plants found. Two of them in flower. They are lovely.

We didn't stay many mins on the site. We are always uneasy some one may see us. And of course this information is not for Broadcast. Except to let your members know we still have the Orchid with us, and as there are now 2 in flower there is a chance at long last they may seed,

Yours sincerely

Mr R. Jarman

p.s. There is just one thing in regard to them. In the 32 years we have known them they have crept along to the left in nearly a straight line for about 6 yards. The present 4 are now nearly in a straight line, and at some future time I may be able to show the colour slides of my niece and let you see them.

They also gave records of the plant's performance to Mr Peter F. Hunt at Kew Gardens and to Mr D. G. Smith at Harlow Carr.

Reports that the plant might still be extant began to appear in the press. An article in *The Times* dated 6 August 1965, from an unnamed correspondent, was entitled 'Hunting the Lady's Slipper Orchid', and concluded with its discovery. It was probably only a matter of time before a member of the secret society, perhaps inadvertently, let enough information slip, or was followed by a plant hunter to the site. In part to guard against this possibility, a member of the secret society removed the flower buds in years when it flowered so that it remained relatively inconspicuous. This latter course of action removed any prospect of the plant reproducing by seed, and was a point of disagreement among members of the society. It would most certainly have interfered with studies on the plant's fertilisation by *Andrena* bees. This may have been the eventual catalyst for Eric Hardy to reveal the secret. He gave the approximate position of the site in his regular column in the *Liverpool Daily Post* in 1966 and in a programme for Yorkshire Television. In 1990, in another letter to Ben Mercer, he justified his action as follows: 'Publication as I did was the only way I had to retaliate against the person who ruined our experimental plans ...'

Dr Sledge, having seen the programme, was very upset, and in no doubt that it revealed enough of the location for anyone familiar with the area to recognise the site immediately, but he still would not reveal the location to John Lovis. John

Lovis recalls the aftermath:

> *The inevitable consequence followed within a day or two, there was a hole in the ground where the orchid had been. Whether by design (perhaps to remove only part of the plant to a more secure location in a botanical garden) or by accident, it ultimately proved that not all the rhizome was taken, otherwise the story would have ended there and then.*

There followed a number of articles in the press, including one by David Seymour in the *Yorkshire Post* in 1967 entitled 'Thief wins the game of hunt the Lady's Slipper'. The following is an extract:

> *More than 40 years ago three Yorkshire naturalists formed a secret society pledged to protect the Lady's Slipper ... One of the protectors Dr Arthur Raistrick ... was stalked and shadowed. He visited the plants only once every five years taking care not to be followed ... But inevitably one of the hunters finally found what is thought to be the last home in Britain of the Lady's Slipper. He dug up the roots and took the blooms. Dr Raistrick said yesterday: 'This was an act of vandalism. Over the years we have done everything possible to preserve the remaining plants.'*

Another letter from Bob Jarman to Mrs Joan Duncan, dated 12 June 1967, reported that all was not lost:

> *Dear Mrs Duncan,*
>
> *Re Newspaper cutting enclosed*
>
> *I now find the report of the plants being dug up is not correct ... As I visited the site yesterday I found 4 plants one of which is just coming into flower so I (am) very pleased we still have it.*
>
> *Yours sincerely*
>
> *Mr R Jarman*

Shortly after the theft, John Lovis found the site for himself, and went on to play an important part in the early conservation efforts. I saw the plant for myself in 1970 with colleagues from the University of Manchester when two shoots were in flower, and when the hole was still obvious.

For many years the site discovered by the Jarmans had been kept secret even from Nature Conservancy staff, and it is possible that there were one or two other sites which also remained closely guarded secrets. But by the late 1960s they were aware that the plant was still extant at only one site, and of the need to decide how best both to protect the site and to conserve the plant. A further complication, of which the staff were also aware, was an attempt by a well-meaning amateur naturalist to reintroduce *Cypripedium* into five sites in the Dales; but these reintroductions were said to be of the closely related North American species *Cypripedium parviflorum* and thus potentially detrimental to conservation efforts.

CONSERVATION

In September 1969 a meeting was called in Grassington under the chairmanship of Edgar Milne-Redhead, Deputy Keeper of the Kew Herbarium, which was attended by representatives of the Nature Conservancy, the Botanical Society of the British Isles, the Yorkshire Naturalists' Union and the Yorkshire Wildlife Trust, including Arthur Sledge and John Lovis, to discuss the conservation of the *Cypripedium* plant and its habitat. It was clear that just protecting the site was unlikely to be other than a short-term solution. The plant was probably a small single clone consisting of a few shoots, one or two of which were in flower in any one year; but from the Jarman records it was apparent that flowering had occurred in rather less than half the years between 1930 and 1967. Somehow it was necessary to increase the number of plants in the population. The likelihood of a single flower being pollinated naturally was very small, even if the plant was self-fertile. The best solution was to pollinate the plant artificially when it flowered. This course of action was agreed, and John Lovis undertook the task. Meetings to consider the orchid's conservation became an annual event, and in 1971 the present-day *Cypripedium* Committee was formed.

Nature Conservancy staff were aware of at least one plant of Yorkshire origin in a northern garden, and this could provide a source of pollen in the event that *Cypripedium* was self-incompatible. After experimentation on a plant of Swiss origin in the Leeds University Botany Department, John Lovis made a first attempt at pollinating *Cypripedium* in the field:

> *Two flowers appeared on separate shoots. I transferred the contents of two stamens, left two plastic labels indicating this was a Nature Conservancy project, and*

returned a couple of days later to transfer the two remaining stamens, only to find that both shoots had been cut down to the base and removed.

Whether or not the person responsible for this was the member of the secret society previously responsible for removing the flowers is a matter for conjecture. The immediate outcome was a decision by the Nature Conservancy that in future 24-hour protection for the site was essential in the critical late spring and early summer period. This was provided from 1971 onwards. But even with this protection, part of the plant was secretly dug up in 1975, further emphasising the urgent need to increase the number of plants.

The wardens' reports indicate a steady stream of people wanting to see the plant in the flowering period. In 1973, the warden reported 35 groups of people, ranging from one to seven in number, visiting the site, and most, on questioning, said that they had been on at least one previous occasion. The continuing pressure on the plant and its habitat that this was generating increased the urgency of its successful reproduction.

John Lovis continued to attempt to fertilise the plant each summer until 1977, when he left to take up a chair at the University of Canterbury in New Zealand. Dr David Harberd, a colleague at the University of Leeds, and an expert on the orchid genus *Pleione*, then took on the role (Fig. 72). Capsules with viable

FIG 72. Dr David Harberd fertilising the Lady's Slipper Orchid at its sole remaining site in the 1980s. (Phillip Cribb)

seeds were produced, and by and large were allowed to disperse their seeds naturally, but establishment of many rare plants from seed in the field can be problematic, and in the case of a long-lived orchid it might take several years, at least, before any success could be demonstrated. Therefore David Harberd also attempted to germinate seeds in the laboratory using media on which he had successfully grown *Pleione* species. This proved unsuccessful, probably because the commercial media then in use were not suitable for *Cypripedium*.

The annual meetings of the *Cypripedium* Committee initially encouraged enquiries on vegetative propagation, seed germination, and the search for more plants of known Yorkshire origin in gardens. An early attempt was also made to discover the fate of the unauthorised *Cypripedium parviflorum* introductions, and exhaustive searches by Dr Sledge showed that none survived.

The committee was particularly anxious to learn of any additional sites with native *Cypripedium* in the Dales or elsewhere in northern England. There had been persistent rumours of one or two other sites, also being kept closely guarded secrets, perhaps reinforced by a flower shown to Arthur Raistrick in about 1960 which was said to have come from near Austwick – where a plant of currently uncertain origin exists today. To this end in 1976 John Lovis wrote a paper in *The Naturalist* entitled 'Lady's Slipper Orchid (*Cypripedium calceolus* L.): a plea for help in its conservation'. In this he stressed the potential importance of a second colony for cross-pollination studies, and also that Nature Conservancy Council staff would handle any new site information with complete discretion. If some readers of *The Naturalist* had such information, they remained loath to entrust their secret to the national conservation body!

The germination and subsequent propagation of plants under laboratory conditions provided the most likely source of new plants from native stock for establishment in the field. The Sainsbury Orchid project was established at the Royal Botanic Gardens Kew in 1983 to pioneer methods of propagating and conserving European orchids, including methods of propagating *Cypripedium* plants from Dales seed. This was always going to involve time and considerable trial and error, not least because a method had to be found to replace infection of the seed with the specific fungus species that was required for germination. Peter Corkhill was now the member of the Nature Conservancy Council's staff primarily responsible for the conservation of *Cypripedium* in the field, and he worked initially with Robert Mitchell and then Margaret Ramsay at Kew.

To limit the trial and error it was essential to draw on expertise in the cultivation of *Cypripedium* species from abroad, and a visit to a Swedish orchid enthusiast, Svante Malmgren, proved important. He had developed a medium on which seeds which were immature, but contained mature embryos, collected

40–50 days after pollination, could be induced to germinate on a sterile agar medium including 'Vamin' as the source of amino acids, 'Soluvit' as a source of vitamins, and pineapple juice. This system was successfully adopted at Kew with immature seeds from the Dales. Germination occurred within two months in the dark. Once the seedlings developed a shoot and two roots, they were transferred to larger vessels and grown on for a further 1–2 years on the same medium before being planted in a loam compost.

The first few seedlings, germinated from seed gathered in 1987, were planted out close to the parent plant in the Dales in 1989. Initially there was a 75 per cent seedling survival rate, but none survived long term. In the early 1990s over 1,000 seedlings were planted out in various locations, but all apparently failed, partly at least as the result of damage from molluscs, Short-tailed Field Voles (*Microtus agrestis*) and Badger (*Meles meles*) activity. There were two questions arising from this: (1) how could the plants be grown to have a better chance of successful establishment in the field, and (2) what were the most suitable field sites? Peter Corkhill visited European field sites to gain greater knowledge of the habitat factors likely to lead to successful establishment. Success would probably be more likely if older and larger plants were planted out rather than small seedlings. He experimented with various composts before deciding on a medium consisting of a 4:1 mix of perlite and rotted wood chips with a liquid feed every 3–4 weeks. The plants were grown in open polytunnels at Colt Park Barn on Ingleborough (Fig. 73).

FIG 73. Young *Cypripedium* plants established in pots at Colt Park Barn prior to planting in the field.

FIG 74. Successful establishment of Lady's Slipper Orchid plants in the field to flowering and seed production at Gait Barrows Wood, Lancashire.

In this way he was able to grow plants on for 5–7 years, giving a much greater chance of successful establishment in the wild. These plants were all raised from seed resulting either from self-pollination of the Dales plant or from cross-pollination of the Dales plant with plants of Hornby Castle stock (thought to have come originally from the Ingleton area), or from self-pollinated Hornby Castle plants.

The *Cypripedium* Committee decided on a plan to establish populations in at least 12 sites across the recorded range of the plant, using if possible sites where it had been known to grow. This plan has been successfully put into action. By 2003 nine sites had been successfully established. The first flowering on an introduction site was observed in 2004 (Fig. 74). The first naturally pollinated flower producing a seed pod was in 2008, and by 2010, when a total of 16 sites had been established, plants at four sites had naturally produced seed pods.

CONCLUDING REMARKS

It is over 40 years since the *Cypripedium* Committee was established, and despite several setbacks the fruits of this considerable conservation effort are now being realised. This is in no small measure due to the dedicated staff past and present of the Nature Conservancy and its successor bodies, but also due to help from landowners, professional scientists in other organisations and expert amateur naturalists. The committee recognises the importance of demonstrating the success more widely by establishing populations on some sites where the general public can see this beautiful orchid growing in the wild. Currently Kilnsey Park in Wharfedale (Fig. 75), near several sites for which there are old records, is one location chosen for this purpose, taking advantage of the annual orchid festival held there in late May and June. Another site, outside the Dales, is Gait Barrows National Nature Reserve near Morecambe Bay, at the western end of its historic geographical distribution. But history teaches us that we should not be complacent. These new populations can be easily lost, for example by theft and vandalism, and most will remain unpublicised for years to come.

FIG 75. Kilnsey Crag, an area of Wharfedale which was once a stronghold of the Lady's Slipper Orchid, and where at nearby Kilnsey Park the flowering of reintroduced plants can be observed.

CHAPTER 6

Pavements, Scars and Screes

Limestone pavements are amongst the most characteristic landscape features of the Dales, but are unusual in Britain as a whole, covering only *c.*2,600 hectares. The National Park contains more than a third of this total area, some 1,050 hectares (Webb, 2013), and some of the finest examples in the country, making this nationally one of the Dales' most important habitats. However, the pavements are not uniformly distributed across the Dales. Major areas occur around the Three Peaks of Ingleborough, Pen-y-ghent and Whernside, and in the Malham High Country between Arncliffe and Malham. Many of the finest pavements occur on benches of the Great Scar Limestone, but the Devensian ice entombed the whole region, and pavements are also found on the Yoredale limestones which overlie them. From a distance, the bare grey expanses of rock which constitute many of the pavements are visually striking, but appear almost desert-like, largely devoid of vegetation with the fissures scarcely visible. But close up, their important geomorphological and botanical features can both be readily appreciated.

The scars or exposed rocky cliffs with the screes below them are also important features of the stepped valleys which constitute the characteristic Dales landscape. At first sight the pavements, scars and screes would appear to have little in common apart from exposures of apparently bare rock, but in the stepped landscape they can be closely associated: a scar, and the scree below it, grading onto a bench fronted by a band of pavement. An important feature common to all three landforms is that they provide some protection from grazing pressure. In the case of scars this can be appreciated very readily, given their many near-vertical slopes, parts of which at least are inaccessible to all but the most agile large herbivores. Protection from grazing is less obvious on the near-horizontal limestone benches where the pavements are mostly situated. Here the protection is provided by the structure of the pavements themselves, largely resulting from weathering of the limestone since the Devensian glaciation. Grazing and browsing animals can venture across the pavement surfaces, but the vegetation in the deep and sometimes narrow fissures in the limestone is inaccessible to sheep, cattle and deer. This protection from grazing in these two habitats has greatly contributed to their rich biodiversity today. Screes are open to grazing animals, but they often occur on very steep slopes below the scars, and their inherent instability provides some deterrence to herbivores, while at the same time providing crevices in the rock talus in which plants can become established.

FORMATION AND STRUCTURE OF LIMESTONE PAVEMENTS

During the Devensian period (115,000–12,000 years ago) ice sheets plucked and scoured the near-horizontal limestone benches, removing any vegetation, soil and loose surface rock. Glacial drift and erratic boulders littered the newly exposed strong limestone beds as the ice retreated and, in the periglacial conditions which resulted, a layer of silt in the form of wind-blown loess was also deposited on them from large source areas in what is now the Irish Sea. Glacial drift and loess layers were not uniformly distributed across the benches, but it is generally considered that most of the bare pavements we see today were formed under at least a thin soil cover. This view is supported, for example, by excavations for road widening in Stainmore, north of the National Park, which revealed a pavement buried beneath 50 cm of soil (Webb & Glading, 1998). Although most of the loess deposition occurred during the Late-glacial period, there is evidence of it being reworked in the Holocene when periglacial conditions returned in a brief period of major cooling lasting perhaps 100 years and about 8,200 years ago (Wilson *et al.*, 2012). These researchers suggest that increased snow fall and prolonged snow lie at this period contributed to the reworking of the loess deposits, resulting in loss of soil cover. Much of this loss from the near-horizontal pavements must have occurred by soil disappearing into the developing fissures, a process probably accelerated from Neolithic times onwards by forest clearance and grazing livestock.

Carboniferous limestone weathers as the result of the action of carbon dioxide dissolved in rainwater, and this weathering is greatest along vertical lines of weakness or joints in the limestone. Such joints, some of which may have been opened up a little by glacial drag, are abundant. Over time they are enlarged as the limestone dissolves, leaving little or no mineral material and producing fissures. This process occurs, albeit very slowly, without any plant or soil cover, but it is accelerated once plants and microorganisms become established in the fissures and in the covering of loess and/or glacial till, not least because of the creation of a more or less permanently damp interface with the limestone surface. Plant roots and microorganisms in the skeletal soils raise the carbon dioxide concentration in the percolating rainwater through respiration, thereby increasing the solubility of the limestone. Organic and humic acids are also released, and these increase the water's corrosive power. The net result is to increase the rate of limestone weathering over that produced sub-aerially, which over millennia has not only slowly lowered the pavement surface, but also widened the fissures appreciably. These wide fissures are today known as grykes or kluftkarren, and the blocks of limestone between the fissures are known as clints or flachkarren, The grykes vary considerably in their depths and widths both within and between pavements. Maximum depth is determined by the depth of the surface limestone bed, since grykes usually only extend through a single bed. Many grykes are between 50 cm and 2 metres deep and between 50 mm and 50 cm in width, but there are many exceptions. Size and density within and between pavements both vary considerably. At one extreme, there are heavily dissected pavements with a high density of grykes and extremely small clints (Fig. 76). Some of the best examples of these occur close to the Craven and

FIG 76. An example of a heavily dissected limestone pavement with many small clints and a high density of grykes, Moughton, Ingleborough NNR.

FIG 77. An area of limestone pavement with massive clints and a low density of grykes, Scar Close, Ingleborough NNR.

Dent faults. At the other extreme there are pavements, or areas within pavements, with few widely spaced joints giving rise to massive clints and few grykes (Fig. 77).

There has been discussion as to whether the pavements that we observe today, some of which have very large and deep fissures, can have resulted simply from weathering since the Last glaciation, or whether they have resulted, at least in part, from older weathering processes. Evidence that many pavements are Post-glacial features can be most easily seen on some more steeply sloping pavements such as on Hutton Roof crag in Cumbria. Here bare surface pavement areas often show long shallow drainage runnels (rinnenkarren) in adjacent clint surfaces which appear to have been once continuous and which deepen down slope, but are now separated by a gryke. These shallow runnels could not have survived glacial erosion, and thus must be Post-glacial in origin, as must be the grykes that now cut across the paths they once followed, before appreciable weathering of the joints occurred (Fig. 78). However, several authors have suggested that some pavements may not have been subjected to wholesale stripping by ice, and that areas of pavement with deep wide grykes are probably pre-Devensian in origin, since they would not have had time to produce such large structures by solution processes in the Post-glacial period. These pavement areas have been given the name palaeokarst, and examples can be seen on Scar Close in Chapel-le-Dale. Indeed Vincent (1995) has suggested that some observable features in limestone pavements today may have their origins in luxuriant forests established on stranded Carboniferous coral beaches 300 million years ago.

FIG 78. Rinnenkarren, a Post-glacial feature consisting of small sharp-edged runnels on sloping clint surfaces which were once apparently continuous. The gryke that the rinnenkarren now cross must have developed later. Hutton Roof, Cumbria.

There is little doubt that for much of the Post-glacial period the Dales pavements supported woodland. In bare areas, or areas with only very shallow glacial drift or loess cover, the trees could only establish in the developing grykes where their roots could penetrate small fissures in the limestone. This might suggest that any areas of palaeokarst with grykes already formed would provide the initial foci for woodland establishment. Once a tree canopy was established, this provided conditions for the colonisation of mosses and subsequently herbaceous plants and grasses even on bare, near-horizontal, clint surfaces. Tree growth was probably slow, and in situations where the clints were massive and the grykes widely spaced, it is probable that the canopy remained open, perhaps aided by browsing by deer and other large mammals. However, most of the pavement development must have been under a vegetation cover, and even the apparently bare rocks we see today are in fact covered in saxicolous lichens, which must also appreciably influence weathering processes.

MICROCLIMATES

Aspect is an important property of landscape features, and nowhere more so than on hillsides and their scars in upland areas. Scars on south-facing slopes receive greater amounts of insolation (solar radiation) than north-facing ones. The result is that south-facing scars and screes are warmer and drier than north-facing ones, and this is reflected in the plant communities which have become established on them. The higher the scar, the cooler the climate and the shorter the growing season, producing conditions which on the north- and east-facing slopes of the higher hills have allowed the persistence of some arctic–alpine species: relics of the Dales vegetation immediately following the retreat of the Devensian ice sheets.

Microclimate is also an important feature of limestone pavements. Orientation plays a part in the microclimate within grykes, with grykes that run east to west receiving greater amounts of insolation than those that run north to south. In the Great Scar Limestone the main trend in orientation is northwest to southeast, but the total amount of insolation received drops rapidly with depth whatever the gryke orientation. In deep grykes little direct insolation occurs, and the crevices in which plants can become established remain cool and shaded. However, although little light may penetrate into the deepest grykes, the thermal mass of the limestone provides protection from severe winter frosts, and helps to maintain cool and moist conditions with little air turbulence at depth throughout the year. Alexander *et al.* (2005) recorded freezing events in grykes at Clawthorpe Fell National Nature Reserve, Cumbria, over one winter. The temperature fell below freezing on 23 occasions at the gryke top, but not at all at the bottom (> 100 cm deep). Silvertown (1982) measured the diurnal fluctuation in temperature at the top and bottom of a gryke at Highfolds, Malham, which was approximately 100 cm deep and 20 cm wide. He showed that in July the temperature remained a fairly constant *c.*10 °C at the bottom, whereas at the top it fluctuated from 10 °C, or a little lower near dawn, to over 20 °C in the afternoon (Fig. 79). This damping of environmental variables at depth contrasts markedly with conditions on the exposed clint surfaces, which in the absence of tree or shrub cover receive maximal insolation, and are exposed to the extremes of temperature, precipitation and wind, resulting in rapid wetting and drying cycles, conditions to which few plants except the saxicolous lichens have adapted. Thus this extreme contrast in microclimate is expressed within a metre or two vertically.

However, once trees and shrubs become established in the grykes, and begin to cast some shade on the clints, climatic extremes are reduced and mosses begin to colonise the limestone surface. Over time this allows for the accumulation of organic matter and the beginnings of a skeletal soil development permitting the establishment of flowering plants on the pavement surface (Fig. 80). Where trees have been established for a considerable period of time, the pavement structure is more or less obscured by the vegetation, and little or no bare limestone is exposed. A good example of the latter is Colt Park Wood, where, in summer in particular, it is extremely treacherous to attempt to walk across the pavement

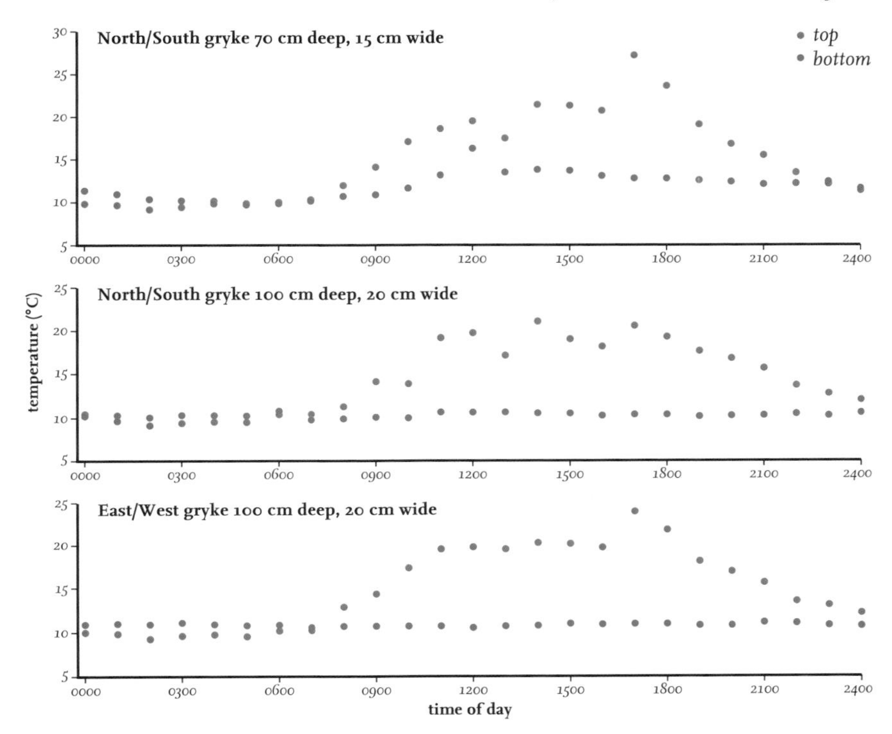

FIG 79. Diurnal temperature variation at the surface and bottom of grykes at Highfolds, Malham, in July, from Silvertown (1982).

FIG 80. Scrub establishment providing conditions suitable for moss encroachment onto the clint surface and the beginnings of soil establishment, Scar Close, Ingleborough NNR.

surface, as the position of the grykes can be difficult to see. Before humans began to remove the forest cover, most if not all the pavement surfaces we see today would have had a vegetation cover, whether or not there was a thin layer of mineral soil. The microclimate created by the forest canopy was essential for this, and once removed, perhaps by fire, the skeletal soils were easily lost as the plants succumbed to climatic extremes, particularly to periodic drought, perhaps also exacerbated by the hooves of grazing animals. A net effect of this vegetation and soil loss was to reduce considerably the rate of limestone solution.

PAVEMENTS

The pavements contain a mosaic of woodland and open-habitat communities. Even the open pavements with little or no scrub development today maintain a woodland flora in the grykes similar to the field layer of the sub-alpine Ash woodlands (W9), which is perhaps a relic of the former Post-glacial forest cover. Common woodland plants such as Wood Anemone (*Anemone nemorosa*), Ramsons (*Allium ursinum*), Sanicle (*Sanicula europaea*), Wood-sorrel (*Oxalis acetosella*), Dog's Mercury (*Mercurialis perennis*), Enchanter's Nightshade (*Circaea lutetiana*), Herb-Robert (*Geranium robertianum*), and Wall Lettuce (*Mycelis muralis*) abound. Woodland ferns are also prominent including Hart's-tongue (*Asplenium scolopendrium*) (Fig. 81), Male-fern (*Dryopteris filix-mas*) and Hard Shield-fern (*Polystichum aculeatum*); but an open-habitat community (OV40) also occurs which includes Maidenhair Spleenwort (*Asplenium trichomanes*), Brittle Bladder-fern (*Cystopteris fragilis*), and Wall-rue (*Asplenium ruta-muraria*) together with common moss species of limestone habitats such *Ctenidium molluscum, Fissidens dubius, Neckera crispa* and *Tortella tortuosa.*

However, it is not the common plants alone which make the flora of limestone pavements remarkable; the grykes contain a range of rare and restricted species. These include Baneberry (*Actaea spicata*) (Fig. 82), Angular Solomon's-seal (*Polygonatum odoratum*), Bloody Crane's-bill (*Geranium sanquineum*) (Fig. 83), Downy Currant (*Ribes spicatum*), Herb Paris (*Paris quadrifolia*), Mountain Melick (*Melica nutans*), Dark-red Helleborine (*Epipactis atrorubens*), Alpine Cinquefoil (*Potentilla crantzii*), Lesser Meadow-rue (*Thalictrum minus*), Northern Bedstraw (*Galium boreale*), Stone Bramble (*Rubus saxatilis*), Narrow-leaved Bitter-cress (*Cardamine impatiens*) and Lily-of-the-valley (*Convallaria majalis*). Another important feature is the presence of uncommon ferns such as Green Spleenwort (*Asplenium viride*), Rigid Buckler-fern (*Dryopteris submontana*) (Fig. 84), Holly-fern (*Polystichum lonchitis*) and Limestone Fern (*Gymnocarpium robertianum*).

FIG 81. Hart's-tongue (*Asplenium scolopendrium*) growing near the top of a gryke, Scar Close, Ingleborough NNR.

FIG 82. Baneberry (*Actaea spicata*) growing between limestone rocks at the edge of Southerscales limestone pavement, Ingleborough NNR.

FIG 83. Bloody Crane's-bill (*Geranium sanguineum*) growing in a shallow gryke, Scar Close, Ingleborough NNR.

Species vary in their distribution within grykes. Some flowering plants such as Lesser Meadow-rue, Alpine Cinquefoil, Bloody Crane's-bill, Lily-of-the-valley and Wall Lettuce are typically found near the top of grykes, whereas Sanicle and Wood-sorrel are frequently found in deeper situations. A similar difference in distribution can be found with the bryophytes and ferns. Mosses at or near the lips of the grykes are species found on wall tops and other open

FIG 84. Rigid Buckler-fern (*Dryopteris submontana*), a central and southern European species which in Britain is largely confined to the Carboniferous limestone of the Yorkshire Dales and around Morecambe Bay.

habitats and include *Tortella tortuosa*, *Grimmia pulvinata* and *Bryoerythrophyllum recurvirostrum*. These are usually present as small tufts and cushions, while at the bottom are found mats of typical woodland species such as *Eurhynchium striatum*, *Plagiomnium undulatum* and *Thamnobryum alopecurum*. Ferns such as Wall-rue and Maidenhair Spleenwort commonly occur near the top of grykes, with Hart's-tongue able to survive and thrive at depth. To some extent at least this must reflect the species' individual responses to the variation in the range of environmental conditions. Ability to establish in the deepest situations must depend on a considerable degree of shade tolerance. Porter (1994) showed that prothalli (gametophytes) of the Hart's-tongue fern have a very low light compensation point (the irradiance at which photosynthetic gain of carbon dioxide balances respiratory loss), and the success of the fertile fronds (sporophytes), as measured by the number of fertile fronds, increased with depth in grykes. However, plants more often found lower down grykes on open pavements are found near the top on wooded pavements, probably reflecting plant responses to deep shade.

Although much of the limestone pavement's biodiversity resides in the grykes, the clint surface is not without interest. For example, locally the differential weathering of the impermeable limestone surface has produced runnels. On many pavements these take the form of smooth depressions, usually a few centimetres deep and rounded in cross section. These are known as rundkarren (Fig. 85), and are thought to have been formed under deeper soils compared with the similar structures with sharp edges known as rinnenkarren, which are best developed on sloping pavements. On near-horizontal benches other prominent features include solution cups or kamenitzas (Fig. 86). These are shallow closed depressions, sometimes as small as 20 cm in diameter and a few centimetres deep, in which water accumulates. Given the high precipitation falling on the Great Scar Limestone benches, some of the solution cups and also some of the runnels rarely dry out in summer, and give rise, very locally, to a wetland vegetation in marked contrast to the surrounding freely draining clints and grykes.

FIG 85. Rundkarren, rounded channels on the clint surface formed originally under a soil cover, a common feature of many limestone pavements.

FIG 86. A kamenitza, a hollow in the clint surface in which water collects, and which over time becomes colonised by plants, Scar Close, Ingleborough NNR.

Hairy Stonecrop (*Sedum villosum*) is a prominent plant in these runnels (Fig. 87), while locally on wet limestone surfaces on Ingleborough the English or Yorkshire Sandwort (*Arenaria norvegica* ssp. *anglica*) occurs; this is one of only two known locations for this plant, the other being Dawson Fold, east of Pen-y-ghent (Fig. 88). Kamenitzas are colonised by a variety of wetland organisms, and lichens may play an important role in their development when their thalli expand and contract in wetting and drying cycles, plucking tiny fragments of limestone from the surface in the process (Moses & Smith, 1993). Ivemy-Cook (1965), following investigations at Hutton Roof, Cumbria, suggested that there was a succession in these cups in which mats of the cyanobacterium *Nostoc commune* were followed by colonisation by mosses including *Fissidens adianthoides*, *F. dubius* and *Tortella tortuosa* and lichen species. This in turn was followed by the establishment of Jointed Rush (*Juncus articulatus*) and Yellow Sedge (*Carex viridula* ssp. *oedocarpa*). As the skeletal soil accumulated, Flea Sedge (*Carex pulicaris*) invaded and became dominant. These cups in the Malham area also support a specialist cyanolichen flora including *Lempholemma botryosum* and *L. cladodes*, and are also notable for an abundant midge species, *Dasyhelea lithotelmatica*, which Henry Disney recorded there and was new to Britain in 1974.

FIG 87. A partially vegetated damp runnel with Hairy Stonecrop (*Sedum villosum*) in flower, Scar Close, Ingleborough NNR.

FIG 88. English Sandwort (*Arenaria norvegica* ssp. *anglica*), endemic to bare limestone in the Dales, Ingleborough NNR.

The pavements of the Great Scar limestone on the northern side of Ingleborough are amongst the finest in Britain. From Southerscales in the west (Fig. 89) through Scar Close to Colt Park Wood in the east is a series of pavements of outstanding conservation interest, all now part of the Ingleborough National Nature Reserve. It also represents the full range of vegetation cover, from the largely bare pavements of Southerscales, managed by the Yorkshire Wildlife Trust, which are still open to cattle and sheep grazing, to the complete woodland cover of Colt Park (see Chapter 4), which is ungrazed by domestic livestock; this

FIG 89. Limestone pavement at Southerscales, a Yorkshire Wildlife Trust reserve and part of the Ingleborough NNR.

has been so since at least 1962 when it was declared a National Nature Reserve, and was probably so for long before then. The long-standing importance of the wood can be judged by the then owner Thomas Dugdale including in the 1937 tenancy agreement with George Pratt for Colt Park Farm the stipulation that 'the tenant shall preserve all timber and other trees and shall not cut down, lop, top or injure them.'

Scar Close is to some extent intermediate between Colt Park and Southerscales, containing open areas of pavement with patches of scrub development (Fig. 90) from which grazing by domestic livestock was removed in 1975. Scar Close also contains small areas of vegetation which are in marked contrast to the freely drained calcicole (lime-loving) limestone flora. Locally patches of heath vegetation are established on glacial till or shallow peat over the limestone with affinities to the *Calluna vulgaris – Eriophorum vagnatum* blanket mire (M19). This calcifuge (lime-fleeing) vegetation includes Heather (*Calluna vulgaris*), Bilberry (*Vaccinium myrtillus*), Crowberry (*Empetrum nigrum*), Hare's-tail Cottongrass (*Eriophorum vaginatum*) and Wavy Hair-grass (*Deschampsia flexuosa*). These islands are thought to be remnants of the once more extensive soil cover over the pavements which continues to be eroded into the grykes despite nearly

FIG 90. Scar Close, Ingleborough NNR. A view from a massive limestone clint towards a deep pocket of soil supporting Heather (*Calluna vulgaris*) and other calcifuge plants with developing woodland on the pavement beyond. The exclusion of grazing by domestic livestock is resulting in the expansion of shrubs and trees on the pavement.

40 years' absence of grazing by sheep. Some of these islands have bare white regions around them which have been taken to indicate freshly exposed areas of limestone that have not had time for lichen colonisation to occur, and thus they signify active erosion. However, some caution is required in this interpretation (see below).

There are also patches of deeper soil in which the limestone influence remains despite the leaching tendency of the area's high precipitation. Here a tall herb community is developed with Globeflower (*Trollius europaeus*) (Fig. 91), Melancholy Thistle (*Cirsium heterophyllum*), Meadowsweet (*Filipendula ulmaria*) and Water Avens (*Geum rivale*) among the most prominent members, with similarities to the northern hay meadow community (MG3). Although Scar Close is fenced to exclude domestic livestock, grazing still occurs: Rabbits (*Oryctolagus cuniculus*) and much less numerous Brown Hares (*Lepus europaeus*) occur on many pavements, and grazing pressure fluctuates in intensity with population numbers. Rabbits may also exacerbate erosion around the vegetation islands. Deer still have access, and Roe Deer (*Capreolus capreolus*) in particular visit the pavements. In 2012, Natural England's senior reserve manager on Ingleborough, Colin Newlands, found the remains of a Roe Deer which had fallen into a deep gryke on Scar Close and had been unable to extract itself, thus graphically illustrating the potential perils for large grazing animals on limestone pavements; the same fate sometimes befalls sheep.

FIG 91. Tall herb community with Globeflower (*Trollius europaeus*) on a moist calcareous soil pocket at Scar Close, Ingleborough NNR.

Mollusc grazing is also important, and affects seedling establishment within grykes where the cool, moist conditions are suitable for snail activity and fissures provide some protection from avian predators. What is less readily appreciated is that snails can influence the distribution of organisms on the apparently bare clint surfaces. These surfaces support two forms of saxicolous lichens: epilithic lichens (growing on the rock surface) and endolithic lichens (growing between 0 and *c.*7 mm within the rock surface). Lichens are a mutualism between a fungus (mycobiont) and a green alga or a cyanobacterium (photobiont), but these surfaces also support populations of free-living cyanobacteria. It is this combination of lichens and cyanobacteria which give the characteristic grey colour to the clint surface and, when they are removed by heavy mollusc grazing or by the deposition of aerial pollutants, the rock appears white. As we have seen, the rock may also appear white when it appears for the first time from underneath any eroding vegetation and soil cover. In a study of limestone pavements on the Baltic island of Öland, Froberg *et al.* (2011) showed that grazing by snails decreased cyanobacterial abundance and lichen diversity along narrow cracks on the limestone pavements. Two common lichens which contain cyanobacterial photobionts, *Placynthium nigrum* and *Collema fuscovirens*, had low abundance up to 25 cm from crack edges when snails were present in high densities. By transplanting rocks close to cracks with and without high snail densities these workers were able to show that cyanobacterial colonies on the rocks were grazed out within 19 months at sites with high snail densities, but not where snails were absent. The most common snail species on these pavements was *Chondrina clienta*. To what extent mollusc grazing on the clint surfaces is affecting the distribution of saxicolous lichens and cyanobacteria in the Dales is unknown. Robert Cameron (1978) recorded 29 species of molluscs on pavements ungrazed by cattle or sheep, and 26 species on grazed pavements in the Ingleborough and Malham areas, but these assemblages did not include *Chondrina clienta*. The most frequently recorded species on grazed pavements were *Pyramidula rupestris* and *Vitrea contracta*. The former species was amongst the most frequently recorded species on ungrazed pavements, together with *Clausilia dubia, Discus rotundatus* and *Oxychilus alliarius*.

Certainly in the past atmospheric pollution from the local lead industry and the nearby major towns and cities will have had some effect on the lichen flora. Seaward & Pentecost (2001) list 69 lichen species on well-illuminated rock surfaces in the Malham area, but they also note the potential past influence of atmospheric pollution on the flora, and record John Lund's observation of seeing soot fall on the pavements before the enforcement of the 1956 Clean Air Act. Smelting of lead ore (galena) was a significant source of sulphur dioxide in the Dales during the eighteenth and nineteenth centuries. However, the peak of coal smoke pollution from northern industrial towns, another major source of this gas, was in the period just before and after the First World War, providing what Albert Wilson described to the British Association for the Advancement of Science in 1900 as 'The great smoke cloud of the North of England'. Thus the lichen communities may have been modified by more than two centuries of acidic deposition, and this deposition may well have accelerated weathering of the limestone.

SCARS

The Grassington Grit and inter-bedded shales exposed on the higher hills in several dales, such as Arkengarthdale, Ribblesdale, Sleddale and Swaledale, give rise to acidic skeletal soils in the rock crevices. These crevices support ericaceous dwarf shrubs including Heather, Bilberry and Cowberry (*Vaccinium vitis-idaea*); also calcifuge grasses and herbs such as Wavy Hair-grass, Heath Bedstraw (*Galium saxatile*) and Tormentil (*Potentilla erecta*). Common fern species present include Hard-fern (*Blechnum spicant*), Broad Buckler-fern (*Dryopteris dilatata*) and Lemon-scented fern (*Oreopteris limbosperma*). Most of these species are common in heathland and pastures developed on acidic soils with light grazing pressure, but some are much rarer, for example Serrated Wintergreen (*Orthilia secunda*), which occurs on ungrazed ledges of the Silurian slate cliffs at Cautley Spout in the Howgills near Sedbergh. Other uncommon species include Fir Clubmoss (*Huperzia selago*), which is found on some high-altitude cliffs, and rarely also Beech Fern (*Phegopteris connectilis*) and Oak Fern (*Gymnocarpium dryopteris*), which are more typically woodland plants. However, the vast majority of scars in the Dales are Carboniferous limestone cliffs with a very different and much richer flora.

Below the gristone caps of Ingleborough and Pen-y-ghent are scars of the Main Limestone that locally support remnants of the arctic–alpine flora which covered much of the Dales as the Devensian ice retreated. The most attractive of these is the Purple Saxifrage (*Saxifraga oppositifolia*), which was first described from Ingleborough by John Ray in the late seventeenth century. From March to May its purple flowers cover the mats of shoots trailing from rock crevices (Fig. 92). It is the more attractive because its flowers, produced in the previous growing season, appear long before those of the majority of other herbs, and when vegetation on the nearby slopes may appear still to be in the depths of winter. Another remarkable plant on the Ingleborough cliffs close to 700 metres

FIG 92. Trailing shoots of Purple Saxifrage (*Saxifraga oppositifolia*), which adorn the Main Limestone cliffs of Ingleborough and Pen-y-ghent in early spring.

in altitude is the Alpine Meadow-grass (*Poa alpina*) (Fig. 93). This species in Britain is usually viviparous; that is its spikelets proliferate forming small plantlets. These become detached and can establish new plants in a form of asexual reproduction. However, the Ingleborough population reproduces sexually, although there is little published evidence to show how frequently

FIG 93. Alpine Meadow-grass (*Poa alpina*) growing on Ingleborough. This race of the grass reproduces sexually, whereas at most of its British sites the species is viviparous.

FIG 94. Viviparous Sheep's-fescue (*Festuca vivipara*) on exposed sandstone rocks with its spikelets proliferating to form small plantlets, Ingleborough NNR.

seed production and seedling establishment is successful. Ingleborough does support a viviparous grass, Viviparous Sheep's-fescue (*Festuca vivipara*) (Fig. 94), which occurs on rocky exposures a little below the limestone cliffs.

The Ingleborough cliffs also support some other arctic–alpine species, notably Yellow Saxifrage (*Saxifraga aizoides*) (Fig. 95) and Roseroot (*Sedum rosea*) (Fig. 96); and also the moss (*Encalyptra alpina*) at its most southerly location in Britain. These remnants of the once ubiquitous Late-glacial vegetation do not survive under tree canopies and were gradually eliminated from all but the tops of the highest hills by spreading forest cover in the Post-glacial period. These high and north- or east-facing cliffs have growing seasons which are short and

FIG 95. Yellow Saxifrage (*Saxifraga aizoides*), on a Main Limestone cliff, Ingleborough NNR.

FIG 96. Roseroot (*Sedum rosea*), Ingleborough NNR.

cool, providing conditions suitable to the growth and survival of arctic–alpine plants. They also provide protection from sheep grazing, favouring these species and some more common limestone plants such as Small Scabious (*Scabiosa columbaria*), which is an important component of the vegetation on cliffs and rocks at lower altitudes.

The limestone scars at lower altitudes include some of the most admired landscape features of the Dales, including for example Kilnsey Crag, Malham Cove and Gordale Scar. The plants which colonise them include many of the species found on limestone pavements, together with some tree and shrub species which cannot establish on the highest cliffs (Fig. 97). Again on these scars the apparently bare limestone is in fact colonised by saxicolous lichens which, along with cyanobacteria and some bryophyte species, help to produce the dark vertical stripes seen where water seeps down the rock face of Malham Cove. The scars contain small vertical fissures in which plants can establish, but also more or less horizontal ledges which, if they are large enough, can support scrub woodland and tall herb communities. On drier, sunnier rocks the latter may contain species such as Wild Marjoram (*Origanum vulgare*), Common Knapweed (*Centaurea nigra*) and Small Scabious. The larger damp ledges support a vegetation

FIG 97. Yew Cogar Scar near Arncliffe, an example of a well-wooded cliff at low altitude.

which includes Water Avens, Globeflower, Marsh Hawk's-beard (*Crepis paludosa*) and Melancholy Thistle. In addition some damp cliffs, particularly in Swaledale and Wensleydale, support Pyrenean Scurvygrass (*Cochlearia pyrenaica*) (Fig. 98) and Mossy Saxifrage (*Saxifraga hypnoides*), but both species are also found on and around the high cliffs of Ingleborough and Pen-y-ghent.

Trees are established in some crevices and on some of the larger ledges, sometimes giving rise to patches of scrub or open woodland. One of the best examples of this is Yew Coger Scar, where, as the name suggests, Yew (*Taxus baccata*) is prominent. Ash is the most abundant tree on many scars, but Hawthorn (*Crataegus monogyna*), Rowan (*Sorbus aucuparia*) and Sycamore (*Acer pseudoplatanus*) are common, with Rock Whitebeam (*Sorbus rupicola*) being more locally distributed. In sunny crevices and on shallow ledges a characteristic assemblage includes Hairy Rock-cress (*Arabis hirsuta*), Thale Cress (*Arabidopsis thaliana*), Hoary Whitlowgrass (*Draba incana*), Biting Stonecrop (*Sedum acre*) and winter annuals, species which set seed and die in the spring, such as Common Whitlowgrass (*Erophila verna*), Rue-leaved Saxifrage (*Saxifraga tridactylites*) and Wall Whitlowgrass (*Draba muralis*). On cliffs in Swaledale and Wensleydale the rare Hutchinsia (*Hornungia petraea*) can be found. Another now rare plant, abundant in

FIG 98. Pyrenean Scurvygrass (*Cochleria pyrenaica*), Ingleborough NNR.

the Dales immediately following the retreat of the Devensian ice, is the Mountain Avens (*Dryas octopetala*) (Fig. 99). It grows on a few exposed northwest-facing rocks in Cowside Beck valley near its confluence with Littondale, at its southern limit in England. The limestone cliffs support a rich fern flora including Maidenhair Spleenwort, Wall-rue, Green Spleenwort, Hard Shield-fern and Hart's-tongue. The Lesser Clubmoss (*Selaginella selaginoides*) is found around areas of seepage, and the scars also support many common mosses and liverworts of limestone districts, but also several uncommon ones including *Pseudoleskella catenulata*, *Cololejeunea rossettiana* and *Pedinophyllum interruptum*.

One of the attractive features of Malham Cove to visitors in spring and early summer is the presence of Peregrine Falcons (*Falco peregrinus*), just one of perhaps 20 pairs nesting on cliffs throughout the Dales. Scars also provide nesting sites for Jackdaws (*Corvus monedula*) and Ravens (*Corvus corax*) amongst the larger bird species. Before there were many buildings in the Dales, the overhangs on cliffs such as at Malham (Fig. 100) and at Kilnsey would have been major nesting sites for House Martins (*Delichon urbicum*).

FIG 99. Mountain Avens (*Dryas octopetala*), a rare plant of a few exposed rocks in the Cowside Beck valley, where it is at its southern limit in England. It also occurs very locally in calcareous grassland in the vicinity.

FIG 100. The Great Scar Limestone cliff at Malham Cove, showing overhangs and vegetated ledges, an attraction for naturalists, climbers and many tourists.

SCREES

Screes are typically found on steep slopes below scars and are the result of chemical and physical weathering of rock. Today the processes leading to the production of scree, or talus as it is more generally known, are most easily observed in much colder climates than those currently occurring in Britain, such as in the High Arctic in summer. The repeated freezing and thawing of water penetrating narrow fissures in the rock results in fragments of rock falling under gravity from the cliffs to the slopes below, producing fans or aprons of rock particles of many sizes. These assemblages tend to be very unstable because of the steep slopes on which they have accumulated and the continued rain of new rock falling from above. The conditions existing in the Arctic today are similar to those which must have occurred in the Dales at the end of the Devensian glaciation, and the screes we observe must have largely been formed at that time. Today few new rock fragments fall from the scars, but the screes are still poorly colonised by plants in many locations, not least because many remain inherently unstable, and this may be exacerbated by both freezing and thawing in even our currently mild winters, as well as by the movement of animals across them.

Screes come in a variety of fragment sizes, and not all are entirely natural in origin. The scree on the south slope of Pen-y-ghent is formed of massive blocks of Grassington Grit (Fig. 101). More typically the screes are formed of much smaller rock fragments, but they are nonetheless difficult for plants to colonise, particularly on the many steep talus slopes below limestone scars. Some areas of shattered rock found on the shoulders of hills have many of the features of scree but probably arose differently. These may have been areas of heavily weathered and shattered limestone pavement which have resulted in a scree-like structure of loose stones on shallow slopes, and these areas are also sparsely colonised. The Dales also contain areas of manmade scree below large quarry faces, and particularly extensive screes in some old lead-mining districts associated with former crushing mills.

Although the screes are open to grazing animals, the steep slopes and the unstable substrate probably act to reduce some at least of the potential grazing pressure. Plants become established in small pockets of soil between the stones and boulders. Millstone Grit screes have pockets colonised by acid grassland species including Wavy Hair-grass, Bilberry, Foxglove (*Digitalis purpurea*) and Heath Bedstraw. Parsley Fern (*Cryptogramma crispa*), which is such a characteristic plant of similar screes in Lakeland and Snowdonia, is rare in the Dales, where it is mostly confined to scree in old lead-mining districts.

FIG 101. The large-block gritstone scree below the summit of Pen-y-ghent.

On limestone screes, prominent colonisers are the ferns Maidenhair Spleenwort and Wall-rue, but more locally the Limestone Fern can also be abundant. Blue Moor-grass (*Sesleria caerulea*), which can be dominant in the surrounding grassland, is a prominent coloniser together with Sheep's-fescue (*Festuca ovina*), Herb-Robert, Wild Thyme (*Thymus polytrichus*), Harebell (*Campanula rotundifolia*), Fairy Flax (*Linum catharticum*) and the occasional tree seedlings, most notably Ash. But these limestone screes can contain some uncommon plants. Thus Clapham (1954) records the presence of Purple Saxifrage on a coarse scree slope at 1,225 feet (373 metres) in the Moughton area of Ingleborough. A rare plant found in a similar situation on Ingleborough is the Teesdale Violet (*Viola rupestris*) in one of only a few localities in Britain. Another rare plant found in a few screes is the Prickly Sedge (*Carex muricata* ssp. *muricata*).

Aspect and hydrology can also influence scree vegetation. On hillsides, with some flushing in the soils down slope, the scree surface may become partially stabilised by vegetation cover, and at a few sites uncommon species such as Jacob's-ladder (*Polemonium caeruleum*), Dwarf Milkwort (*Polygala amarella*) and Dark-red Helleborine occur.

FIG 102. Extensive artificial screes, the result of old lead-mining and smelting activities, Gunnerside Gill, Swaledale.

FIG 103. Spring Sandwort (*Minuartia verna*) growing in Arkengarthdale. This species is a metallophyte frequently associated with old lead workings in the Dales and elsewhere in Britain.

The screes below old lead workings (Fig. 102) have not only the physical constraints of natural screes, but may also have the chemical constraints of growth on soils enriched in metals, notably lead and zinc. These give rise to a flora in which two metallophytes are amongst the most prominent colonisers: Spring Sandwort (*Minuartia verna*) (Fig. 103) and Alpine Penny-cress (*Noccaea caerulescens*); together with rather stunted specimens of Sheep's-fescue, Common Bent (*Agrostis capillaris*), Wild Thyme and Harebell. This is the *Festuca ovina – Minuartia verna* (OV37) community. A rich metallophyte flora is found in several sites in Arkengarthdale, Swaledale

FIG 104. Mountain Pansy (*Viola lutea*) growing in Arkengarthdale on metal-contaminated soils.

FIG 105. Moonwort (*Botrychium lunularia*) growing on metal-enriched soils at Grinton, Swaledale. (Falgunee Sarker)

and Wharfedale, but probably nowhere better than in the Ox Close Special Area of Conservation in Wensleydale. This large site contains old spoil tips, metal-enriched alluvium and little-disturbed scars. As well as Spring Sandwort and Alpine Penny-cress, other species associated with the metal-enriched soils include Thrift (*Armeria maritima*), a plant more often associated with sea cliffs and salt marshes, Pyrenean Scurvygrass, Mountain Pansy (*Viola lutea*) (Fig. 104) and Moonwort (*Botrychium lunularia*) (Fig. 105).

CONSERVATION

It may at first seem that little action would be required to conserve these rocky habitats apart from perhaps preventing the ravages of plant collectors, which in the past may have had a detrimental effect on the flora – as for example when there was a craze for fern collecting in the nineteenth century. This may be true for many scars and screes, but not so for the limestone pavements, and the fact that more than a third of the total area of limestone pavement in Britain is found in the Dales makes them of special conservation importance here.

A walk around many villages in limestone pavement districts of northwest England will reveal houses and gardens containing rocks lifted from the surface of these pavements. Many of these have been there for a century and more, and at this small scale of activity it is unlikely that much damage was caused. In any case, on common land many of the villagers would have had rights to remove stones for building purposes. However, the national craze for water-worn limestone for garden rockeries had a markedly detrimental effect on many pavements in northern England, particularly in the decades immediately following the Second World War. In one sense pavement lifting could be seen to be desirable from a farmer's point of view: it might improve the grazing, remove a potential hazard to stock, and at the same time provide an immediate cash return. However, pavement lifting usually involved removing the surface limestone bed, leaving the bed beneath in which the joints were often little weathered. A local desert was the immediate result, leaving bare limestone surfaces with few if any crevices in which plants could establish; and of course the gryke vegetation, one major nature conservation interest, was completely destroyed. The other major conservation interest is in the geomorphology of the pavements, many with unique features, which were also entirely lost.

This destruction accelerated when heavy machinery such as JCBs and rock drills came into widespread use in the late 1950s and 1960s. The matter came to a head in the early 1970s when, for example, Gait Barrows in Cumbria was increasingly being subjected to damage. Protection for this site, with its unrivalled limestone pavements situated near sea level, was achieved when it was acquired by the Nature Conservancy Council as a National Nature Reserve to mark the Queen's Silver Jubilee in 1977. But shortly afterwards, legislation in the form of the 1981 Wildlife and Countryside Act provided for more general protection. Section 24 of this Act imposed legal protection through Limestone Pavement Orders on landowners to conserve pavement areas of outstanding ecological and geological interest. Philpin Sleights in Chapel-le-Dale was an early subject of such an order. At least 3,000 tonnes of rockery stone had been extracted from there between 1954 and 1958 and, by the time it was acquired by the Nature Conservancy Council in 1991, only 60 per cent of the pavement was intact. Today many Dales pavements are also designated Special Areas of Conservation under the European Union Habitats and Species Directive.

Some control of grazing is essential to maintain and enhance the biodiversity of both pavements and screes. The vast majority of these habitats are grazed and have been grazed by domestic livestock since the Iron Age. Their open nature today depends on sheep and/or cattle grazing to prevent succession to woodland. However, low rather than high stocking levels are usually beneficial to the conservation interest of both screes and pavements. Grazing pressure on many upland pastures increased markedly from historic levels in the second half of the twentieth century. Work by the Nature Conservancy and its successors suggests that optimum long-term stocking levels to maintain open upland limestone pavement may be less than one ewe per hectare (or the cattle equivalent) over the whole year, and this stocking level is also likely to be beneficial to the conservation interest of screes. This is based on a variety of management regimes trialled in the Malham–Arncliffe SSSI during the 1990s. For example at Knotts, where both cattle and sheep were stocked, a regime was established in 1994 which consisted of two ewes (or the cattle equivalent) per hectare in April, no stock between May and August and between November and March, and 1.25 ewes per hectare in September and October. The result was that there was a 100 per cent increase in frond numbers of the Limestone Fern in the pavement between 1994 and 1996, and in 1996 the Northern Brown Argus butterfly (*Aricia artaxerxes*) appeared.

A similar management trial at West Gordale, using differing levels of low-intensity grazing at different periods in the year, resulted in the short term in increased fruiting of Baneberry, while Lily-of-the-valley was recorded at the site after a 20-year absence. Management of Southerscales since 1991 by the Yorkshire Wildlife Trust originally involved a stock-free period every May followed by light cattle grazing in the summer months (10 beasts in the 43-hectare reserve), but latterly light sheep grazing (20 sheep) has replaced the stock-free period. Sheep grazing occurs throughout the autumn and winter, with a higher stocking rate in September and October (either 100 sheep and no cattle or 50 sheep and 10 cattle) than in November to the end of April (a maximum of 40 sheep). The aim of such management schemes is to maintain open limestone pavement, but it serves to increase populations and species which favour gryke-top position such as Bloody Crane's-bill and also grazing-intolerant species such as Baneberry and Lesser Meadow-rue. A further aim is to give more structure to the vegetation above the clints, which provides shelter for the butterflies such as the Northern Brown Argus and the Dark Green Fritillary (*Argynnis aglaja*) whilst preventing scrub development. But unforeseen problems can arise in any new management plan. An example is an increase in Ragwort (*Senecio jacobaea*) at Southerscales; this has been controlled partly by slightly adjusting the grazing regime, and partly by volunteers removing the plant.

In the past, non-native trees have been deliberately planted on several limestone pavements in northern England, including for example in Chapel-le-Dale Beech, which is not native in northern England, European Larch and Sycamore. This is certainly detrimental to the biodiversity and conservation interests, and, in recent years on some of these pavements, alien conifers have been removed in an attempt to reverse this – for example on Hutton Roof and Whitbarrow in Cumbria. Sycamore, introduced into Britain in the fifteenth or sixteenth century, and commonly planted as a shelter belt around farmsteads, has also naturally invaded many pavements, where it can cast deep shade. At Southerscales and Scar Close systematic attempts have been made over the last few decades to remove Sycamore, partly by glyphosphate injection into the trunks. The desired result of this management, which has largely been successful, is to ensure that the trees and shrubs present are components of the presumed semi-natural sub-alpine Ash woodlands of the district, as exemplified by the neighbouring Colt Park Wood.

CONCLUDING REMARKS

Looking northwest from the gritstone screes near the summit of Ingleborough, walkers have one of the finest views of pavements, scars and screes anywhere in the National Park. The Great Scar Limestone bench immediately below shows almost the full range of vegetation cover on pavements, from the partially wooded Scar Close to the northeast, through Southerscales with a few isolated trees, to the bare pavements of Sleights to the southwest. Across the valley, the northern flank of Chapel-le-Dale supports rows of scars, some partially wooded, with their associated screes below. And above the scars a bare grey expanse of limestone pavement occupies the wide bench of Scales Moor extending south from Whernside towards Kingsdale beyond. Scales Moor is the largest continuous area of pavement in the National Park (> 100 hectares), and famed as the site of early investigations to discover the processes involved in pavement formation (see e.g. Sweeting, 1973). One suspects that there is still much to be learnt about these landscape features, particularly about the pavements, from an ecological viewpoint. Much effort thus far has gone into understanding the geomorphological processes involved, conserving the pavements and optimising the management of the finest examples. The pavements have also been much used in ecological teaching, notably those around the Malham Field Centre, but research studies published in the ecological literature are few and far between.

Human activity continues to produce new scars and screes in the Dales, none larger than those at Horton-in-Ribblesdale, but, as quarrying comes to an end in some locations, there is the potential for ecological gains. A good example is the Ribblehead quarry, which became part of the Ingleborough National Nature Reserve in 2000. Here cliff faces, boulder fields and stone piles are being left to colonise naturally, providing opportunities for both naturalists and professional ecologists to study the succession of plants and animals on them.

CHAPTER 7

Meadows and Pastures

In the Dales today, particularly in the upper dales, the climate is unsuitable for the growth of arable crops, and farmers largely rely on sheep and beef cattle to make a living. Historically, dairying was also important. Bradley (2014) recalls that as late as the 1960s it was possible to look out from his family farm in Ribblesdale and count two dozen or so other dairy farms, whereas by the early 2000s such farms in this view could be counted on the fingers of one hand. In his words, 'Dairy farms left the Dales and became concentrated in areas such as Cheshire and the Southwest.' However dairy farming remains important in one dale, Wensleydale, because of the success of the Wensleydale Creamery in Hawes in making and marketing Wensleydale cheese, which involves taking milk from 36 local farms.

In the past many farms were small, offering little more than a subsistence income, and much of the farming was part-time, particularly in the smallholdings occupied by lead miners and their families. Raistrick (1967) describes the farms in the parish of Linton in Wharfedale at the time of the 1851 census. Thirty of the farmers in the parish had farms of less than 10 acres (4 ha), and 35 had farms between 10 and 50 acres (4–20 ha). Only 13 farmers had more than 100 acres (40 ha). A typical small farm comprised a few fields on the better soils in or near the dale bottom containing the meadows, and fields on the dale sides which might once have supported arable crops, and where the remains of the ancient common-field system of strip lynchets can sometimes still be seen. Unimproved pastures unsuitable for mowing also occurred on the valley sides, sometimes on the site of the village's former common cow pasture, or more rarely on rock-strewn valley-bottom fields. Winter housing for cattle was often in field barns within the meadows, with the hay crop stored in the loft above

FIG 106. Field barns within the meadows, in which cattle were housed below and hay stored above, Yockenthwaite, Wharfedale.

(Fig. 106). These barns provided a source of well-rotted manure (muck) which was spread on the meadows in winter and early spring to maintain their fertility. The meadows and pastures around the farmstead constituted the so-called in-bye land. But integral to the agricultural system was access to grazing on the fells and commons on the dale sides and ridge tops above the in-bye land. These pastures were essential to the farming system because the meadows had to be shut up (the livestock excluded) after lambing in the early spring to allow the grass to grow, and the hay crop to be taken after midsummer.

THE GRASS CROP

The earliest farmers probably relied largely on leaf fodder cut from forest trees such as Ash, elm and lime as a winter supplement for their animals (see e.g. Peterken, 2013), but, from the Iron Age onwards, as sharp metal sickles became available, it became increasingly possible to harvest grass efficiently. As the forests contracted, the result of the demands for timber, fuel and pasture for grazing animals, the use of trees for winter fodder declined, being replaced by a grass crop. For many centuries thereafter, until the last few decades of the twentieth century, the hay crop was exceptionally important to each and every farmer, not least because before the Industrial Revolution there was no easy transport of fodder between districts, and fodder supplies effectively determined how many beasts could be kept through the winter. However, although some local trading of hay within a dale may have been possible, this would have been very restricted, not least because weather conditions are all important in haymaking, and similar weather conditions within a dale led often to the same poor crops along its length.

To make hay, three or four successive dry days are required, and there was very little certainty of these occurring at the optimal time for cropping in the damp summers of the upper dales. As John Tuke recorded in 1794:

> *[Hay is] the grand object of the farmer and ... he has many difficulties to combat: the season commences late, the surrounding hills occasion frequent and sudden showers and the meadows abound with ... [herbs] ... which being more succulent than the grasses properly so called, are more difficult to harvest than the produce of meadows where the grasses greatly predominate.*

Experienced judgement and speed were of the essence to make use of the narrow windows of opportunity, and all the family, combined often with the addition of casual labour from the village and further afield, were required to expedite the harvest. The fact that many barns were situated in the meadows was helpful here. However, the vagaries of the climate meant that the harvest was often poor in both quantity and quality, particularly in the latter if cutting was delayed until very late in the summer. With limited labour, even on small farms with very few meadows, it was not possible to cut the entire crop at once in early summer, and harvesting of some fields was inevitably delayed to a later dry period. Marie Hartley and Joan Ingilby (1956) record visiting Garsdale in about 1950 ...

> *on a brilliantly fine day in early August, a hay day in a wet summer. The hillsides were alive with people. Groups of men, women and children armed with wooden rakes strewed and turned the hay, rhythmically raking backwards and forwards across the steep meadows. The whole dale was astir with feverish activity.*

These authors also provide many photographs of traditional haymaking in the Dales in the days before mechanisation (Hartley & Ingilby, 1968).

Increasingly in the twentieth century there was an emphasis in Britain on agricultural production aided by improving mechanisation. The latter also reduced both the labour required and the time necessary to make the hay harvest. During the Second World War many meadows were ploughed up to increase cereal production, even in some areas such as the Dales where the generally short, cold growing seasons are unsuitable for these crops. In the post-war years, following the 1947 Agriculture Act, the emphasis on increasing agricultural production was continued by the introduction of subsidies, and a renewed effort emanating from the Ministry of Agriculture to improve the productivity of grasslands. This resulted in many meadows and permanent pastures being ploughed up, treated with inorganic fertilisers, and re-sown with more productive grasses. This emphasis on increased production was continued after Britain joined the European Economic Community (EEC), thanks to the Common Agricultural Policy. The headage payment system encouraged increased stocking rates (sheep numbers in the National Park increased by 70 per cent between the 1950s and 1997) and led to the increasing use of inorganic fertilisers. It has been estimated that of the 44,571 hectares of grassland in the National Park, over a quarter has been 'improved' by fertiliser addition, and sometimes also by replanting meadows and pastures with seed mixes of more productive grasses.

The end result was to encourage the growth of productive grasses at the expense of many wildflower species. Over-stocking and late exclusion of livestock from the meadows also led to a reduction in traditional hay-meadow species, the encouragement of weeds such as docks and thistles, and increased soil compaction. Fairly rapidly the vast majority of the remaining species-rich wildflower meadows were lost, and less than 1 per cent of the National Park remains as upland hay meadow today.

The increasing replacement of the hay crop by silage and haylage after the Second World War also exacerbated the loss of biodiversity. These crops involve early cutting, before many flowers have set seed and ground-nesting birds have raised their young. Cutting is usually repeated later in the summer and into the early autumn if the meadows are not required for the immediate grazing of the aftermath. The distinct advantage of silage and haylage production from the farmer's viewpoint is that it is much less weather-dependent, given that maybe only a single dry day is required to wilt the crop after cutting, and it is also much less labour-intensive than hay time used to be. The move to silage was also one major factor in making many field barns at least partially redundant, as today the crop is often in the form of large bales wrapped in plastic, and stored in a corner of a field (Fig. 107).

FIG 107. The modern method of storing winter fodder, large bales covered in black plastic stored in a field corner, Malham.

THE MEADOWS

Before the Second World War the flower-rich hay meadows were outstanding colourful features of all the dales in early summer; now they are rare. Very many meadows were subjected to agricultural improvement in the post-war years, but here and there wildflower meadows survived under traditional management systems. Where they have survived, farmers and landowners have been encouraged by Natural England, the Yorkshire Dales National Park Authority and the Yorkshire Dales Millennium Trust to conserve them, and also, where possible in suitable semi-improved fields, to re-establish wildflower meadows. Importantly, the remaining species-rich meadows provide the opportunity to understand the factors affecting their biological diversity, and this knowledge is vital for the successful re-establishment of these meadows more widely in the Dales.

The meadows have similarities with the tall-herb communities which covered much of the Dales in the Late-glacial; these must have persisted in the Post-glacial woodland, perhaps within some mosaics of closed-canopy woodland,

FIG 108. A tall-herb community amongst scrub and limestone pavement, Scar Close, Ingleborough NNR, with Globeflower (*Trollius europaeus*) in flower.

scrub and small clearings (Fig. 108), maintained as such by large herbivores, as proposed by Frans Vera (2000). The meadows originate mostly from the Ash–Rowan–Mercury woodland (W9) on the better-drained soils, and from the Alder–Ash flush woodland (W7) along the becks and spring lines. Many of these woodland species found in the meadows today can also be found on cliff ledges free from grazing animals. While many open-woodland species have adapted to the centuries-old cutting and grazing regime, some such as Baneberry (*Actaea spicata*) and Dog's Mercury (*Mercurialis perennis*) are not found in meadows.

The meadows are often essentially mesotrophic or neutral grasslands found on soils which are neither markedly acidic nor strongly calcareous. Several meadow types can be found in the Dales, but perhaps the most characteristic of these is the *Anthoxanthum odoratum – Geranium sylvaticum* grassland (MG3) or northern hay meadow, which as the latter name suggests is largely confined to the northern counties of England. These meadows were typically found in the upper dales between 200 and 400 metres in altitude, but are now restricted to a few sites. The surviving meadows contain a rich range of herbs including some species which for example are prominent members of semi-natural birch forests on lime-rich soils north of the Arctic Circle in Scandinavia today. These include some of the most prominent and attractive meadow species such as the Globeflower (*Trollius*

FIG 109. A tall-herb community in the meadows at Yockenthwaite, Wharfedale, with Melancholy Thistle (*Cirsium heterophyllum*) in flower.

europaeus), Wood Crane's-bill (*Geranium sylvaticum*) and Melancholy Thistle (*Cirsium heterophyllum*) (Fig. 109). Other northern species in a few meadows include rare lady's-mantles such as *Alchemilla monticola* and *A. subcrenata*. Lady's-mantles are apomicts, in which seed production occurs without sexual reproduction, leading to the perpetuation of often small mutations, and to the recognition of micro-species.

In contrast to these northern herbs, the grasses are all common and widely distributed in Britain. Perhaps the most iconic of these is the Sweet Vernal-grass (*Anthoxanthum odoratum*). In agricultural terms this is an unproductive grass, and

FIG 110. An inflorescence of Sweet Vernal-grass (*Anthoxanthum odoratum*). This grass is common and widely distributed in the Dales, as elsewhere in Britain. It is considered to be worthless agriculturally, and is excluded from seed mixes in improved pastures and meadows. However, it contains coumarin, which gives the characteristic odour to new-mown hay in unimproved meadows.

has been largely eliminated from reseeded meadows, but it contains coumarin, which once provided the characteristic sweet hay smell of mown meadows throughout the country (Fig. 110). Northern hay meadows contain a diversity of other common grasses including Common Bent (*Agrostis capillaris*), Crested Dog's-tail (*Cynosurus cristatus*), Cock's-foot (*Dactylis glomerata*), Quaking-grass (*Briza media*), Red Fescue (*Festuca rubra*), Rough Meadow-grass (*Poa trivialis*) and Yorkshire-fog (*Holcus lanatus*). The commoner herbs include buttercups, particularly Common and Bulbous Buttercups (*Ranunculus acris* and *R. bulbosus*), Pignut (*Conopodium majus*), Common Sorrel (*Rumex acetosa*), Red and White Clover (*Trifolium pratense* and *T. repens*), Great Burnet (*Sanguisorba officinalis*), lady's-mantles (*Alchemilla glabra* and *A. xanthochlora*), Meadow Vetchling (*Lathyrus pratensis*) and Rough Hawkbit (*Leontodon hispidus*). In less well-drained areas within the meadows other herbs include Common Bistort (*Persicaria bistorta*), Marsh Hawk's-beard (*Crepis paludosa*) and Water Avens (*Geum rivale*).

Another common and important herb in these meadows is Yellow-rattle (*Rhinanthus minor*). Yellow-rattle is one of very few annuals in meadows, and is a hemiparasite which attaches to the roots of other plants to obtain nutrients and water from its hosts (Fig. 111). In this process it reduces the vigour of at least some of its hosts, particularly the grasses, and is thought to be important in the maintenance of the species richness in the community as a whole. The rattling of ripe dry seeds within the capsules gives the plant its name, and this rattling was taken as one indicator that the hay crop was ready to harvest. However, it is a species without a persistent seed bank in the soil, and is readily lost from the sward if the harvest is taken before the seed is ripe, thus releasing the grass species from an important constraint on their growth. Other annual hemiparasites in these meadows are the eyebrights (*Euphrasia* species), a critical genus of plants with many hybrids. The commonest species in

FIG 111. Yellow-rattle (*Rhinanthus minor*), a hemiparasite which is able to reduce the vigour of grasses in meadows and pastures, and an important species in meadow restoration.

FIG 112. A species-rich northern hay meadow community (MG3) in Dentdale, an intricate mixture of grasses and forbs with Arctic Eyebright (*Euphrasia arctica* ssp. *arctica*) and Red Clover (*Trifolium pratense*) prominent in the foreground.

the Dales is Arctic Eyebright (*Euphrasia arctica* ssp. *arctica*) (Fig. 112). However, the Red Data Book species Montane Eyebright (*Euphrasia officinalis* ssp. *monticola*) also occurs in a few places, mostly in upper Ribblesdale and Langstrothdale. A recent survey of 91 potentially suitable meadow fields in the Dales found the species in only seven (Ptyxis Ecology, 2012).

The National Vegetation Classification recognises several other meadow communities which are present in the Dales. These occur in fields which are subjected to some grazing before and after the hay crop is taken, but some may also occur in graveyards and roadsides which are only subject to cutting. An example of the latter is the *Arrhenatherum elatius* grassland (MG1) or oat-grass meadow in which the False Oat-grass (*Arrhenatherum elatius*) is abundant. This grass is particularly sensitive to trampling by livestock, but thrives in grassland only subjected to cutting regimes. Other characteristic species in this community include Cow Parsley (*Anthriscus sylvestris*), which is such an attractive feature of roadside verges in late May and early June. Many roadsides in the Dales also contain Sweet Cicely (*Myrrhis odorata*), a native of central and southern European mountains, which has spread from habitation along the verges providing often

FIG 113. A road verge in Littondale in early May, colonised by Sweet Cicely (*Myrrhis odorata*), an introduced plant which is both a common and an attractive feature of roadsides in the Dales in spring.

FIG 114. Greater Knapweed (*Centaurea scabiosa*), an important component of the *Centaurea – Cynosurus* grassland community or knapweed meadow (MG5) found mostly in the drier and warmer regions of the lower dales. (Falgunee Sarker)

the first white-flowered umbels in spring (Fig. 113). Later in the summer two other umbellifers are prominent in the vegetation, as Hogweed (*Heracleum sphondylium*) and Rough Chervil (*Chaerophyllum temulum*) continue the sequence of white flowers. Lower down the dales, the blue flowers of Meadow Crane's-bill (*Geranium pratense*) and Greater Knapweed (*Centaurea scabiosa*) (Fig. 114) also provide an attractive feature in the vegetation.

The *Cynosurus cristatus – Centaurea nigra* grassland or knapweed meadow (MG5) is mostly found in the drier and warmer regions of the lower dales, and elsewhere in lowland Britain and Europe where traditional meadow management persists. This community contains a diverse mixture of grasses and herbs, many of which are found in the northern hay meadow community, but lacks those herbs with northern or montane distributions such as Globeflower, Wood Crane's-bill, the less common lady's-mantles, and Melancholy Thistle. A number of herbs present in the northern hay meadow community are more abundant in the knapweed meadows, in particular Common Knapweed (*Centaurea nigra*). Other species which are widely distributed in Britain, such as Autumn Hawkbit (*Scorzoneroides autumnalis*), Bird's-foot Trefoil (*Lotus corniculatus*) and Oxeye Daisy (*Leucanthemum vulgare*), are also more prominent. The soils can vary even within a single field, and this is reflected in the vegetation. Less well-drained regions encourage the growth of rushes such as Soft-rush (*Juncus effusus*) and Jointed Rush (*J. articulatus*). Where the limestone is near the surface, the soils are calcareous, allowing species such as Yellow Oat-grass (*Trisetum flavescens*) and Lady's Bedstraw (*Galium verum*) to flourish. Conversely, on small pockets of deeper soils with little or no limestone influence, Betony (*Betonica officinalis*), Devil's-bit Scabious (*Succisa pratensis*) and Tormentil (*Potentilla erecta*) are more prominent.

Another meadow community found in fields flushed from springs or periodically inundated by becks is the *Cynosurus cristatus – Caltha palustris* grassland or kingcup meadow (MG8). Although some fields containing this community have often been used as permanent pastures, others have also been cut for hay. They are particularly attractive in spring, when the abundance of Kingcup or Marsh-marigold (*Caltha palustris*) flowers gives the meadows a golden-yellow appearance (Fig. 115). The community contains Crested Dog's-tail and other common hay-meadow grasses such as Red Fescue, Sweet Vernal-grass and Yorkshire-fog, but also a range of plants common on soils with impeded drainage. These include herbs such as Creeping Buttercup (*Ranunculus repens*), Cuckooflower (*Cardamine pratensis*), Meadowsweet (*Filipendula ulmaria*) and Marsh Valerian (*Valeriana dioica*), but also several species of rushes, sedges and horsetails including Jointed Rush, Carnation Sedge (*Carex panicea*) and Marsh Horsetail (*Equisetum palustre*).

The most restricted meadow community in the Dales is the *Molinia caerulea – Crepis paludosa* fen meadow or hawk's-beard fen meadow (M26), which is largely to be found at Malham Tarn. It occurs on areas of fen peat flushed with calcareous groundwater which are periodically flooded in winter. Although this community is very localised, and is probably not suitable for mechanised haymaking, in earlier years it provided a useful addition to the hay crop. Today this community has a very high biodiversity, and is of great conservation value. Purple Moor-

FIG 115. A field rich in Marsh-marigolds (*Caltha palustris*) supporting the *Cynosurus – Caltha* grassland (MG8) or kingcup meadow, Arkengarthdale.

grass (*Molinia caerulea*) is the most abundant grass, forming prominent tussocks, but there is a rich range of herbs including Marsh Hawk's-beard, Meadowsweet, Common Valerian, Devil's-bit Scabious, Globeflower, Wild Angelica (*Angelica sylvestris*), Marsh Bedstraw (*Galium palustre*) and Saw-wort (*Serratula tinctoria*). Many sedge species occur including Carnation Sedge, Glaucous Sedge (*Carex flacca*), Flea Sedge (*C. pulicaris*) and Common Sedge (*Carex nigra*). Horsetails, notably Marsh Horsetail, are prominent, as are mosses and liverworts in the ground layer.

It is the succession of colourful flowers from spring to summer which is the most attractive feature of these meadows for many people, but there are other reasons for conserving them. The plant diversity is large, with some fields having up to 150 species, but this is only a small part of the overall biodiversity. The soils contain many microorganisms and invertebrates, some of which at least are vital for nutrient recycling and the maintenance of plant growth. Perhaps the most characteristic fungal species of permanent grassland are the waxcaps (*Hygrocybe* species). Evans (2004) classified pastures at Austwick and Malham as being of national importance, both having 18 waxcap species, with the former site containing Pink Waxcap (*Hygrocybe calyptriformis*), a UK Biodiversity Action Plan species. For comparison, 33 species have been recorded for the internationally important pastures of the Longshaw Estate in the southern Pennines (Evans, 2004). A more recent study of the permanent grassland on the Malham estate (Graham, 2013) also recorded 18 species of waxcaps, but in addition two subspecies. A total of 53 species of fungi were recorded in the grassland, and 65 species from Tarn Moss and fens, but these numbers are likely to be only the tip of a very considerable iceberg. For example, DNA studies elsewhere have revealed very considerable fungal diversity in pasture soils, far more than can be accounted for from fungal fruit bodies.

The vegetation also provides shelter and/or a food resource for many invertebrates, including a large diversity of insects, molluscs and spiders, as well as mammals and birds. A recent study of slug communities in meadows at five sites in Swaledale and Wensleydale showed that there was a positive response of slug abundance and species richness to decreasing management intensity (Barlow, 2013). The most abundant slug species in these meadows were *Deroceras reticulatum* and *Arion fasciatus* and, later in an experimental study, Sarah Barlow was able to show how these might be able to influence meadow plant communities through preferential seedling herbivory of some species and avoidance of others. Species negatively affected by slugs in her experiment were Red Clover and Yellow-rattle, whereas several species were avoided, including Wood Crane's-bill, Common Sorrel and Rough Hawkbit. The importance of slug herbivory in structuring plant communities clearly has implications for hay-meadow restoration techniques which involve the addition of seeds.

Flowers lost from improved meadows are clearly potentially vital to populations of insect pollinators, amongst which bumblebees are particularly important. Sarah Barlow continued her study of invertebrates in northern hay meadow communities by investigating the foraging behaviour of bumblebees in five connected Northumberland meadows. She observed seven bumblebee species using the meadows, including the rare/scarce species *Bombus jonellus*, *B. monticola* and *B. muscorum*. She went on to show that the bumblebees were predominantly foraging on the flowers of only four species, Red and White Clover, Wood Crane's-bill and Yellow-rattle, with the last of these being the most frequently visited. The decline or loss of these species from improved meadows considerably reduces the potential food sources for these bees.

The loss of plant species from improved meadows not only affects those insects visiting flowers but also those dependent on particular food plants such as Common Bird's-foot Trefoil. These include the Burnet moths (*Zygaena filipendulae* and *Z. lonicerae*) and the Burnet Companion (*Euclidia glyphica*). The Chimney Sweeper moth (*Odezia atrata*) is abundant in northern hay meadows where Pignut, its food plant, is a prominent component of the vegetation, but is lost in improved meadows (Fig. 116). Even without improvement and the loss of their food plants, early and late cutting of the meadows for silage with modern machinery may prevent many insects from completing their life cycles. It also removes the possibility of Yellow-rattle setting seed, and so the plant is rapidly lost from the sward, as is any other species lacking a persistent soil seed bank. Silage making has a considerable impact on the seed production of other species as well, reducing both their contribution to the seed bank and their availability as a food source for seed-eating birds such as finches.

FIG 116. Chimney Sweeper moth (*Odezia atrata*), a day-flying moth common in meadows where its food plant, Pignut (*Conopodium majus*), is abundant.

Changes in the above-ground plant and animal communities in agriculturally improved meadows are also associated with changes below ground. The proportions of fungi and bacteria in the soil community change. Unimproved meadow soils have a fungal to bacterial ratio of *c.*0.083, whereas improved meadows have a lower ratio of *c.*0.032, reflecting the proportionally increased bacterial activity. This change in the microbial populations may also be responsible for a lower total carbon content of improved grassland soils, around a third less than those of unimproved grasslands, which may be associated with bacterially driven increased rates of organic matter mineralisation.

MEADOW CONSERVATION AND RESTORATION

With such a small area of the species-rich meadows surviving in the Dales today, and their importance for biodiversity, they are of great conservation value. Initially conservation efforts by the Nature Conservancy were centred on the remaining species-rich meadows, most of which had been declared Sites of Special Scientific Interest (SSSIs), and were managed through agreements with local farmers and landowners including the National Trust. Conservation was aided by the 1981 Countryside and Wildlife Act, which established the Wildlife Enhancement Scheme (WES) designed to stop damage to SSSIs by providing annual payments to farmers through management agreements. Payment was on an area basis, but also provided restrictions on farmyard manure and fertiliser use, as well as on the grazing period. Species-rich meadows were to be shut up by 15 May and the hay cut after 15 July.

To some extent the conservation importance of species-rich meadows was reduced by their being present as small isolated fragments in the landscape. The appreciation that restoration of semi-improved meadows (those which have not entirely lost their species richness) in the wider landscape would also be of considerable value was aided by the 1986 Agriculture Act. This made provision for the establishment of Environmentally Sensitive Areas (ESAs). These involved farmers being rewarded for entering voluntary management agreements designed to maintain existing landscapes and wildlife, and, where possible, to recreate features lost through modern agriculture. The Pennine Dales ESA covered most of the Yorkshire Dales National Park as well as areas further north, and provided an opportunity for many Pennine farmers to adopt more environmentally friendly management regimes. The management agreements included dates before which the grass crop could not be taken; these were, for example, 1 July in Dentdale, 8 July in Langstrothdale and Wharfedale and 15 July in Arkengarthdale and Swaledale. However, these rigid dates were one major reason why some farmers would not enter into ESA or WES agreements, given the overriding importance of dry periods for hay harvest – often very few – in the course of late spring and early summer. Thus these agri-environment schemes were not necessarily preventing further loss of species-rich meadows.

The ESA and WES have been progressively replaced by Environmental Stewardship schemes, but from 2016 a new three-tier scheme will come into operation. The Higher Level Environmental Stewardship scheme provides for more flexibility than the older schemes, in that management regimes can be made site-specific. For example, although the current species-rich meadow regime must include appropriate grazing and haymaking periods together with no ploughing, reseeding or new drainage work, farmyard manure applications and supplementary stock feeding regimes are adjustable. Restoration of semi-improved meadows is also provided for under this scheme if the soil fertility – as judged by the plant-available phosphate level – is not too high. Environmental Stewardship Schemes cover 1,150 hectares of species-rich hay meadows in the National Park, but a further nearly 6,000 hectares of potentially improvable meadows are also included.

Restoration is neither easy nor quick, particularly so if it depends on lowering the fertility of soil enriched by previous inorganic fertiliser additions. This has been demonstrated by a long-running experiment designed and established by Roger Smith of the University of Newcastle upon Tyne at Colt Park (part of the Ingleborough National Nature Reserve), which has proved important in determining meadow management plans (Smith *et al.*, 1996, 2000, 2002, 2003). The experiment, managed by English Nature/Natural England staff from 1990, was established in meadows which had been agriculturally improved, but still contained a range of herb species (Fig. 117). It was designed to investigate the most effective management regime to promote herb-rich grassland. This involved different treatments including grazing treatments (sheep grazing in spring or cattle grazing in autumn, or both), three hay cut dates (14 June, 21 July and 1 September) and two inorganic fertiliser additions (none or 25 kg nitrogen, 12.5 kg phosphorus and potassium per hectare per year). Previous studies had demonstrated that many herbs of northern hay meadows do not have seed persisting in the soil seed bank, and seed dispersal from these meadows to restoration sites would be negligible, if any at all. Therefore no management regime could bring these species back to meadows undergoing restoration without collecting and sowing seed from other sites. The two final treatments were seed of many species broadcast by hand after the hay crop in each year 1990–92, and no seed addition.

FIG 117. Experimental plots for the study of meadow management at Colt Park, Ingleborough NNR, 1990–2008, and continuing to being used to investigate the effects of the treatments on carbon sequestration.

The response to the treatments was slow, and it only became clearly apparent after 8 years that grazing regime and hay cut date were both important. The plant diversity increased in plots (1) to which seeds of missing meadow herbs were added, (2) which were grazed in the spring and autumn, (3) which received no fertiliser addition and (4) when the hay crop was taken on 21 July. This led to the recommendation that hay should be cut after mid-July and the aftermath should be grazed by cattle in the autumn. After 1998 two-thirds of the experiment was abandoned, but it continued on the autumn and spring grazing plots with the 21 July hay cut applied to all treatments. A farmyard manure treatment was added in 1999 by subdivision of the original plots. Between 2005 and 2008 the importance of Yellow-rattle, one of the species added in the seed mix, to overall species diversity was investigated by removing it from half of each plot. Farmyard manure when added with inorganic fertiliser reduced species diversity, but by 2008 in the most favourable treatment combination, several extra species from the 1990–92 seed additions were still established in the sward; perhaps this was partly at least the result of Yellow-rattle helping to reduce the vigour of the grasses.

The Colt Park meadow experiment demonstrates that it is possible to restore, at least partially, herb-rich meadows, given appropriate management and a soil of low enough fertility to limit the growth of the most vigorous grasses. But it also clearly demonstrates that change is a slow process, and it may take commitment to apply the most appropriate management regime over several decades at least to create the diversity observable in the remaining northern hay meadows today.

The Hay Time project was successfully launched in May 2006 and ran to December 2011. It was a partnership between the Yorkshire Dales Millennium Trust and the National Park Authority, supported by Natural England, the Yorkshire Wildlife Trust and other bodies with funding from a variety of sources including the Tubney Charitable Trust and Countdown 2010. The project initially aimed to restore at least 200 hectares of upland and lowland meadows within and close to the National Park (Gamble & St Pierre, 2010; Gamble *et al.*, 2012). This involved collecting seeds and harvesting green hay from surviving species-rich meadows, and using these to enrich the flora of neighbouring semi-improved grasslands. Care was taken to avoid damaging the donor meadows by not harvesting more than a third of each meadow in any one year, and not re-harvesting the area for at least three years. The receptor meadows were chosen for their low residual soil fertility, and prepared by harrowing to produce suitable gaps for plant establishment in the form of 30–50 per cent bare ground. By the end of the project, 69 restoration schemes covering 279 hectares had been undertaken, with field-scale seed additions applied to 170 hectares in total. This resulted in increased species number and diversity in the fields. The annuals, Eyebright and Yellow-rattle, established easily in the harrowed fields, as did less readily a number of perennials including Common Knapweed, Meadow Vetchling (*Lathyrus pratensis*) and Selfheal (*Prunella vulgaris*); but the establishment of some characteristic meadow species, such as Wood Crane's-bill and Great Burnet, was less successful, as indeed it had been in the earlier Colt Park experiment. But five years is far too short a time in which to assess the full success of the restoration programme. Although species-rich meadows can be easily and quickly destroyed by modern agricultural methods, it should be no surprise that the re-creation of such communities – which have been many centuries, at least, in the making – cannot be fully achieved in so few years.

In another way the Hay Time project was remarkable, in that it engaged with a large public through the annual Flowers of the Dales Festival, which included around 120 events per year spread through the spring, summer and autumn months. These events brought the importance of the meadows and their conservation to a wide audience both inside and outside the National Park. In just three years, between 2009 and 2011, more than 10,000 people participated in expert-guided walks and events in the meadows themselves, and in other sites of wildlife interest in the Dales.

In 2013 the Prince of Wales launched the national Coronation Meadows initiative to mark the 60th anniversary of the Queen's coronation. This initiative is designed to protect our remaining meadows and to use them as a springboard to restore other sites. It involves the establishment of at least one Coronation Meadow in each county. In North Yorkshire four small meadows at Muker owned by William and Carole Raw and Kathleen Raw and David Hill, amongst the best upland hay meadows in the Dales, form the Coronation Meadow. Coronation Meadows also act as donor sites for seed to promote meadow restoration at nearby sites.

PASTURES

Grasslands in their many forms cover approximately 75 per cent of the National Park. The in-bye meadows and pastures are perhaps the most familiar of these to visitors, but grasslands extend much above the enclosed fields, and can be found over the whole altitudinal and climatic range.

The most productive permanent pastures are to be found in the in-bye fields on moderate slopes which have been, and are, subject to agricultural improvement in terms of regular manure, inorganic fertiliser and, where and when necessary, lime additions. But less accessible fields and the fell sides will have been largely untouched. As in the case of the meadows, improved pastures have fewer species than pastures receiving little or no inputs, while the 'out-bye' grasslands are largely unimproved and contain a wider range of communities and species.

The grasslands exhibit a mosaic which reflects the underlying geology and to a lesser extent the climate. The Great Scar Limestone gives rise to calcareous grassland. The Yoredale limestones also support calcareous grassland, but the shales and sandstones of this series and the Millstone Grit support largely acidic or sometimes neutral grassland, as do areas of all these rocks overlain by loess and glacial drift. Soils on shales and drift often show impeded drainage, which adds wet grassland communities to the mosaic. Superimposed on the soil mosaic is the grazing history which itself largely produced the grasslands. Grazing pressure has fluctuated with the state of agriculture, which has varied over and within centuries. The in-bye pastures have been grazed intensively for many centuries by domestic livestock – milk cows, beef cattle, sheep and horses – but particularly so in the second half of the twentieth century as farm livestock numbers increased. This increase in livestock also affected the 'out-bye' grasslands, the domain of fell sheep and beef cattle, which were lightly grazed by modern standards. Millward (1988) records that for the 18 parishes in Wensleydale, sheep numbers increased from 79,800 in the period 1894–97 to 155,300 in 1986 – when sheep numbers were not yet at their twentieth-century peak – and noted that 'this increase is undoubtedly taking its toll on the flora.' An example of this toll at a landscape scale is the conversion of areas of heather moorland into grassland as coverage of Heather (*Calluna vulgaris*) and other ericaceous dwarf shrubs was selectively reduced by sheep browsing.

Upland calcareous grassland (CG9 *Sesleria caerulea* (*albicans*) – *Galium sterneri* grassland) covers over 5,500 hectares in the National Park, and, although it is mostly found at altitudes above 250–300 metres, the name is a bit misleading because it is also found at lower levels and almost down to sea level on the Carboniferous limestone outcrops fringing Morecambe Bay. Blue Moor-grass (*Sesleria caerulea*) (Fig. 118) is largely confined to these two regions in Britain, and as such these grasslands are of considerable ecological interest. Blue Moor-grass is the earliest flowering of British perennial grasses, with often its bluish-violet tinged panicles showing anthers in April. It is short in stature, even in the absence of grazing, when it can become dominant on rock ledges with few other associated species except Glaucous Sedge. In contrast, in areas with appropriate grazing regimes this community is species-rich. The Limestone Bedstraw (*Galium sterneri*), a small mat-forming species, is an important component of these grasslands, having a somewhat similar distribution in Britain to the Blue Moor-grass. The community also includes calcicole (lime-loving) flowering plants and mosses which are common on the chalk and limestone throughout Britain, including Common Rock-rose (*Helianthemum nummularium*) (Fig. 119), Salad Burnet (*Poterium sanguisorba*), Small Scabious (*Scabiosa columbaria*), Wild Thyme (*Thymus polytrichus*), Fairy Flax (*Linum catharticum*) and the moss species *Ctenidium molluscum* and *Homalothecium lutescens*. Other important grasses and more widely distributed species include Crested Hair-grass (*Koeleria macrantha*), Sheep's-fescue (*Festuca ovina*), Quaking-grass, Bird's-foot Trefoil, Common Dog-violet (*Viola riviniana*), eyebright species and Harebell (*Campanula rotundifolia*). In some localities in Ribblesdale and Swaledale a distinctive sward rich in sedges occurs, notably Flea and Carnation Sedge; however, both species are common in this grassland elsewhere.

Very locally the limestone pastures contain some rare or uncommon plants including Dwarf Milkwort (*Polygala amarella*), Alpine Cinquefoil (*Potentilla cranzii*), Mountain Avens (*Dryas octopetala*), Field Gentian (*Gentianella campestris*), Bloody

FIG 118. Blue Moor-grass (*Sesleria caerulea*), Colt Park, Ingleborough NNR. This coarse and vigorous grass flowers very early in the spring. The *Sesleria caerulea (albicans) – Galium sterneri* (CG9) calcareous grassland is abundant in the Dales.

FIG 119. Common Rock-rose (*Helianthemum nummularium*), an important plant of calcareous grassland, where it is the food plant of the Northern Brown Argus butterfly (*Aricia artaxerxes*) and other insects.

Crane's-bill (*Geraneum sanguineum*), and orchids such as Dark-red Helleborine (*Epipactis atrorubens*) and Frog Orchid (*Coeloglossum viride*). Although Mountain Avens is perhaps best known as occurring on exposed rocks above Littondale, it can also be found in a fairly extensive area of limestone grassland in this vicinity

(Kevin Walker, personal communication). In contrast to plants with northern and montane distributions such as Alpine Cinquefoil and Mountain Avens, Horseshoe Vetch (*Hippocrepis comosa*), a species more typical of the southern chalk and limestone, occurs very locally too. Other southern species occurring locally within the Dales are Green-winged Orchid (*Anacamptis morio*) and Burnt Orchid (*Orchis ustulata*).

Perhaps the most enigmatic of all the plants recorded from the Dales is the lady's-mantle *Alchemilla minima*. This species was first described from Simon Fell, Ingleborough, by Max Walters in 1947 as a dwarf species easily separable from the much more common *A. filicaulis* subsp. *vestita*. Margaret Bradshaw (1964) later described the species as occurring on damp intensively grazed *Festuca – Agrostis* grassland, either on limestone or in areas flushed with lime-rich water. Although the species was thought originally to be confined to Ingleborough and Whernside, Halliday (1997) lists records from Garsdale Head and upper Dentdale. *Alchemilla minima* has claim to be Britain's only endemic flowering plant species, but doubts have persisted about its taxonomic status. Clive Stace (2010) still gives it specific rank, but concludes that it is possibly better regarded as a subspecies of *A. filicaulis*. Mark Lynes (2014), reviewing all the most recent evidence, is firmly of the opinion that it conforms to the latter species.

Damper depressions and areas of seepage on slopes in these grasslands contain perhaps the most characteristic of all Dales plants: Bird's-eye Primrose (*Primula farinosa*) (Fig. 120), growing often with Common Butterwort (*Pinguicula vulgaris*), an insectivorous plant, and Grass-of-Parnassus (*Parnassia palustris*). Bird's-eye Primrose is a delightful feature of these grasslands, particularly in late May and June when the pinkish-violet flowers with yellow throats borne in umbels on short, mealy scapes abound on moist slopes. These flushes are often rich in sedge species, including Yellow Sedge (*Carex viridula* ssp. *brachyrrhyncha*), Tawny Sedge (*C. hostiana*), Common and Carnation Sedges. Rush species are also prominent, including Jointed Rush and Sharp-flowered Rush (*Juncus acutiflorus*). Lower plants frequently present include the mosses *Ctenidium molluscum*, *Palustriella commutatum* var.*commutatum* and *Philonotis calcarea*, and less commonly the Lesser Clubmoss (*Selaginella selaginoides*). More locally some of these flushes contain Black Bog-rush (*Schoenus nigricans*), Flat-sedge (*Blysmus compressus*) and Broad-leaved Cottongrass (*Eriophorum latifolium*).

Very locally on lightly grazed steep slopes a meadow-like tall-herb grassland occurs: the *Arrhenatherum elatius – Filipendula ulmaria* tall-herb grassland (MG2). This community includes Jacob's-ladder (*Polemonium caeruleum*) as a characteristic species which was widespread in the Late-glacial but now restricted to a very few sites, including at Malham.

FIG 120. Bird's-eye Primrose (*Primula farinosa*), a plant of damp calcareous grassland, fens and flushes and amongst the most attractive and characteristic of all the Dales flora.

In contrast to the upland calcareous grassland, the lowland calcareous grassland (CG2 *Festuca ovina – Avenula pratensis* grassland) is much more localised, covering a very much smaller area in the Dales, only 200 hectares compared with over 5,500. It occurs in the south and west Craven region. This grassland largely lacks Blue Moor-grass and several of the plants of northern distribution, but contains many of the common calcicole species of the upland grassland.

The need to conserve the rich biodiversity of these calcareous grasslands, particularly the upland community, has led to studies of the most appropriate grazing regime. Ashley Lyons and her co-workers at Edge Hill University are studying the effects of grazing regime (no grazing, or sheep or cattle at the same low stocking density) on upland calcareous grassland communities at Malham and Ingleborough, as well as at Great Asby Scar outside the current National Park boundary. On large plots (ranging between 50 and 526 hectares) at all three sites the data show that, after a minimum of 10 years, sheep grazing has led to the highest plant diversity so far, significantly higher than in the ungrazed sites. As the investigation proceeds, its results may have long-term implications for the recent trend towards the increased use of cattle grazing as a conservation tool on upland calcareous grasslands.

The better-quality pasture on acidic soils, often on free-draining slopes, is the *Festuca ovina – Agrostis capillaris – Galium saxatile* (U4) grassland. It can be found in enclosed pastures as well as on the open fells, where it is attractive to livestock and is important in sustaining upland farming in Britain. Sheep's-fescue and Common Bent are the most important grasses, but other species such as Sweet Vernal-grass, Crested Dog's-tail and Yorkshire-fog are common constituents of the sward, as is the Field Wood-rush (*Luzula campestris*). Heath Bedstraw (*Galium saxatile*) and Tormentil are the most characteristic herbs in this community, but on the better soils, often within enclosed pastures, a wide range of species can occur including Common Mouse-ear (*Cerastium fontanum*), dandelions (*Taraxacum* species), Germander Speedwell (*Veronica chamaedrys*), Ribwort Plantain (*Plantago lanceolata*), White Clover, Pignut and Yarrow (*Achillea millefolium*). On more neutral soils which retain some limestone influence Lady's Bedstraw, Wild Thyme and Mountain Pansy (*Viola lutea*) can be found in the community. Mountain Pansy, one of the most attractive of pasture flowers, is also often found in soils enriched in metals in lead-mining districts. The common calcifuge moss species in these grasslands include *Hylocomium splendens, Pleurozium schreberi, Rhytidiadelphus squarrosus* and *Hypnum cupressiforme.*

These better-quality pastures, particularly on fairly deep soils, can become invaded with Bracken (*Pteridium aquilinum*), which much reduces their grazing value. Young Bracken has the added disadvantage that it is toxic to cattle. Bracken produces a dense canopy and a litter which few other species are able to tolerate – but among these are Heath Bedstraw, Tormentil and Sheep's Sorrel (*Rumex acetosella*). This is the *Pteridium aquilinum – Galium saxatile* fern community (U20). Another fern which occurs very occasionally in this community is Lemon-scented Fern (*Oreopteris limbosperma*). Bracken, a woodland plant, spread very considerably in upland grassland areas of Britain in the twentieth century, particularly where sheep replaced cattle on the hills and when it was no longer cut to provide bedding for stock. Cutting and trampling by cattle can considerably reduce its vigour. Bracken is essentially a calcifuge species; however, it will also occur on some calcareous soils, but it rarely grows vigorously in this situation, partly at least because the growth of its rhizome is often restricted in the usually shallow limestone soils. It is also susceptible both to late frosts and to exposure, and is thus largely excluded from frost pockets and from higher hillsides. However, the community still covers more than 2,000 hectares in the National Park.

Mat-grass (*Nardus stricta*) grasslands (*Nardus stricta – Galium saxatile* grassland, U5) provide the poorer-quality fell pastures on acidic soils (Fig. 121). Again,

FIG 121. Mat-grass (*Nardus stricta*) in flower, a major component of poor-quality pastures supporting the *Nardus stricta – Galium saxatile* grassland (U5).

Heath Bedstraw, Tormentil, Sheep's-fescue and Common Bent are important components of the vegetation, but Mat-grass is usually dominant. Wavy hair-grass (*Deschampsia flexuosa*) is an important component of the vegetation too, and other monocotyledons commonly occurring are Heath-grass (*Danthonia decumbens*), Velvet Bent (*Agrostis canina*), Green-ribbed Sedge (*Carex binervis*), Common Sedge, Heath Rush (*Juncus squarrosus*) and Heath Wood-rush (*Luzula multiflora*). Great Wood-rush (*Luzula sylvatica*), predominantly a woodland species, can also be found locally in these grasslands forming dense patches over small areas. Common calcifuge bryophytes, notably *Rhytidiadelphus squarrosus, Lophocolea bidentata* and haircap mosses (*Polytrichum* and *Polytrichastrum* species) are important, and can be more abundant here than in the better-quality acidic pastures. Bilberry (*Vaccinium myrtillus*) is the most common dwarf shrub, occurring as scattered shoots often much browsed by sheep. Heather and Crowberry (*Empetrum nigrum*) are also widespread, but make up a small proportion of the overall above-ground biomass. In many places these plants are indicators of former heathland communities which are now grasslands as the result of grazing pressure.

Damp grasslands on thin peaty soils can often be dominated, not by a grass, but by the Heath Rush. Grasses in this community include Wavy Hair-grass, Common Bent and Mat-grass, while Heath Bedstraw is often the only herb and Common Sedge the only sedge. But where the peat is a little deeper, other sedges including Hare's-tail Cottongrass are found as scattered tufts and *Sphagnum* species may also occur. This is the *Juncus squarrosus – Festuca ovina* grassland (U6), which is found extensively not only in the Dales but also in the neighbouring areas outside the National Park including Nidderdale, the Lakeland fells and the north Pennines.

Flushes are interspersed into the sloping ground of these acidic grasslands. The water emerging from these springs and seepages is usually acidic, but locally more calcareous flushes occur along spring lines. Many of the acidic flushes are dominated by Soft-rush with a carpet of bog-moss species below (notably *Sphagnum fallax*) (Fig. 122), but some, perhaps those with slightly less acidic water, are more species-rich, containing Lesser Spearwort (*Ranunculus flammula*), Round-leaved Crowfoot (*Ranunculus omiophyllus*) and Pale Forget-me-not (*Myosotis stolonifera*). A few calcareous flushes on the spring line just below the summit of Great Shunner Fell have long been noted for the presence of Marsh Saxifrage (*Saxifraga hirculus*), but in recent years two other remarkable finds have been made in these flushes: Sheathed Sedge (*Carex vaginata*) and Alpine Foxtail (*Alopecurus borealis*) have been recorded in the Dales for the first time (Robinson, 2008). These discoveries may have been aided by increased flowering following a reduction in

FIG 122. A flush community, important for ground-nesting birds, with Soft-rush (*Juncus effusus*) growing through a *Sphagnum fallax* lawn. (Roger Meade)

grazing pressure after the foot and mouth epidemic of 2001. But a decrease in grazing pressure may not always prove beneficial. Linda Robinson suggested that Marsh Saxifrage flushes need some grazing and trampling to open up the sward in order to reduce competition from other species, including tall herbs.

In the past these moorland flushes have been put to agricultural use. Pearsall (1950) described how these flushes were once used in an attempt to improve the productivity of the surrounding grassland by replacing nutrients which had been removed by the grazing animals and leaching. This involved extending the area of seepage by cutting a number of oblique channels downslope from the flush into the grassland, a practice no longer encouraged today.

CONCLUDING REMARKS

The spread of both *Nardus stricta – Galium saxatile* and *Juncus squarrosus – Festuca ovina* grasslands at the expense of both heathland and the better-quality *Festuca ovina – Agrostis capillaris – Galium saxatile* grassland is the result of the grazing history over the last few centuries. This reflects not only increased stocking rates in these upland pastures, particularly in the second half of the twentieth century, but also the earlier switch in many upland areas from cattle to sheep grazing. Formerly sheep grazing on the fells was often by wethers when mutton rather than lamb was in demand. Both cattle and wethers will graze Mat-grass and Heath Rush to some extent, but ewes now largely avoid them, leading to the dominance of these species over Sheep's-fescue and Common Bent.

Pastures on SSSIs and nature reserves are managed to optimise the biological diversity whether on acidic or calcareous soils. Inevitably this means the establishment of appropriate grazing regimes. This invariably has resulted in a reduction in stocking levels from those present at the end of the twentieth century, but also adjustments have been made both to the grazing period and to the livestock used. Cattle have once again become important, particularly the use of native breeds such as Belted Galloway and Shorthorn, but further adjustments to existing regimes may prove necessary as current grazing studies come to fruition.

Hill farming can only currently be sustained at these stocking levels and under these management regimes by some form of financial support such as from Environmental Stewardship Schemes. Relaxation of grazing pressure and change in grazing regime can be shown to be beneficial in the short term, and may help to reverse some of the decline in biodiversity – this was spectacularly demonstrated in 2001 by mass flowering in areas affected by foot and mouth. But other factors may be at work both in the pastures and in the meadows: Carly Stevens and her co-workers (2004), in a study of the species composition of British acidic grasslands, showed a linear negative correlation of species number with increase in atmospheric nitrogen deposition, suggesting that even with optimal grazing and cutting management, biodiversity in these grasslands may still be in the process of being lost. Atmospheric deposition has been, and is, largely discounted by farmers as an important nitrogen source, but it increased markedly in the second half of the last century, and is likely to be having long-term ecological effects which are not yet entirely apparent.

CHAPTER 8

Moorland

Although grassland covers large areas of the pastures, and forms the most vital part of the farming system above the enclosed dale-side fields, communities in which dwarf shrubs, particularly Heather (*Calluna vulgaris*), are prominent are also very important (Fig. 123). In August the mauve-purple Heather flowers provide a major landscape feature, particularly

FIG 123. An example of an extensive managed Heather moor near the head of Arkengarthdale, with a strip in the foreground recovering from burning in the year before.

above parts of Nidderdale, Swaledale and Wharfedale where the moors are managed as shooting estates for Red Grouse (*Lagopus lagopus scoticus*). Red Grouse, a subspecies of Willow Grouse endemic to Britain, is much prized as a fast-flying game bird.

Heather, together with several other species of dwarf shrubs, most notably Bilberry (*Vaccinium myrtillus*), Crowberry (*Empetrum nigrum* ssp. *nigrum*) and more locally Cowberry (*Vaccinium vitis-idaea*), forms dry heaths on sandstone and gritstone outcrops and on well-drained slopes supporting acidic soils – providing they have not been subjected to heavy sheep-grazing pressure. On less freely drained soils wet heath communities occur locally, with some peat accumulation (< 0.5 metres deep). But over large areas on rounded hill tops and ridges, where the slopes are gentle and the drainage strongly impeded, Heather is an important component of another community, blanket mire, which is developed over peat often of several metres depth. Here it is joined by another ericaceous shrub, the Cross-Leaved Heath (*Erica tetralix*), and more locally by Cranberry (*Vaccinium oxycoccus*); but other important and conspicuous plants are the bog-mosses (*Sphagnum* species) and the cottongrasses. Hare's-tail Cottongrass (*Eriophorum vaginatum*) can form large grass-like tussocks over much of the bog surface, and Common Cottongrass (*E. angustifolium*) grows vigorously in damp depressions and pools. These heathland and mire ecosystems are of major importance, covering over 30 per cent of the Yorkshire Dales National Park. But it is not simply their large total land cover that makes them important. These ecosystems support the grouse moors that are one of the mainstays of the local economy, providing full- and part-time employment as well as attracting many visitors to the Dales. In addition, the blanket mires have an importance both inside and far outside the National Park. They act as gigantic sponges, except when saturated, storing water which is slowly released to the becks and rivers, and thence to the reservoirs. They also provide both large sinks and stores of carbon which are increasingly regarded as important in terms of global climatic change.

HEATHS

Heathland covers over 100,000 hectares in the National Park. The best-developed heather moors are on estates which are actively managed for Red Grouse (Fig. 124), and since at least the 1980s these have been seen as a conservation priority. Predominantly these are covered by the *Calluna vulgaris – Vaccinium myrtillus* heath (H12), but locally, particularly in the south of the region, the *Calluna vulgaris – Deschampsia flexuosa* heath (H9) is widespread. In both these communities

FIG 124. Red Grouse (*Lagopus lagopus scoticus*), an important part of the Dales economy. (Phil Mclean)

Heather is generally dominant. The latter community, in which the Wavy Hair-grass (*Deschampsia flexuosa*) is prominent, contains Bilberry but is often poor in species. This is particularly so in areas which were subjected to high levels of atmospheric pollution during the nineteenth and twentieth centuries. The moss *Pohlia nutans* is a characteristic plant in this community, which includes, amongst other bryophytes, the moss *Orthodontium lineare*, which was first recorded in West Yorkshire in 1920 but has now spread throughout much of Britain, and the leafy liverwort *Gymnocolea inflata*. *Cladonia* lichens, notably *Cladonia squamosa*, form scattered patches over the ground.

In the *Calluna vulgaris – Vaccinium myrtillus* heath, Heather is usually dominant and can form almost a monoculture, with the more shade-tolerant Bilberry occurring sparsely below the developing canopy. Where the growth of Heather is less luxuriant, other shrubs are often found in this community, including Crowberry, Cowberry and very locally Bell Heather (*Erica cinerea*). This last species is much rarer in the Dales than in the Pennines further south. Other rare species found at very few sites include Chickweed Wintergreen (*Trientalis europaea*) and Common Cow-wheat (*Melampyrum pratense*), both essentially woodland species possibly indicative of the former forest cover.

These heaths are interspersed with wetter soils around flushes where groundwater reaches the surface. As in the acid grasslands, these give rise to communities in which clumps of the Soft-rush (*Juncus effusus*) grow through *Sphagnum* lawns often dominated by *Sphagnum fallax*, but also containing other species, most notably *S. denticulatum* (*auriculatum*). The largest British moss, *Polytrichum commune* var. *commune* (Fig. 125), is also prominent in the community. In the National Vegetation Classification (NVC) this is the *Carex echinata – Sphagnum recurvum/auriculatum – Juncus effusus* sub-community (M6c), which is very common throughout the Pennines. Among the plants found more locally in these flushes are Star Sedge (*Carex echinata*) and Marsh Violet (*Viola palustris*). These flushes, although often occupying only a small area within the moorlands, are important for moorland-nesting birds and as feeding sites for their young.

FIG 125. A hummock of the largest British moss species, *Polytrichum commune*, a common plant of flushes in the Dales moorland.

Another heath community found very locally in the National Park, notably on Threshfield Moor west-southwest of Grassington, is a wet heath developed over very shallow peat. Heather is present, but Purple Moor-grass (*Molinia caerulea*) is dominant and Cross-leaved Heath is the most abundant dwarf shrub. This community has affinities with the *Molinia caerulea – Potentilla erecta* mire (M25). The mosses *Sphagnum compactum* and *S. capillifolium* are also locally abundant in the vegetation cover.

Montane heath is also very restricted in its distribution. The hills in the National Park are not high enough to support extensive examples of this community, but very locally near the summits of some of the higher hills – including Fountains Fell, Great Shunner Fell, Great Whernside, Ingleborough, Pen-y-ghent and Whernside – small patches of it occur (Fig. 126). Here the dwarf

FIG 126. The summit of Ingleborough, where the desert-like state of the montane heath is the result of sheep grazing and the boots of generations of walkers.

shrubs are Bilberry, Cowberry and Crowberry, but other plants of northern montane communities include Dwarf Willow (*Salix herbacea*), Stiff Sedge (*Carex bigelowii*) and Viviparous Sheep's-fescue (*Festuca vivipara*). Among the moss species occurring is *Racomitrium lanuginosum*, which together with Stiff Sedge is an important component of the extensive moss heath communities in the Scottish Highlands, for example in the *Vaccinium myrtillus – Racomitrium lanuginosum* heath (H20). In the Dales the moss does not form the extensive mats found on Scottish mountains, perhaps in part because of visitor pressure on some summits, the long grazing history and the nearer proximity to major sources of atmospheric pollution (Baddeley *et al.* 1994). However, in the Dales it can be found growing more vigorously on walls and screes, suggesting that the activities of grazing animals may be an important factor limiting its vigour and distribution at the present time.

Most heaths are subject to at least light sheep grazing, while grazing and/or burning is essential in their maintenance to limit tree establishment, particularly at lower altitudes and on well-drained soils. When these heaths are not well managed, they often have an open Heather canopy allowing grasses, herbs and Bracken (*Pteridium aquilinum*) as well as large woody plants to establish. Bracken poses a considerable threat to these heaths. It can grow vigorously on deep well-drained soils, and it suppresses the shade-intolerant Heather over wide areas. Once established, Bracken also reduces the grazing value by limiting the vigour of the subordinate grasses and herbs. In the absence of Bracken, Wavy Hair-grass is prominent in the open Heather canopy, but other grasses commonly found include Sheep's-fescue (*Festuca ovina*), Common Bent (*Agrostis capillaris*), Velvet Bent (*A. canina*) and Mat-grass (*Nardus stricta*). The calcifuge herbs Heath Bedstraw (*Galium saxatile*) and Tormentil (*Potentilla erecta*) are common, and several mosses are often prominent, notably *Pleurozium schreberi, Hypnum jutlandicum, Hylocomium splendens* and *Dicranum scoparium. Cladonia* lichen species including C. *impexa*, C. *pyxidata* and C. *uncialis* are common, growing both on the stems of the dwarf shrubs and on the ground. Increase in grazing pressure can readily convert this community to grassland dominated by Mat-grass, and has done so widely in the past, particularly as a result of sheep selectively browsing the dwarf shrubs in winter.

Even without grazing the growth of these subordinate species is enhanced as the Heather canopy ages. Old Heather stems become woody and fan out like wheel spokes, allowing light to penetrate and enabling the subordinate species to expand around the base of the heather stems (Fig. 127). Over a century ago it was recognised that old Heather stands were not optimal for Red Grouse, not least because of the paucity of young Heather shoots on which the birds feed, and the much reduced cover particularly from avian predators.

FIG 127. Leggy Heather (*Calluna vulgaris*), with the old shoots collapsing to expose the vegetation below, Ingleborough NNR.

MOORLAND MANAGEMENT

Moor burning or swaling of the commons was an age-old practice used to remove old woody heather growth to provide a 'soft bite' for sheep in the subsequent new growth. It was given fresh impetus by the rise of grouse-shooting estates. Grouse shooting was first recorded as being introduced into the Dales by the Whartons of Swaledale in 1725 (Done & Muir, 2001), and the parliamentary enclosures later in the century and the first half of the nineteenth century provided the opportunity for the expansion of grouse moors onto what once had been common land. In 1797 the Duke of Devonshire advertised grouse shooting in 14 manors in the Dales to 'gentlemen resident in the neighbourhood upon application to Mr Swale of Settle for tickets'. And by the end of the nineteenth century some estates, for example the Yorke estates in Nidderdale, found letting of shooting rights more profitable than farming tenancies.

To optimise the area suitable for the vigorous growth of Heather, and thus also for Red Grouse, many shooting estates indulged in moor gripping (the digging of drainage ditches), particularly where the moors extended over shallow peat soils. This was designed to improve the drainage and thus the vigour of the Heather, which grows poorly in waterlogged soils, where it is confined to the tops of hummocks. These drainage activities were combined with a burning regime designed to eliminate stands of old 'leggy' Heather (Fig. 127). This regime, which is widely used today on moorland, involves controlled burning designed to be hot enough to remove the surface vegetation (*c.*500 °C) while limiting the nutrient losses in smoke, and not so hot as to destroy the underground Heather stems (< *c.*200 °C). This allows the Heather to shoot vigorously from the latter as well as providing a bare ash-covered soil in which seedlings can become established. Vegetative regeneration leads to a more rapid recovery of the Heather canopy than from seed. Immediately following a burn, Bilberry and Wavy Hair-grass plants can become prominent, but soon young shoots of heather appear and carpet the ground. Alex Watt (1955), in describing cyclical changes in Heather growth, termed this the pioneer stage. This stage is followed by the building stage, in which Heather grows vigorously and the canopy closes. The mature stage occurs when a dense canopy is established, but the productivity of the Heather begins to decline. As the stand ages, the old Heather stems separate and become prostrate, and their cover and productivity declines further as other plants become more prominent in the moorland community. This is the so-called degenerate stage.

The whole process may take well in excess of 25 years, but the object of good moorland management is to eliminate the mature and degenerate phases while maintaining both good cover and an optimal supply of young Heather shoots on which the birds can feed. Burning of the moor proceeds sequentially in a series of strips during the period from 1 October to 15 April when suitable dry weather conditions allow, although in wet springs and on land above 450 metres the latter date can be extended. Each strip is burnt roughly every 12–15 years at a time approximating to the end of the building stage; in well-controlled burns this can produce a complete heather cover in little more than four years from the burn. Many small long strips are burnt preferably to large single areas of moorland. The moor thus becomes a patchwork of strips of differing post-burn ages, providing the necessary cover and food resource for the birds (Fig. 128).

But burning and drainage can be counterproductive if carried out to excess. Drainage can reduce the availability and quality of flushes, which are important for young Red Grouse chicks as well as for several wader species. Uncontrolled burns can lead to very high temperatures, and short exposure to temperatures of

FIG 128. A recently burned strip (right) and a mature Heather strip (left), part of the moorland patchwork above Arkengarthdale producing even-aged stands of young Heather shoots to provide both food and cover for Red Grouse (*Lagopus lagopus scoticus*).

*c.*400 °C kill Heather stem bases in the soil, as well as burning the surface organic matter. On shallow peat this can mean burning down to the subsoil, not only markedly increasing the time for a vegetation cover to return, but also potentially causing a public nuisance. Mismanaged swaling in the nineteenth century on Earl de Grey and Ripon's estate at Dallowgill Moor caused smoke discomfort to the populace in Ripon 16 kilometres away (Done & Muir, 2001). It also potentially causes soil erosion and increases the dissolved organic carbon, causing brown colouration in drainage water which water companies have to remove for domestic supplies. After mismanaged swaling, the recovery of a Heather cover can take many years.

Heather cover can also be lost as the result of Heather Beetle attack. Heather Beetle (*Lochmaea suturalis*) caterpillars are capable of defoliating large areas of moorland, but it is unclear whether the periodic outbreaks of this pest are directly related to moorland management. In the Netherlands infestations have been shown to restrict Heather regeneration, and the outbreaks have been linked to high atmospheric nitrogen deposition in the latter part of the twentieth century, but it is uncertain whether outbreaks in Britain have become more common in this period.

Management certainly influences invertebrate diversity (see e.g. Coulson, 1988; Usher & Gardener, 1988). When comparisons have been made between managed and unmanaged Heather communities, the latter have been shown to have a higher biodiversity, with many of the taxa being more numerous. This is a reflection of the fact that unmanaged stands have all stages of Heather, whereas managed stands usually lack the mature and degenerate stages. Studies of ants and spiders in southern heathlands show changes in species abundance and composition from pioneer to mature stages. Haysom & Coulson (1998), studying blanket peat communities in northern England and southern Scotland, showed that there was a significant increase in the density and diversity of Lepidoptera larvae with increase in the height of Heather, and this was common to most species and families at all their study sites. Other work on Scottish moorlands has shown that pioneer-stage heather supports largely ground-dwelling and feeding species of Carabidae, Collembola, Acarina and Araneae, whereas building and mature stages were dominated by sap and shoot feeders such as Cercopidae, Psyllidae and Curculionidae. However, in general, building and mature stages have the greatest invertebrate diversity.

Grouse moors have been managed to optimise the Red Grouse population, and this has meant the control of potential predators. Historically it has meant gamekeepers shooting avian predators such as Buzzards (*Buteo buteo*), Hen Harriers (*Circus cyaneus*), Peregrine Falcons (*Falco peregrinus*) and Short-eared Owls (*Aseo flammeus*); this has been illegal since the 1950s, but still occurs, as evidenced by a Hen Harrier being found shot dead on a Dales moorland in 2012. Carrion Crows (*Corvus corone*) are shot legally, and control of mammalian predators such as Foxes (*Vulpes vulpes*), Stoats (*Mustela erminea*) and Weasels (*M. nivalis*) is also seen as important. Foxes are the main predators of adult birds. In a ten-year study in Scotland, Foxes took 38 per cent of radio-tagged hen grouse on their nests. Most mammalian predators also take eggs and chicks, as do some avian predators including Carrion Crows, and, where they are present, Hen Harriers will also take grouse chicks. In an experimental study of legal predator control in northern England, Fletcher *et al.* (2010) showed that a reduction of Fox (–43 per cent) and Carrion Crow (–78 per cent) abundance led not only to an increase in breeding number and success in Red Grouse, but also to similar increases for other ground-nesting birds including Curlew (*Numenius arquata*), Golden Plover (*Pluvialis apricaria*) and Lapwing (*Vanellus vanellus*). Without predator control on similar moorland areas, breeding numbers of all these species declined. The aim of predator control on well-managed estates is to arrive at a density of not less than 65 Red Grouse per square kilometre in the autumn, which is thought to be the minimum necessary to sustain profitable driven shooting. Predator control has advantages for small mammal species such as Pygmy Shrews (*Sorex minutus*) as well as birds, and, close to some well-controlled grouse moors, Rabbit (*Oryctolagus cuniculus*) populations also benefit in the absence of attention on them from keepers and landowners!

On some estates attempts are made to control the parasite which causes so-called 'grouse disease' or tricostrongylosis. This organism is the caecal threadworm *Trichostrongylus tenuis*. Larvae of the threadworm move onto young Heather shoots which are ingested by the birds and move through their guts to the caeca where they develop into adult threadworms (for further details see Watson & Moss, 2008). Heavy infestations lead to the bird's demise and can cause population declines. Attempts to manage the disease involve the use of anthelmintic drugs, usually by laying out medicated grit. In a five-year study in county Durham, birds in an area of moorland treated with medicated grit were compared to those in a control area receiving grit without drug addition. Medicated grit treatment led both to a lower threadworm parasite burden and to a higher mean number of chicks reared per hen. On average twice the number of chicks were raised by hens from the treated area compared to birds in the control area, suggesting that drug treatments should enhance the viability of shooting on this and perhaps also other estates (Newborn & Foster, 2002).

The looping ill virus can also cause heavy mortality in grouse chicks. This is a viral disease spread by the Sheep Tick (*Ixodes ricinus*), which also carries Lyme disease. On Scottish moors Red Deer (*Cervus elaphus*) and Mountain Hare (*Lepus timidus*) are important hosts for the tick, but in northern England the major mammalian host is the fell sheep. Where sheep and grouse are the principal hosts for the tick, controlling the ticks in the sheep through the use of acaricides and vaccination can be important for the birds. Newborn & Baines (2012) showed that enhanced acaricide treatment in sheep grazing at densities of 1.3 and 1.4 per hectare reduced the tick burdens of grouse chicks by 90 per cent, allowing more birds to be shot.

The grouse moors within and around the National Park have been and remain amongst the best managed and most productive in the country. On 30 August 1888 at Blubberhouses Moor between Nidderdale and Wharfedale Lord Walsingham shot 1,070 birds in 20 drives. In one week in 1901, a Richmond game dealer dispatched 17,352 Grouse by rail. And between 1867 and 1895, 47,468 birds were shot on Lord de Grey's Dallowgill Moor alone (Done & Muir, 2001).

BLANKET MIRES

As the name suggests, the blanket mires or blanket bogs cover the gentle slopes and hill plateaux, extending to approximately 44,000 hectares in the National Park. They are essentially precipitation-fed ecosystems insulated from the mineral soils by layers of peat extending from around half a metre to several metres in depth. Although blanket mire and heath vegetation share some species in common, perhaps most notably Heather, it is the presence of an underlying deep peat layer in the blanket mires which effectively separates the communities and determines the very different plant growth conditions. As on the raised bogs discussed in Chapter 9, the peat layer determines that mire plants are largely dependent on the atmospheric supply in the form of rain or dust rather than the mineral soil as a source of nutrients. Blanket mires form only in regions where precipitation greatly exceeds loss of water to the atmosphere by evaporation from the ground surface and transpiration through the plants, so-called evapotranspiration.

John Tallis (1991) showed that peat began forming on the south Pennine hills as early as approximately 9,000 years ago. In the north Pennines peat formation began later (c.5,000 years ago), and the major spread was between 4,000 and 3,000 years ago at a time when human populations were beginning to clear the upland forests. Under the prevailing climate, the soils became leached and waterlogged, providing conditions suitable for the bog-mosses (*Sphagnum* species) to grow over the surface. These species acidify further the developing mire and act like a sponge. They have the ability to drag up the water table as they grow, and in some parts of the Pennines may have drowned woodland in the process, as has happened on Blubberhouses Moor. Under the acidic and anaerobic conditions which result a few tens of centimetres below the growing moss surface, decomposition by both soil bacteria and fungi is strongly suppressed, and dead organic matter accumulates as peat.

Although containing some moss-dominated flats, these mires are not now, and never have been, more or less flat *Sphagnum* lawns, but have a varied topography of hummocks and hollows interspersed with drainage gulleys (Fig. 129). *Sphagnum* species are the major peat-forming plants, and occupy the full range of microhabitats within the mire from species such as *S. cuspidatum*, which grows submerged in the bog pools as well as around their edges, through *S. fallax* and *S. magellanicum* (Fig. 130) growing in lawns around the pools, to hummock-forming species such as *S. capillifolium* and *S. papillosum*.

This difference in species distribution in relation to topography is also reflected in the flowering plants and their relative abilities to grow in relation

FIG 129. An example of the hummock and hollow topography within blanket mire and raised bog ecosystems. Raised bogs are discussed in Chapter 9.

FIG 130. A small section of a lawn containing *Sphagnum magellanicum* (red) and *Sphagnum papillosum*. (Roger Meade)

to the water table. The Common Cottongrass colonises the bog pools (Fig. 131), Cross-leaved Heath, Cranberry and Bog Asphodel (*Narthecium ossifragum*) the lawns, and Hare's-tail Cottongrass (Fig. 132) and Heather, which is intolerant of waterlogging, the hummocks. The last two species are very conspicuous when they are in flower, the former usually in May and early June and the latter in August and early September. They give their names to the community, the *Calluna*

FIG 131. Common Cottongrass (*Eriophorum angustifolium*), a plant of pools and hollows in both blanket and raised mires, Swarth Moor, Ingleborough NNR.

FIG 132. Hare's-tail Cottongrass (*Eriophorum vaginatum*), Swarth Moor, Ingleborough NNR. The plant forms prominent tussocks, and is an important member of the *Calluna vulgaris – Eriophorum vaginatum* blanket mire (M19), where it can become dominant over large areas.

vulgaris – Eriophorum vaginatum blanket mire (M19), which covers much of the Pennine bogs. Crowberry is another shrub which is prominent in many Pennine bogs, but there are more local species too including Bog Rosemary (*Andromeda polifolia*) (Fig. 133). This species is commonly infected by the fungus *Exobasidium karstenii*, which causes gall formation consisting of prominent shoots with reddish-purple enlarged leaves (Fig. 134). Deergrass (*Trichophorum cespitosum*),

FIG 133. Bog Rosemary (*Andromeda polifolia*), a plant of both raised bogs and blanket mires in the Dales. (Roger Meade)

FIG 134. A reddish-purple galled shoot of Bog Rosemary infected by the fungus *Exobasidium karstenii* (left) and an uninfected shoot (right) at Swarth Moor, Ingleborough NNR.

which like the Cottongrasses is a sedge rather than a grass, is abundant and Purple Moor-grass, which is a grass, is common, but it does not usually form the large tussocks associated with its growth in wet heaths. Although *Sphagnum* species are the major peat-forming plants, there are many other bryophytes in the community including the leafy liverworts *Odontoschisma sphagni*, *Mylia taylorii* and *Mylia anomala*. Lichens, particularly *Cladonia* species, are common. A notable northern lichen, *Cetraria islandica*, rare in England, whose common name is confusingly Icelandic Moss, is found in mires above Swaledale.

There are several other interesting flowering plants on the blanket bogs, including the insectivorous Round-leaved Sundew (*Drosera rotundifolia*). Another rather inconspicuous plant which is often overlooked is the Lesser Twayblade Orchid (*Neottia cordata*). This is a plant with a northern montane distribution in Europe, as is the Cloudberry (*Rubus chamaemorus*) (Fig. 135). Cloudberry is dioecious, having separate male and female plants, and its fruits are much prized in Scandinavia (and also in Newfoundland, where they are called bakeapples). Although there are old records of the fruits being sold in markets in northern England, it is rare to see collectable quantities of fruit on Pennine bogs today, for they are eaten by birds including Red Grouse, but the large (2–3 cm) white flowers are an attractive feature of the mires in June and early July.

FIG 135. Cloudberry (*Rubus chamaemorus*) leaves growing through Heather on blanket mire, Fleet Moss, near the head of Raydale.

The mires are grazed, and the abundance of Hare's-tail Cottongrass inflorescences provides an early bite for the Swaledale and other fell sheep in the spring. The higher the grazing pressure the greater abundance of the cottongrass, and the lesser the abundance of Heather. But these mires have had other human uses in the past, not least as a source of peat for domestic heating and as a fuel in lead production. In the second half of the twentieth century they have been partially drained with government/European Union grant support, both to increase the grazing value of the land and also to encourage the growth of Heather for Red Grouse. Where the mires have been burnt to encourage Heather regeneration, this has often led to a marked reduction in *Sphagnum* abundance, as observed by Pearsall (1941) on the Stainmore Mosses just to the north of the National Park. This reduction in cover and vigour of the major peat-forming plants exposes bare peat and accelerates the drying and potential erosion of the peat surface. Even where the bog surface remains intact, burning leads to a reduction in the rate of peat formation and thus of carbon storage (see e.g. Garnett *et al.*, 2000). Recent studies of burned and unburned catchments in the north and south Pennines, including one site (Snaizeholme) in the Dales (Ramchunder *et al.*, 2013; Brown *et al.*, 2014), have also shown that prescribed rotational burning regimes affect not only the mires themselves, but also water quality and macroinvertebrate populations in the rivers draining them. Streams draining burned catchments were characterised by lower calcium concentrations and lower pH, but higher concentrations of aluminium, iron and manganese ions than those draining unburned ones. The former had a higher abundance of non-biting midge larvae (Chironomidae) and burrowing stonefly larvae (Nemouridae), but a lower abundance of mayflies (Ephemeroptera).

Cutting peat at the edges of the mires and gripping to improve the drainage also leads to the exposure and drying of bare peat, with concomitant release of carbon dioxide. Both of these activities are markedly detrimental to the mires and contribute in a small way to global warming.

Throughout the Pennines the blanket mires have become seriously eroded (Fig. 136), most extensively in the southern Pennines where the additional long history of coal-smoke pollution during the nineteenth century and the first half of the twentieth from the great industrial cities of Manchester and Sheffield and the nearby towns has had a markedly detrimental effect on *Sphagnum* species. Although the most extensive blanket mires in the Dales, above Wensleydale and Swaledale, are much more remote from major industrial towns, they are close to the former centres of lead mining and smelting which also provided significant local sources of pollution including sulphur dioxide released from galena, the major lead ore. The smelt mills for example in Arkengarthdale and near Grassington also would have polluted the mires above, a process which may have been exacerbated by the construction of long flues, here and elsewhere in mining districts, running up the hillsides towards the bogs (see Fig. 41). Sulphur dioxide is markedly toxic to many of the bryophytes and lichens which are vital components of mire ecosystems, and their loss will have helped to accelerate erosion processes. In lead mining districts hushing, small reservoir constructions and interference with natural drainage patterns to improve water supplies to the crushing mills will in many cases have markedly impacted the mires, exposing bare peat, which is readily eroded by rain and wind.

The end result of these several factors which predispose the bog ecosystems to erosive forces is the extensive gulleying of the mire surface, often with the gulley sides devoid of vegetation and the mineral substrate exposed on the gulley floor. At the extreme the whole mire surface can be lost. Plants only re-colonise bare subsoil and peat very slowly, particularly in the short, cold growing seasons of the upper dales where, in severe winters, young seedlings can be destroyed by frost heaving. The marked lowering of the water table in the peat on and close to the gulley sides makes conditions inimical to the growth of many mire plants, including *Sphagnum* species, while grazing greatly reduces the ability of vegetation to re-establish. Sheep may also directly accelerate erosion as they seek shelter and rest under vegetation near the top of eroding slopes.

FIG 136. Fleet Moss, showing eroding blanket mire with deep gulleying.

Erosion of particulate matter and the colouration of water draining the blanket peats have long been of concern to the water industry, reducing the capacity of reservoirs and adding to the expense of water treatment. However, the realisation that northern peatlands are important in providing a net sink of atmospheric carbon dioxide has only received widespread recognition in the last two decades. This has focused much more attention on the current state of British mire systems and their role in carbon storage. Carbon accumulates because of carbon dioxide uptake in photosynthesis by the bog vegetation; this exceeds carbon dioxide loss from plant and microbial respiration and other losses such as dissolved organic and inorganic carbon in the bog drainage water, and methane production by microorganisms. The net result is peat formation. Eroding and drained blanket peat is thus a source of carbon rather than a carbon sink. Unfortunately drainage was encouraged after the Second World War up until the late 1970s through the provision of government grants to improve agricultural production. In the UK as a whole Milne and Brown (1997) estimated that 1.5 million hectares out of a total of 2.9 million hectares of peatland had been drained.

Common Standards Monitoring for SSSIs was instigated by the Joint Nature Conservation Committee early in the new millennium. This involved assessing each site at least once over a period of six years as being in favourable or unfavourable condition or destroyed. Those judged unfavourable were further subdivided into recovering to the desired state, declining, or no change. In England in 2003 only 35 per cent of units in the uplands were in a favourable or recovering condition, and this led to a considerable drive by English Nature/Natural England to improve the situation, particularly in blanket bogs and heaths, which accounted for the great majority of the land area in unfavourable condition in the English uplands, a result of burning, drainage, overgrazing and atmospheric pollution. On blanket mires this led to mitigation treatments blocking previously cut drains and erosion gulleys in an attempt to re-wet the bog surface: a process which also reduces loss of dissolved organic carbon and water colour, as demonstrated by Wallage *et al.* (2006) from Oughtershaw Beck, a tributary of the River Wharfe. This is attempted and sometimes achieved by the insertion into the channels of corrugated plastic sheets, wood planks, heather bales, peat blocks or even stone rubble. As a result of this, combined often with a reduction in grazing pressure and burning frequency, by the beginning of 2008 nearly 72 per cent of units were in a favourable or recovering condition.

Under Defra's Heather and Grass Burning Code, burning as a management tool on bogs is proscribed, but it certainly was used widely in the first decade of this century. Yallop *et al.* (2006) showed that, in the English uplands as a whole, 17 per cent of the area in 2000 had been burnt within the previous four years. They concluded that 'It is now nearly impossible to find any extensive or continuous areas of ericaceous dominated moorland in the uplands of England that have not been burnt in the past 10 years.' Burning of some blanket mires in the Dales continued in the first decade of the twenty-first century, a process which at the very least results in some drying out of the bog surface and oxidation of the upper peat layer. The adverse result is the increased export of dissolved organic carbon in the drainage water. Yallop *et al.* (2010) estimated that in the last three decades, carbon export by this route had doubled in a number of south Pennine catchments where burning for grouse-moor management occurred, possibly converting the blanket mires from carbon sinks to sources over this period. They showed no such trend at Moor House in the northern Pennines, where the mires had not been subjected to burning over this period.

CONCLUDING REMARKS

These moorlands, and to some extent the mires, have largely resulted from the destruction of the once ubiquitous deciduous forest by human activities from Mesolithic times onwards. As Holden *et al.* (2007) point out in a review of moorlands, change has been a more or less permanent feature of these ecosystems in the UK. In the Dales moorlands have been used in turn for hunting wild animals, as hunting forests, as commons for livestock grazing, as sources of building stone, peat for domestic fuel and heather for thatching roofs, and as a resource of water and fuel for the lead industry. Since the eighteenth century, and particularly following the parliamentary enclosures, grouse-shooting estates have risen to prominence as a major land use, while moors and mires used as catchments for the water industry have also become important. During this period the atmospheric environment has also changed considerably with the rise and fall of sulphur dioxide pollution, to be replaced by increased deposition of nitrogenous pollutants in the second half of the twentieth century, having potentially serious effects on these nutrient-poor ecosystems. The use of moorland and mires as extensive grazing in upland agriculture continues as it has for centuries. Since the Second World War this has been supported by government and EC/EU subsidies which have resulted in greater grazing pressure than at any time in the past, converting many areas of heathland to grassland. In the last two decades agri-environment schemes have begun to be used to reduce the grazing pressure and to reverse this process, enhancing the wildlife interest. However, nature conservation is a very recent concern when contrasted with this long history of land management, and the importance of peatlands in carbon farming and storage has been recognised much more recently still.

It is likely, though not inevitable, that future moorland management will be more sharply focused on environmental sustainability than it has been for much of the past, but there is likely to continue to be some tension between management processes necessary to maintain grouse moors in optimal condition and those to conserve and enhance soil carbon storage. Environmental sustainability will largely continue to be driven by EU or direct government support. The Higher Level Stewardship Scheme for hill farms, as part of the Common Agricultural Policy, has provided one mechanism by which a reduction in grazing pressure can be utilised, for instance, not only to reverse the decline of Heather cover on mires, but also to help limit peat erosion and aid restoration processes. Typically the fells and hill tops are covered by a mosaic of heath, mire and acidic grassland communities. During the latter part of the twentieth century, grassland expanded at the expense of heathland, as Heather cover was removed by high sheep stocking densities; this process is fairly readily reversed by appropriate adjustment to the grazing regime. But some changes are not so easily reversible, particularly areas of blanket mire undergoing erosion, and areas already very extensively eroded probably can never be fully restored. Nevertheless considerable effort is now going into the successful restoration of Yorkshire's 40,000 hectares of eroding blanket peat through the Yorkshire Peat Partnership. This involves gulley blocking and re-profiling eroding gullies (Fig. 137) combined

FIG 137. A recovering blanket mire following grip blocking at Cam Houses, showing ponding after heavy rain the night before, 7 January 2014. (Ribble Rivers Trust)

with spreading Heather brash containing *Sphagnum* fragments onto bare peat surfaces. By April 2013 it was estimated that nearly a quarter of Yorkshire's damaged peatlands had been restored, including areas in the National Park.

A further complication with blanket mires is that they are very dependent on a climate in which precipitation exceeds evapotranspiration. Climate change scenarios suggest that the climate in northern and western Britain will become warmer and wetter as we move towards the middle of the twenty-first century, which, if so, will probably encourage bog growth. But a greater frequency of extreme events is also predicted, and this could be markedly detrimental, both through intense rain events, potentially accelerating erosion processes, and through droughts, effectively stopping bog growth and increasing the possibility of accidental fires.

CHAPTER 9

Tarns and Wetlands

As the glaciers melted at the end of the Devensian glaciation, many of the dale bottoms were covered in shallow lakes, often dammed by moraines. But the power of water, on the one hand carrying debris from the fell sides onto the dale floors, and on the other eroding both the moraine dams and, once the permafrost melted, the underlying Carboniferous limestone, meant that most lakes were short-lived, and today only two large natural lakes survive: Semer Water in Raydale and Malham Tarn. However, there are also some reservoirs, most notably Grimwith Reservoir, built to provide a water supply for Bradford in the nineteenth century and greatly extended in the late twentieth century, and many much smaller tarns on moorland over the Millstone Grit, such as Fountains Fell Tarn above Malham Moor. Some of these natural tarns and small artificial dams provided important water resources for the former lead industry.

The margins of many lakes have regions where wetland vegetation rafts over the open water, particularly where sedimentation has reduced the water depth to allow emergent plants to become established, for example where stems of the Common Reed (*Phragmites australis*) or the Bottle Sedge (*Carex rostrata*) spread landward in so-called reedswamp communities. As sedimentation increases, it allows fen communities to develop in areas that are influenced by base-rich lake water, which provides a source of minerals. This enriches the accumulating organic material, resulting in minerotrophic peat formation. In winter the lake water floods the surface, and in summer the water table is maintained near the surface, resulting in anaerobic conditions in the waterlogged ground that lead to peat accumulation, raising the surface level and allowing over time for willow (*Salix* species) and Alder (*Alnus glutinosa*) seedlings to become established, eventually forming carr woodland. But where organic matter accumulates to such a height that base-rich water no longer floods the surface in winter, particularly in cool, wet climates, surface conditions can become acidic and allow the establishment of bog-mosses (*Sphagnum* species). The result is the formation of raised bogs dependent solely on the atmospheric supply of elements. Under these conditions rain-fed or ombrotrophic peat accumulates, which is acidic and low in nutrients. *Sphagnum* species have the ability to act like a sponge and hold on to the atmospheric water and nutrient supply, and the water table effectively rises as the mound grows. The waterlogged acidic substrate is inimical to the growth and regeneration of most trees; those which do succeed can also sink into the peat as their mass increases. On their margins, these bogs are still influenced to some degree by base-rich minerotrophic water, and organic matter accumulates more slowly there, in the so-called lagg, than in their centres. The end result is a dome-shaped structure known as a raised bog, the often steep sides of which are known as the rand. Raised bogs were once major landscape features in northern England, but little-disturbed examples are now rare, as a result of for example drainage, peat extraction and other human activity.

Examples of all these types of communities occur at Malham Tarn, and contribute to its great ecological importance as part of the National Nature Reserve and as a wetland of international importance under the Ramsar Convention. Reedswamp, fen and carr woodland also contribute to the ecological importance of Semer Water, which, at its southwestern end, is a Yorkshire Wildlife Trust nature reserve. Swarth Moor, an SSSI in Ribblesdale, is another rare example of a raised bog within the National Park

LAKE CHEMISTRY AND CLASSIFICATION

The chemical composition of the water draining from the catchments into lakes determines their ecological characteristics. Where the catchment rocks are resistant to weathering and the soils are unproductive, the water entering the lakes is low in nutrients. These lakes, which are often clear, reflecting the low productivity of the phytoplankton, are described as being oligotrophic. Wastwater in the Lake District is a good example of an oligotrophic lake. At the other extreme, where catchment rocks weather more easily and the soils may have greater agricultural potential, the water entering the lakes is much higher in nutrients, particularly in phosphorus and nitrogen. The end result is a much greater productivity in the phytoplankton, leading to algal blooms and poor light penetration through the water column. These lakes are termed as being eutrophic, examples of which can be found in the Cheshire and Shropshire meres. Lakes with an intermediate nutrient status between the two are described as mesotrophic. Small water bodies in moorland have water very low in nutrients, but can have appreciable suspended and dissolved organic matter in the water column as the result of drainage from blanket mires. These small tarns, although essentially oligotrophic in terms of nutrient supply, are called dystrophic, and can be very acidic.

Other lake systems which can be considered to fall outside the oligotrophic–eutrophic water-body continuum are marl lakes. These occur where the water flowing into a lake from its catchment is essentially saturated with calcium bicarbonate, as can occur in chalk and limestone districts. If carbon dioxide is lost from the water column as a result of photosynthesis by submerged plants and phytoplankton, or directly to the atmosphere above the lake surface, calcium carbonate or marl is precipitated. Typically, temperate hard-water marl lakes contain an average of 100 parts per million calcium bicarbonate in the water and sediments containing over 60 per cent calcium carbonate dry weight (Pentecost, 2009). These lakes, although rich in calcium and bicarbonate ions and with a high pH (> 7.5), often are essentially oligotrophic in terms of nutrient supply. This may at least in part result from the fact that phosphate can be co-precipitated with carbonate in marl formation. Malham Tarn is the highest, and one of the largest, marl lakes in the United Kingdom.

MALHAM TARN

Malham Tarn (Fig. 138) lies on an inlier of impervious Silurian slate which is covered in glacial drift and contains thick marl and clay deposits of at least

FIG 138. Malham Tarn, Tarn Woods and the Field Centre from Ha Mire. The weather station can just be made out in the south-facing field immediately above the Tarn and below the Centre.

6 metres (Pigott & Pigott 1959, 1963). Its catchment area is predominantly on Carboniferous limestone and extends to 600 hectares. The Tarn has a surface area of 62 hectares, and is a shallow lake with an average depth of 2.4 metres and a maximum depth of 4.4 metres with a total volume of 1.5 million cubic metres. The lake basin is effectively dammed by a moraine on its southern side.

Being an exposed, shallow upland lake, Malham Tarn does not show temperature stratification in summer, which is a warm surface layer of water sitting on a colder, denser bottom layer. The water column in the tarn remains well mixed throughout the year; however, its mean temperature has increased by 2 °C since 1949. The tarn is fed by a series of springs which emerge from the limestone at its junction with the Silurian slate inlier. The main group of these springs occurs in the northwest corner and gives rise to a small stream which meanders through the fen, providing the major inflow to the tarn (Fig. 139). Springs at the foot of Great Close Scar and around Ha Mire provide a smaller inflow in the northeast corner. The water has a mean pH 8.25 and an alkalinity of 105 milligrams per litre, and there is some evidence of nutrient enrichment in that recent measurements of yearly maximum nitrate concentrations are over an order of magnitude higher than those observed in 1949. The mean retention time of water in the tarn is 116 days, but it can be less than 25 days in winter. The outflow is Malham Tarn Beck, at the southern end, which disappears underground at Water Sinks approximately 450 metres from the Tarn after crossing the North Craven fault.

After the retreat of the ice following the Devensian glaciation the Tarn was approximately twice its current size, but it has since shrunk by siltation on its western shore, leading to the development of a fen and subsequently an extensive raised bog. Thomas Lister, later Lord Ribblesdale, artificially deepened the tarn by approximately 1 metre in 1791 through the construction of an embankment and sluice gate. A major effect of this has been partially to expand the area of open water again, producing a new shoreline (Fig. 140), but one negative consequence has been the erosion of the Tarn Moss raised bog along its interface with the tarn (Fig. 141), leading to the deposition of peat in the sediments.

Naturalists have been attracted to visit the tarn and record its plants and animals over many years, but after Malham Tarn House was given to the National Trust in 1947, and the house subsequently leased to the Field Studies Council, a fresh impetus was given to a wide range of ecological and other environmental investigations. These investigations included a general description of the animals and plants in the tarn by the first warden, P. F. Holmes, and a detailed investigation of the algae both in the tarn and in the surrounding district (Round, 1953; Lund, 1961; Holmes, 1965).

FIG 139. The major inflow stream to Malham Tarn as it passes through the fens.

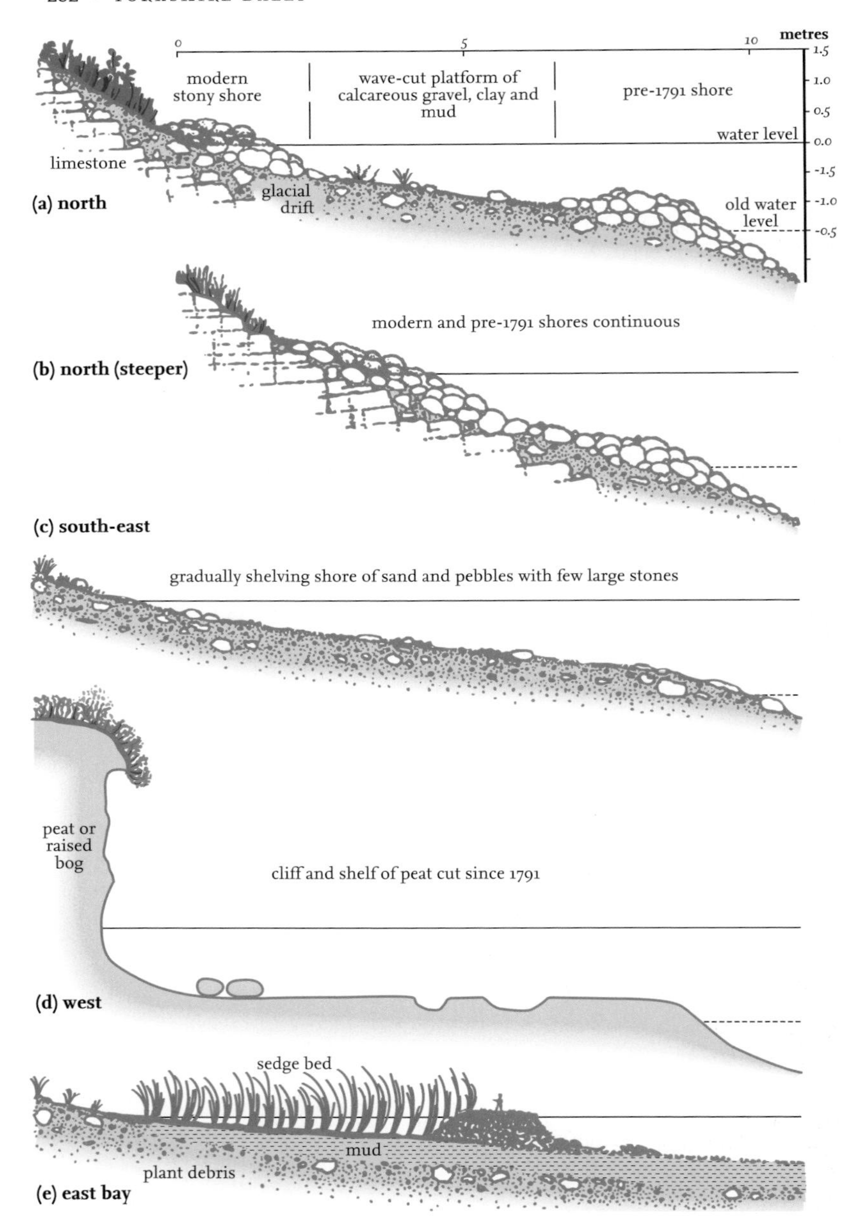

FIG 140. Schematic shore profiles for regions of Malham Tarn, showing modern and pre-1791 shorelines. Reproduced from Holmes (1965).

FIG 141. Erosion of peat from Tarn Moss, a result of raising the level of the Tarn in 1791, photographed in 2013 before restoration work commenced.

John Lund, a member of the Freshwater Biological Association staff, made a detailed study of the plankton in the tarn over eight years during the period 1949–60, comparing his results from Malham with those he had previously obtained from Windermere.

Lund found that the diatom *Asterionella formosa* was the most abundant contributor to the phytoplankton, showing marked spring and autumn peaks in both lakes, but with much smaller peak densities in Malham Tarn than in Windermere, up to an order of magnitude lower (Fig. 142). Despite the very different chemical composition of the two lakes, particularly in calcium bicarbonate concentrations, the phytoplankton in Malham Tarn contained few

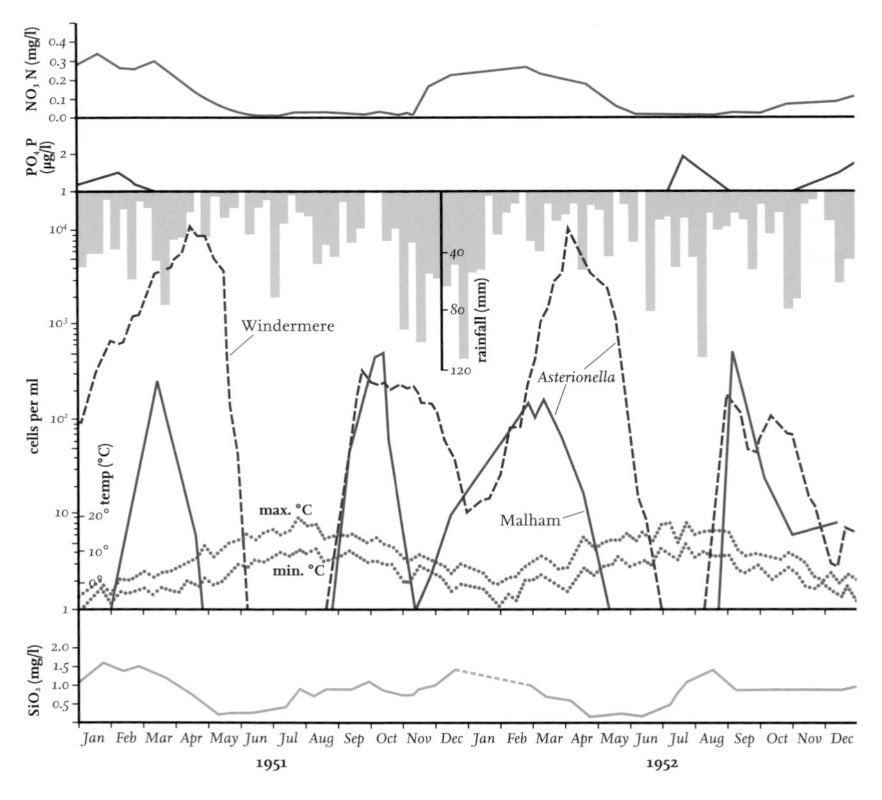

FIG 142. Density of *Asterionella* cells (log scale) in Malham Tarn in 1951 and 1952 together with the concentration of nitrate, phosphate and silica in the water. Rainfall and maximum and minimum air temperatures are also shown. The dotted line shows *Asterionella* cell density in Windermere over the same period for comparison. Reproduced from Lund (1961).

species which were not found in the oligotrophic north basin of Windermere, and other species in common included *Dinobryum divergens* and *Dolichospermum flosaquae* (*Anabaena flos-aquae*). Lund concluded that 'The plankton of the tarn is qualitatively that of a somewhat eutrophic body of water, but quantitatively it is usually sparse, though considerable crops arise occasionally' – perhaps illustrating the difficulty of categorising marl lakes in terms of the oligotrophic–eutrophic continuum.

A later study by Freshwater Biological Association staff, covering the three years 1985–87, confirmed the low to moderate abundance of phytoplankton, which was at a minimum in winter, followed by a spring maximum for diatoms with brief increases in summer which included the colonial cyanobacterium *Gloeotrichia echinulata* (Talling & Parker, 2002). These researchers concluded that the phytoplankton was probably phosphorus-limited, but a vernal depletion of silicon, mainly induced by benthic diatoms, was likely to be limiting diatoms in the phytoplankton. More recently, in studies of the sediment cores, Allan Pentecost (2009; Pentecost *et al.*, 2013) found relatively little change in the diatom flora over the last 9,000 years. However, they observed that *Asterionella formosa* had increased over the last 50–100 years, and that the diatom *Mastogloia lacustris* (*Mastogloia smithii* var. *lacustris*), which was found throughout the lower sections of the cores, often in large numbers, had declined within a similar time period, and was no longer present in the top 10 cm of sediment. Whether these and other changes in the phytoplankton during this period are related to increasing eutrophication is uncertain, but currently Malham Tarn is considered to be a mesotrophic marl lake. Present management of the tarn is designed to maintain, or if possible improve, the water quality in line with the European Union Water Framework Directive, thereby limiting algal blooms to no more than in two weeks per year by maintaining total phosphorus < 0.07 and nitrate < 0.6 milligrams per litre. To achieve this, farmers in the catchment have been encouraged to enter into agri-environment schemes designed to limit nutrient and sediment output from their land.

Lund also found the margins of the tarn to be very rich in algae, notably in filamentous cyanobacteria and diatoms. There were immense growths of epilithic diatoms in spring, especially around the mouth of Malham Tarn Beck, including *Encyonema prostratum* (*Cymbella prostrata*) and *Diatoma tenuis* (*Diatoma elongatum*). Green algae were also important on the margins of the tarn, including *Chaetomorpha incrassata*, *Cladophora glomerata*, *Ulothrix zonata* and *Oedogonium* and *Spirogyra* species. Holmes (1965) observed that the moss *Fontinalis antipyretica* could also be found in some abundance in these areas.

Malham Tarn's benthic flora plays a key role in the sedimentation process. Holmes (1965) recorded that the large alga *Chara globularis* (*C. deliculata*), which forms a dense sward up to 60 cm tall, covered a quarter to a third of the tarn bottom, similar to the first estimate made by Arthur Sledge in 1936, who, in a survey with W. H. Pearsall on 14 September 1936, also recorded the presence of *Chara aspera*. *Chara* species are known as stoneworts because of their large calcium carbonate encrustations. These encrustations result from the fact that bicarbonate ions are taken up from the water for algal photosynthesis, and are exchanged for hydroxyl ions. This local efflux of hydroxyl ions causes the precipitation of calcium carbonate, and the whole plant becomes encrusted. Pentecost (1984) found a significant negative correlation between the calcium concentration in the tarn's water and *Chara* biomass, concluding that seasonal fluctuations in calcium concentration in the water are linked to the growth of *Chara* species, a finding confirmed by Talling & Parker (2002). An observation recorded by Holmes (1965) attests to the large *Chara* biomass in the tarn at that period:

> *During a long calm and hot spell in 1959 so much gas was trapped in this sward off the north shore (as a result of photosynthesis) that great quantities of* Chara *were brought to the surface and a boat could only be rowed through it with difficulty.*

Holmes also recorded the presence of a number of flowering plants in the benthos including a few patches of Spiked Water-milfoil (*Myriophyllum spicatum*) and several pondweed species including Perfoliate Pondweed (*Potamogeton perfoliatus*) and Small Pondweed (*P. berchtoldii*). He also noted that the Shining Pondweed (*P. lucens*) formed large patches, which had apparently increased considerably in the twentieth century. Other *Potamogeton* species found in the tarn today are Curled Pondweed (*P. crispus*), Fennel Pondweed (*P. pectinatus*) and Long-stalked Pondweed (*P. praelongus*). Horned Pondweed (*Zannichellia palustris*) was first recorded in 2005. Holmes recorded the first appearance of the non-native Canadian Waterweed (*Elodea canadensis*) in the tarn as a small patch outside the west boathouse in July 1962, probably introduced on a visiting student's sampling net. A year later it had become a large patch 13 feet by 15 feet (4.0 ×4.5 m). Holmes noted, 'It will be interesting to watch the spread of this species', and was concerned that it might oust *Chara* if indeed it did spread. This has not proved to be the case, as a number of surveys in the intervening years have shown. George Hinton has undertaken annual surveys at peak biomass in late summer since 1994 using a reproducible methodology at up to 60 stations in the tarn. These have demonstrated peaks and troughs in *Chara* cover ranging from 21 to 96 per cent, with appreciable annual fluctuations in the cover of Canadian Waterweed, but with generally much lower cover. The peaks and troughs in *Chara* growth coincide with maxima and minima in inorganic carbon uptake from the water (Fig. 143).

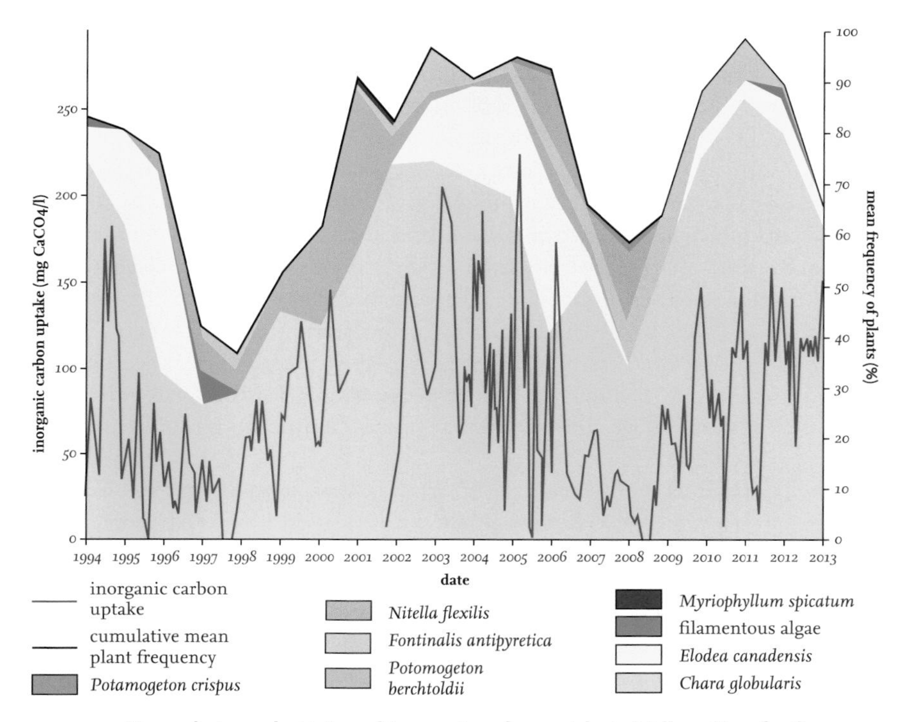

FIG 143. Macrophyte productivity and inorganic carbon uptake in Malham Tarn for the period 1994–2013. The blue line and the blue labels (0, 50, 100, etc.) show inorganic carbon uptake in milligrams of calcium carbonate per litre, as measured by the difference in concentration between the inflow and outflow streams. The percentage figures in red are the mean frequencies of the plants, determined from grapnel samples at set locations. Data of George Hinton, reproduced with permission.

The submerged plants provide important habitats for invertebrates. Holmes (1965) found that the tarn contained 13 species of water snails and nine small bivalve molluscs. Molluscs dominated the fauna of *Chara* beds, with the commonest species being the bivalve *Sphaerium corneum*, but much the largest contribution to the fauna of Shining Pondweed beds was the crustacean *Gammarus lacustris*, at the time known from only four English waters. *Sphaerium corneum*, in contrast to its abundance on *Chara* species, was rare on Spiked Water-milfoil plants. These latter plants harbour large numbers of the coelenterate *Hydra oligactis*. This raises the prospect that changes in the benthic flora may result in changes in the invertebrate fauna with possible consequences for fish species further up the food chain. *Gammarus* species are important food items for both Brown Trout (*Salmo trutta*) and Perch (*Perca fluviatilis*), with *G. lacustris* associated with the submerged plant beds and *G. pulex* mostly confined to stony shores. Holmes recorded one 5 lb (2.3 kg) trout caught on 22 May 1961 as containing 1,117 *Gammarus* specimens. Another crustacean which is found on stone exposed shores is the White-clawed Crayfish (*Austropotamobius pallipes*). Holmes speculated that the crayfish might have been introduced into the tarn in the sixteenth century and might have provided a food source for Otters (*Lutra lutra*) at the time of his survey. However, its stony shores remain a stronghold for the animal today. Other rare crustaceans found include the copepods *Bryocamptus rhaeticus* and *Moraria mrazeki*, uncommon boreo–alpine species known only in England from Malham Tarn, where they are possibly Late-glacial relicts (Fryer, 1993). Stony shores also support the Common Flatworm (*Polycelis nigra*) and five of the seven species of leeches found in the tarn, including the Horse-leech (*Haemopus sanguisuga*).

The insect fauna in the Tarn includes many stonefly nymphs and a small mayfly, *Caenis horaria*. Holmes records that the latter species emerges in vast numbers on calm evenings in July and early August. Caddisfly numbers are also enormous, including species of *Agraylea*, *Hydroptila*, *Polycentropus* and *Tinodes* with differing flight periods during the year (Fig. 144). The larvae of the flightless caddisfly *Agrypnetes crassicornis* live in *Chara* beds. In 1965 this species was known nowhere else in the United Kingdom, and even today it is largely confined to a few sites in the Craven Pennines. The mud below the *Chara* beds supports large numbers of chironomid pupae, which emerge in late May to give rise to clouds of adult midges.

Small fish in the tarn include the Bullhead (*Cottus gobio*) and the Stone Loach (*Barbatula barbatula*), both of which are common under stones on exposed shores. Holmes (1965) recorded that the Three-spined Stickleback (*Gasterosteus aculeatus*) was extremely common in some years, but Minnows (*Phoxinus phoxinus*) were scarce. The tarn only contains two large fish species, Brown Trout and Perch, both of which may have been introduced originally in the twelfth century when fishing rights were granted to the monks of Fountains Abbey by William de Percy. In the nineteenth and early twentieth century the tarn was extensively stocked with Brown Trout, a practice which ceased from the early 1930s. Holmes provided old game-book data for the number of Perch caught in the tarn from the late 1850s to the late 1920s (Fig. 145). Although the numbers of rods used may have varied over time, the data show very large fluctuations in catches. Holmes did not attempt a detailed analysis of these fluctuations, but he noted that large numbers of Perch died after the severe winter and spring of 1947. He concluded that very cold winters might account for some of the observed fluctuations in catches. In

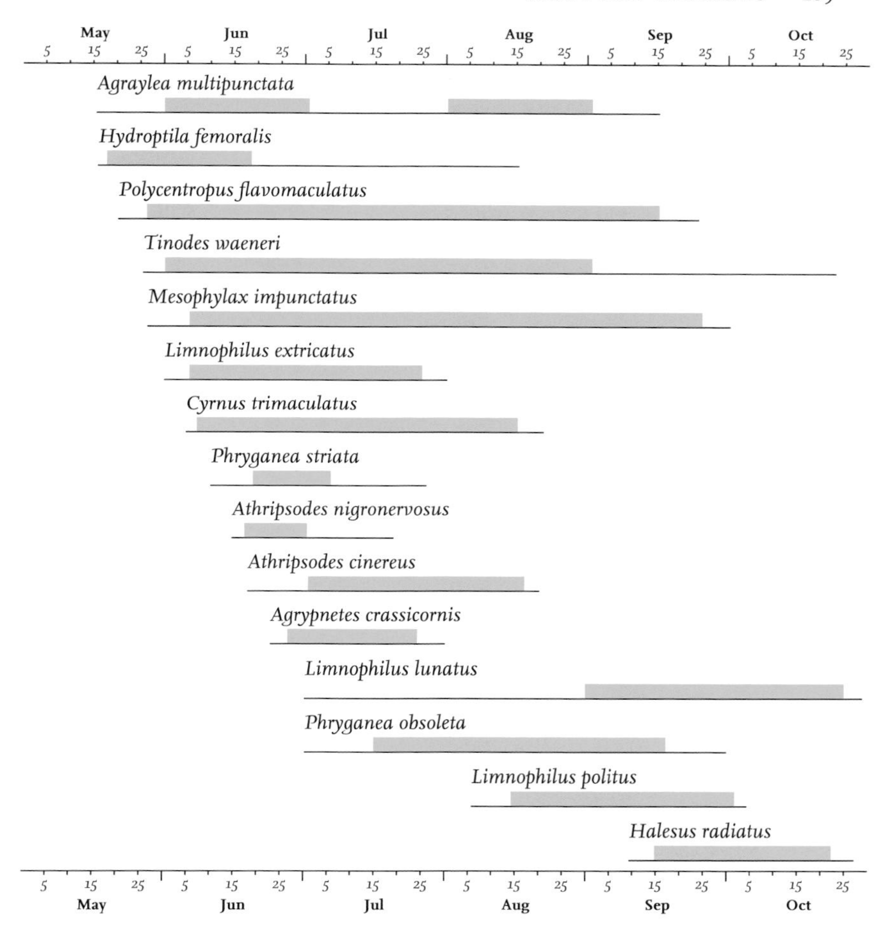

FIG 144. The flight periods of the 15 most frequently recorded species of Malham Tarn caddisflies. The length of the single base line indicates the time over which each species was likely to be in flight; the ends of the lines are the extreme dates at which adult caddisflies were taken. Reproduced from Holmes (1965).

her study of Otter sprraints over the period December 2011 to June 2013, Emily Alderton (personal communication) found remains of Perch only once. Bullhead, followed by small Brown Trout (< 12 cm in length), were the most frequently found remains, but the composition of spraints may reflect the ease of prey species capture as well as their relative abundance. In confirmation of Holmes's speculation, she found that crayfish formed a small component of the Otter's diet.

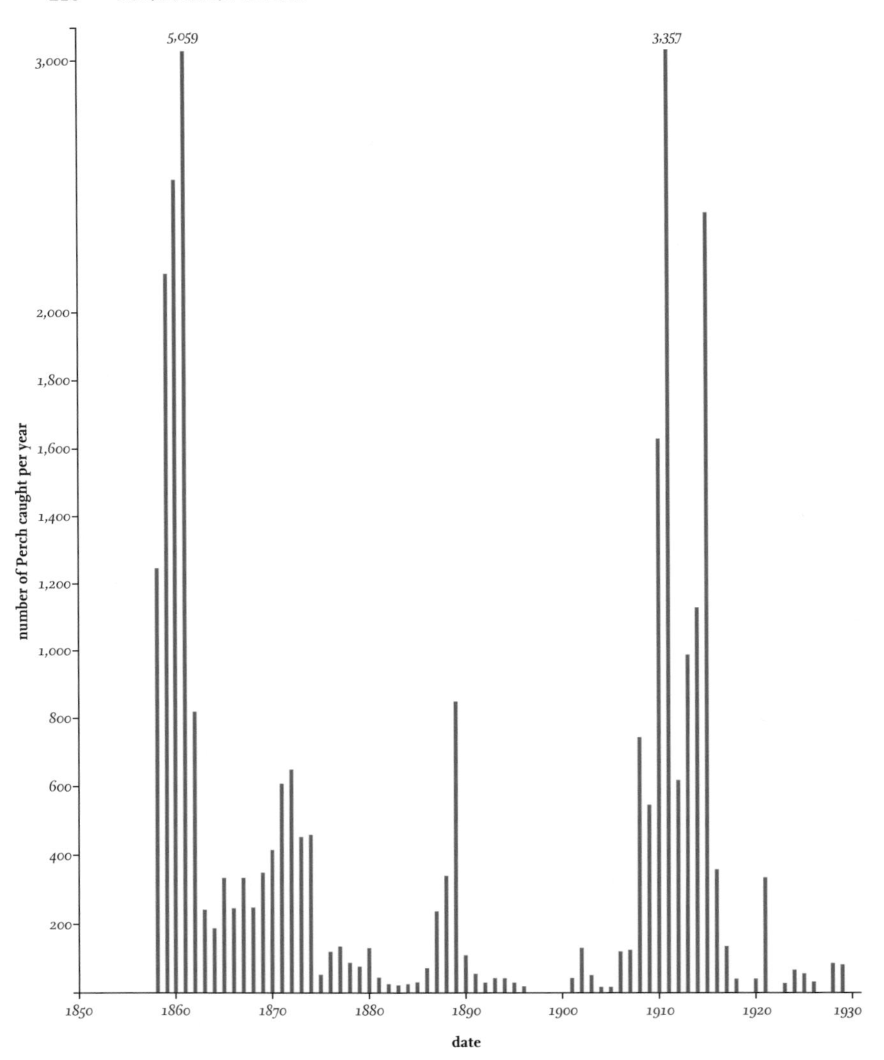

FIG 145. Numbers of Perch caught in Malham Tarn 1858–1929, as recorded in the game books. Reproduced from Holmes (1965).

TARN MOSS AND FENS

Donald and Margaret Pigott made a detailed stratigraphical study of the raised bog and fens at Malham (Pigott & Pigott, 1959, 1963). They showed that in the

Late-glacial open water extended over the whole area now occupied by the tarn, Tarn Moss and the fens, and that Ha Mire to the east was occupied by a separate area of open water. Detailed studies of the sediments revealed that by 8,000–9,000 years ago reedswamp was widely established over much of the western part of the tarn basin, as demonstrated by a thin layer of grass and sedge peat formed over marl deposits. This reedswamp peat was quickly replaced by an amorphous fen peat sometimes containing woody fragments, which continued to accumulate to a depth of several metres around the basin margin.

Away from the basin margin *Sphagnum* remains increased in the woody layer at about 7,000 years ago, which is when Alder first appeared in the pollen record. *Sphagnum* quickly rose to dominance, indicating a transition from carr woodland to ombrotrophic bog, and ombrotrophic peat has continued to accumulate on Tarn Moss to the present day, forming the raised bog, though contemporary deposits are rich in cottongrasses and overlie the large areas from which peat has been extracted. A considerable amount of peat has been extracted, some possibly by boat, as the area between Spiggot Hill and the tarn in particular is deeply cutover (Roger Meade, personal communication).

The ombrotrophic peat extends to a depth of 5–6 metres widely over Tarn Moss, much of it formed of *Sphagnum* remains, but also containing cottongrass (*Eriophorum* species) and Heather (*Calluna vulgaris*), which become more important peat formers near the surface. Close examination of the bog-moss remains revealed that much of the peat was formed by Austin's Bog-moss (*Sphagnum austinii*, formerly known as *S. imbricatum*), a species which used to be the major peat former throughout the Pennines, but which is now very rare and no longer found at Malham.

Various explanations have been advanced for the disappearance of Austin's Bog-moss throughout the Pennines. McClymont *et al.* (2008) studied its disappearance from Butterburn Flow, Cumbria, which they dated to *c.*1300 CE. They concluded that the loss coincided with increasing human disturbance surrounding the bog, which may have altered nutrient inputs to the bog surface from agriculturally derived dust. A similar study of raised bogs in Wales showed a clear temporal relationship within the last 2,000 years between the decline in the moss and woodland clearance, cereal cultivation, soil erosion and contemporary climate change (Hughes *et al.*, 2008). Ombrotrophic bogs are particularly sensitive to pollution because the major peat-forming plants, the bog-mosses, depend on the aerial supply of nutrients, which is readily perturbed by atmospheric pollutants, and Austin's Bog-moss may be much the most sensitive *Sphagnum* species. The demise of Austin's Bog-moss in the Pennines pre-dates major pollution from the nearby industrial towns, but not necessarily localised pollution from lead smelting. Other possible explanations include the sensitivity of the moss to burning and to the modification of the bog surface as the result of peat digging and widespread drainage. Tarn Moss has certainly been subjected to all these possible causes in the past, and one or other, or more probably a combination of several, account for cottongrass and Heather remains having become the most important contributors to the surface peat, as demonstrated by Donald and Margaret Pigott.

Tarn Moss is in fact not one raised bog, but three (Fig. 146). Its apparent single expanse today is the result of three raised-bog domes encroaching on one another. These were initiated northeast, northwest and south of Spiggot Hill, a tree-covered morainic mound immediately around which is a band of minerotrophic fen vegetation. The northeastern and northwestern domes are separated by a ditch carrying a slightly base-enriched seepage from this lagg fen around Spiggot Hill to the main inflow channel, which flows close to the ombrotrophic peat to the south. As the raised bogs grew they progressively restricted the calcareous drainage from the surrounding Carboniferous limestone and from the fluvio-glacial sand deposits (Wheeler *et al.*, 2005) such as Spiggot Hill. This was channelled into the lagg around Tarn Moss and the fens surrounding the main inflow streams.

FIG 146. A view across Tarn Moss in early July showing the abundance of cottongrasses, particularly *Eriophorum vaginatum*, which are in seed.

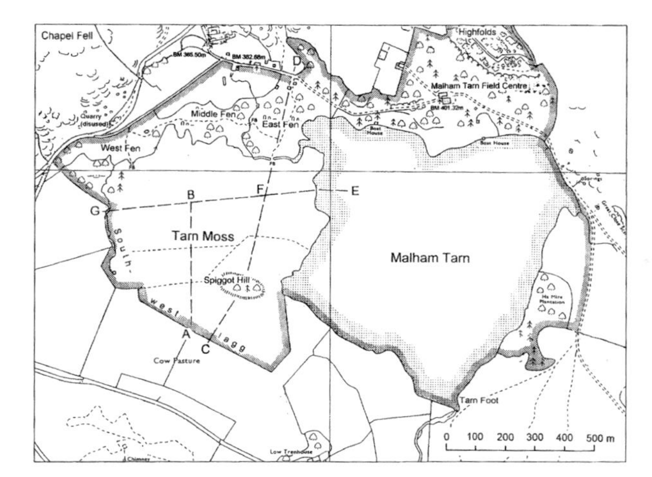

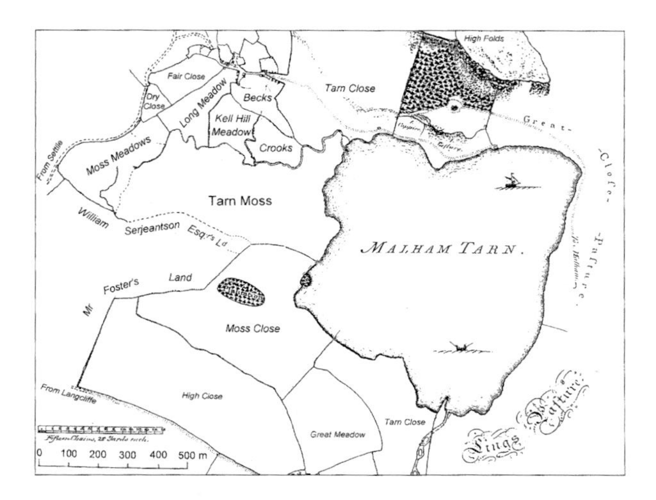

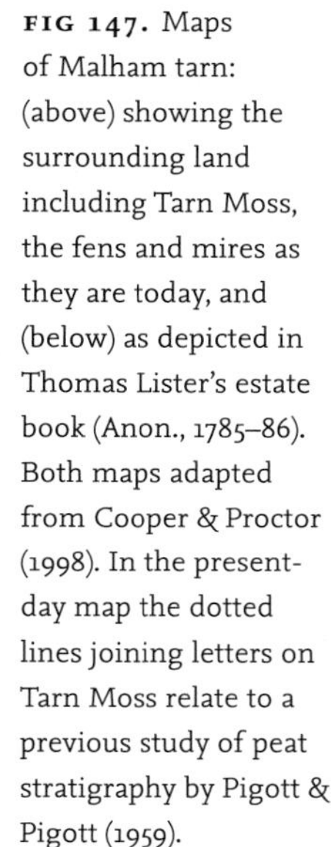

FIG 147. Maps of Malham tarn: (above) showing the surrounding land including Tarn Moss, the fens and mires as they are today, and (below) as depicted in Thomas Lister's estate book (Anon., 1785–86). Both maps adapted from Cooper & Proctor (1998). In the present-day map the dotted lines joining letters on Tarn Moss relate to a previous study of peat stratigraphy by Pigott & Pigott (1959).

Cooper & Proctor (1998) made a detailed study of the present-day vegetation of both Tarn Moss and the fens, together with an account of recorded land management. They concluded that, at least since medieval times, grazing by farm livestock must have had some effect on the vegetation of the mires, most probably limiting tree growth, and thus increasing the area of open fen. They reproduced a 1780s map from Thomas Lister's estate book (Anon, 1785–86) which shows the then division of the Moss and fens (Fig. 147). The fens were divided into compartments under agricultural use. The present West Fen was divided into two and called Moss Meadows. Long Meadow resulted from joining the western third of Middle Fen to Tarn Fen Meadow, and the remainder became Kell Hill Meadow. The present East Fen includes the southern edge of what was Tarn Close together with Crooks and the bottom corner of Becks, the field below Water Houses being divided by the north inflow stream. As the old field names demonstrate, the fens were probably mown for centuries, and they would have provided an important winter food resource before the mechanisation of hay harvesting in the twentieth century.

The fens have a complex hydrology, being fed by the laggs, inflow streams and springs, and their present-day structure has been further complicated by human activity. For example Wheeler *et al.* (2005) showed that at one time much of North Fen was occupied by ombrotrophic rather than minerotrophic peat, but much of the ombrotrophic peat had subsequently been cut away. When the level of the tarn was raised in 1791, it had the effect of increasing the surface water area slightly, undercutting the margin of Tarn Moss abutting on the water, and flooding approximately 1 hectare of fen including some old peat cuttings (Cooper & Proctor, 1998). Later changes in the fen include the digging of two large ponds, in about 1820, to hold young Brown Trout. These were abandoned some time around 1880, and by the 1940s were colonised by reedswamp species including Bottle Sedge, Bulrush (*Typha latifolia*), Common Reed and *Sphagnum* lawns.

The 1785–86 map shows three compartments on Tarn Moss, which almost certainly means it was grazed, and probably also occasionally burnt. Although it is difficult to date when drainage started, almost certainly by the latter half of the nineteenth century grip drains began to be dug across the surface of the raised bog. This process only began to be reversed by Donald Pigott and students from the University of Lancaster in the early 1970s. At this period the bog surface was dominated by tussocks of Hare's-tail Cottongrass (*Eriophorum vaginatum*) with abundant Wavy Hair-grass (*Deschampsia flexuosa*). There was little Heather, and *Sphagnum* species were largely confined to flooded hollows. The mosses *Pohlia nutans* and *Tetraphis pellucida* were abundant on the dry acidic peat surfaces, both species not usually associated with actively growing bogs. Today the three domes of the bog surface are wetter and covered in *Calluna vulgaris – Eriophorum vaginatum* mire (M19; see Table 3 for a list of the major Malham mire communities). This community is also found extensively on blanket bogs in the Yorkshire Dales and further north in the Pennines. Wavy Hair-grass is still abundant, as is Deergrass (*Trichophorum cespitosum*), but the dwarf shrubs Cross-leaved Heath (*Erica tetralix*) and Crowberry (*Empetrum nigrum*) are also prominent. Locally, Bilberry (*Vaccinium myrtillus*), Cowberry (*Vaccinium vitis-idaea*) and Bog Rosemary (*Andromeda polifolia*) occur together with Cloudberry

(*Rubus chamaemorus*). Hollows between the tussocks also contain Bog Asphodel (*Narthecium ossifragum*) with low hummocks of the bog-mosses *Sphagnum capillifolium*, *S. magellanicum* and *S. papillosum* together with their associated leafy liverworts including *Odontoschisma sphagni*, *Mylia anomala* and *Lophozia ventricosa*. Pools are not very extensive on the bog surface, but have floating mats of *Sphagnum cuspidatum* and fringes colonised by lawns of *Sphagnum fallax*. Cranberry (*Vaccinium oxycoccus*) and Round-leaved Sundew (*Drosera rotundifolia*) are common in these lawns (Fig. 148).

In contrast to blanket and raised bogs, fens receive water and nutrients both from the aerial supply and from drainage through their catchments. The status of this mineral water depends very much on the underlying geology and the nature and management of the catchments. Fens can broadly be divided into two classes, as first suggested by the Swedish scientist Du Rietz: poor fens, in which the water feeding them is not derived from calcareous rocks so it has a pH < 6 and in which the more base-tolerant *Sphagnum* species abound; and rich fens, fed by calcareous water pH > 7 in which the so-called 'brown mosses' such as *Scorpidium scorpioides* and *Palustriella falcata* are important components of the vegetation. The Malham fens include examples of both classes (Table 3). Poor fens include the *Carex echinata* – *Sphagnum recurvum/auriculatum* mire (M6), which as well as Star Sedge contains White Sedge (*Carex canescens*) and Common Sedge (*C. nigra*). Moss species in this community include *Sphagnum fallax*, *S. palustre*, *S. fimbriatum* and *Polytrichum commune*. It is found in areas of disturbed wet acidic peat with some influence of more base-rich water. Another important example is the *Carex rostrata* – *Sphagnum squarrosum* mire (M5). In this the Bottle Sedge and other sedges are dominant but there is a distinctive *Sphagnum*-rich moss carpet which

FIG 148. A close-up of the mire surface showing rosettes of the insectivorous Round-leaved Sundew (*Drosera rotundifolia*) growing on the *Sphagnum* carpet, the leaves bearing long sticky glandular hairs.

as well as *Sphagnum squarrosum* also contains *Sphagnum angustifolium, S. palustre, S. fimbriatum* and *S. teres*. In deeper-water areas within this community Bladderwort (*Utricularia australis*) occurs, a plant which uses tiny bladders to catch small aquatic animals. The poor fen communities at Malham are rich in *Sphagnum*, and other species which can be found locally include *Sphagnum warnstorfii* and *S. subnitens*.

Reedswamp and rich fen communities occur close to the major inflow stream. Reedswamp communities occur in Middle Fen and East Fen where the channel of the inflow stream broadens. *Carex rostrata* swamp forms a narrow band in open water behind which is a floating mat conforming to the *Carex rostrata – Potentilla (Comarum) palustris* swamp community (S27). This floating raft, besides Bottle Sedge and Marsh Cinquefoil (*Potentilla palustris*), contains Bogbean (*Menyanthes trifoliata*), Marsh-marigold (*Caltha palustris*), Lesser Spearwort (*Ranunculus flammula*), Water Forget-me-not (*Myosotis scorpiodes*), Marsh Bedstraw (*Galium palustre*) and Creeping Bent (*Agrostis stolonifera*). Water Horsetail (*Equisetum fluviatile*) is an important member of this community, and moss species present include *Plagiomnium elatum* and the Spear-mosses (*Calliergon* species).

TABLE 3. National Vegetation Classification (NVC) communities on Tarn Moss and Fens, as recognised by Cooper & Proctor (1998).

Bog vegetation

M2	*Sphagnum cuspidatum/recurvum* bog pool community
M18	*Erica tetralix – Sphagnum papillosum* raised and blanket mire community
M19	*Calluna vulgaris – Eriophorum vaginatum* mire
M25	*Molinia caerulea – Potentilla erecta* mire

Poor fens

M5	*Carex rostrata – Sphagnum squarrosum* mire
M6	*Carex echinata – Sphagnum recurvum/auriculatum* mire

Rich fens and associated swamps and tall-herb vegetation

S27	*Carex rostrata – Potentilla palustris* swamp
M9	*Carex rostrata – Calliergon cuspidatum/giganteum* mire
M26	*Molinia caerulea – Crepis paludosa* mire

Carr and woodland

W3	*Salix pentandra – Carex rostrata* woodland
W4	*Betula pubescens – Molinia caerulea* woodland
W6	*Alnus glutinosa – Urtica dioica* woodland

Where the fen peat has been kept permanently wet with calcareous water but major growth-limiting nutrients, notably nitrogen and phosphorus, are in short supply, as in parts of East and North Fens and locally in the southwestern lagg, there is a rich assemblage of flowering plants below which is a luxuriant moss carpet. This is the *Carex rostrata – Calliergon* mire community (M9). The most abundant mosses include *Calliergon giganteum, Campylium stellatum* and *Scorpidium scorpioides*, but locally one of the most base-demanding bog-moss species, *Sphagnum contortum*, forms small stands marginally above the level of calcareous groundwater. Water Horsetail is again a prominent member of this community. Flowering plants include Bogbean and Marsh Cinquefoil, but many other species occur, including Yellow-sedge (*Carex viridula* ssp. *brachyrrhyncha*), Carnation Sedge (*Carex panicea*), Lesser Tussock-sedge (*Carex diandra*), Devil's-bit Scabious (*Succisa pratensis*), Marsh Willowherb (*Epilobium palustre*), Marsh Hawk's-beard (*Crepis paludosa*), Meadowsweet (*Filipendula ulmaria*), Marsh Lousewort (*Pedicularis palustris*), Marsh Valerian (*Valeriana dioica*) and Ragged-Robin (*Silene flos-cuculi*).

The Malham fens and carr woodland are known for containing a number of rare plants including the leafy liverwort *Barbilophozia kunzeana*, Narrow Small-reed (*Calamagrostis stricta*), the eyebright *Euphrasia rostkoviana* ssp. *montana*, Downy Currant (*Ribes spicatum*) and Jacob's-ladder (*Polemonium caeruleum*). However, the rarest and perhaps the most enigmatic is the Large Yellow-sedge (*Carex flava*), found in only one other United Kingdom site, Roudsea Wood in Cumbria. Although originally considered to be the Large Yellow-sedge, the Malham plants were later thought to be a hybrid between the Large Yellow-sedge and Yellow-sedge, *Carex* × *pieperiana*. Blackstock & Ashton (2001, 2010), using both a morphological and an allozyme study of the Malham plants, concluded that they were in fact not the hybrid, but *Carex flava*. However, there is 'still some argument about the identity of the Malham Tarn population' (C. A. Stace, personal communication), a lingering doubt which perhaps only DNA studies can resolve.

Uncommon insect species found in the fens and carrs include the beetles *Agonum ericeti* and *Hydrothassa hannoveriana*, the crane fly *Phalacrocera replicata*, the liverwort snipe fly *Spania nigra*, the hoverflies *Eristalis rupium* and *Platycheirus immarginatus*, and the Pygmy Soldier Fly *Oxycera pygmaea*. Scuttle flies are an important group of flower-visiting insects, and Henry Disney recorded two new species from Malham, *Megaselia malhamensis* and *M. parnassia* (Disney, 1980, 1986).

Where the inflow stream regularly deposits silt along its banks, particularly in West Fen, the fen peats are enriched in nutrients and a tall-herb community occurs, the *Filipendula ulmaria – Angelica sylvestris* mire (M27). Meadowsweet is dominant, but Wild Angelica (*Angelica sylvestris*), Sorrel (*Rumex acetosa*), Common Valerian (*Valeriana officinalis*) and locally Melancholy Thistle (*Cirsium heterophyllum*) are prominent. There is also an understorey of herbs including Creeping Buttercup (*Ranunculus repens*), Cuckooflower (*Cardamine pratensis*), Golden-saxifrage (*Chrysosplenium oppositifolium*), Water Avens (*Geum rivale*), Wood Crane's-bill (*Geranium sylvaticum*), Water Mint (*Mentha aquatica*) and Water Forget-me-not.

Another wetland community occurs on North Fen: the *Molinia caerulea – Crepis paludosa* mire (M26). This is effectively a fen meadow community intermediate between mire and damp mesotrophic grassland communities. The community contains Purple Moor-grass, but is rich in sedges and tall herbs including Common Sedge, Fibrous Tussock-sedge (*Carex appropinquata*), Slender Sedge (*Carex lasiocarpa*), Marsh Hawk's-beard, Wild Angelica, Meadowsweet, Common Valerian, Great Burnet (*Sanguisorba officinalis*), Marsh Thistle (*Cirsium palustre*) and Globeflower (*Trollius europaeus*). Smaller herbs include Goldilocks (*Ranunculus auricomus*), Wood Anemone (*Anemone nemorosa*), Grass-of-Parnassus (*Parnassia palustris*) and Northern Marsh-orchid (*Dactylorhiza purpurella*).

In places where fen communities neighbour limestone pastures the *Pinguicula vulgaris – Carex dioica* mire community (M10) occurs. This community is much more extensive on calcareous drift and limestone east of the Tarn on Ha Mire and Great Close Mire, and is one of the most attractive of all Dales communities. In late spring and early summer Birds-eye Primrose (*Primula farinosa*) and Common Butterwort (*Pinguicula vulgaris*) are in flower and, later in the year, Grass-of-Parnassus. Other notable species in the community include Dioecious Sedge (*Carex dioica*), Few-flowered Spike-rush (*Eleocharis quinqueflora*) and the moss *Philonotis calcarea*.

Cooper & Proctor (1998) noted that, in the 1940s, carr was limited to what they thought were long-established woodlands in West Fen and at the boundary of East and Middle Fen close to the inflow streams, and in addition some patches of birch woodland on acidic ombrotrophic peat in the latter two fens. By the late 1990s there had been considerable expansion of carr over open fen and birch woodland over acid peat. The carr woodland is predominantly *Salix pentandra – Carex rostrata* woodland (W3) with a canopy of Bay Willow (*Salix pentandra*) and Tea-leaved Willow (*S. phylicifolia*), but Grey Willow (*S. cinerea*) and Dark-leaved Willow (*S. myrsinifolia*) also occur together with some hybrids between the last three species. The understorey has many features of the fen communities, but with Globeflower and Marsh Hawk's-beard prominent together with Bottle Sedge and Fibrous Tussock-sedge. Silty soils around the margin of West Fen support a fringe of *Alnus glutinosa – Urtica dioica* woodland (W6) in which the presence of Stinging Nettles (*Urtica dioica*) and Cleavers (*Galium aparine*) below the Alder canopy is indicative of nitrogen and phosphorus enrichment.

Where acid peat islands occur across North Fen and on the northern side of Spiggot Hill lagg *Betula pubescens – Molinia caerulea* woodland (W4) has developed over some of them, while others remain open. The canopy is formed by Downy Birch with a little Grey Willow, and the field layer is species-poor, with Purple Moor-grass and Hare's-tail Cottongrass the major flowering plants together with the Broad and Narrow Buckler-ferns (*Dryopteris dilatata* and *D. carthusiana*). The ground layer contains several *Sphagnum* species including *S. fallax*, *S. fimbriatum*, *S. palustre* and *S. warnstorfii*. The spread of woodland during the second half of the twentieth century must reflect changes in management, notably the cessation of mowing of the fen meadows and lack of any grazing by domestic livestock. Cooper and Proctor highlighted the need for the control of willow colonisation to maintain the open fen communities, and suggested that willow carr should be managed to revert to its approximate distribution in 1950. Clearance work began in the winter of 1996–97 when the West Fen was cleared and continued in 1997–98 on East Fen. Management of the carr and birch woodland remains an important priority to conserve the rich variety of the Malham mires.

HA AND GREAT CLOSE MIRES

Ha Mire abuts on the east side of Malham Tarn, immediately below Great Scar Close, and occupies the former separate shallow lake basin (Fig. 149). Pigott & Pigott (1959) and Wheeler *et al.* (2005) showed that much of the peat was less than 50 cm deep, and that the mire is developed over a series of gentle ridges punctuated by outcrops of mineral soils supporting dry grassland. The mire is fed by several springs arising near the base of Great Close Scar at its northeastern margin and from mounds of fluvio-glacial deposits to the east, the streams from which drain into and across its surface and into the tarn. Much of the mire is fed by precipitation, and the combination of this and mineral-rich water from the springs has given rise to vegetation which is a complicated mix of acidic ombrotrophic and calcareous minerotrophic mire communities.

Great Close Mire, south of Ha Mire, is also fed by strong springs emanating from the base of Great Scar Close. It occupies a trough which slopes southwards towards the head of the Gordale Beck valley through which spring water flows in small braided stream channels, with the calcareous mire vegetation developed in between them. Some of the mire is strongly poached by grazing livestock and has a stony, skeletal surface with small peaty hummocks.

Both mires contain *Pinguicula vulgaris – Carex dioica* mire communities, rich in sedges in which Bird's-eye Primrose is among the prominent plants. This community on Great Close Mire contains two uncommon plants, Hair Sedge (*Carex capillaris*) and Alpine Bartsia (*Bartsia alpina*), the latter a hemiparasite, and

FIG 149. Ha Mire, in the foreground, occupies a separate basin from Malham Tarn and Tarn Moss, in the background. The wooded Spiggot Hill is at the top left of the photograph.

one of the Teesdale rarities, at its southern limit in the United Kingdom. Ha Mire is also noted for the rare beetle *Leiodes flavicornis*. As recently as 2013 Robin Sutton and Peter Welsh found a colony of Small Pearl-bordered Fritillaries (*Boloria selene*) on Ha Mire which amazingly, given the much-visited location, may have been overlooked for years (Shorrock & Sutton, 2014). The nearest known colony is on Swarth Moor, approximately 10 kilometres away to the northwest.

SWARTH MOOR

Swarth Moor in Ribblesdale is an SSSI extending to 33 hectares which was once a larger area of raised bog with its associated lagg fen between Foredale and Helwith Bridge. It sits within a once shallow lake basin underlain by impervious Silurian greywackes (Fig. 150). Rather more than half of the SSSI is an area of almost intact raised bog, with the domed structure clearly visible, though its

FIG 150. The raised bog of Swarth Moor in the foreground, with Dry Rigg Quarry, in which the Silurian greywackes are being exploited, forming the background.

shape is exacerbated by shrinkage following peat cutting and drainage around its edge. Fen grassland, carr woodland and pools fringed by reedswamp are found in the lagg around its periphery; a small stream, Black Sike, adds to the diversity of the lagg along its southeastern edge. However, the area known as Studfold Moss to the northeast, now a small area of wet woodland and extensive damp grassland, was once part of the bog from which the peat has been removed.

Past drainage and peat extraction up until the Second World War has not drastically altered the remaining bog structure, but the present surface has become drier, which may account in part for the present abundance of Purple Moor-grass on the bog surface. Swarth Moor lies close to Dry Rigg Quarry, the drainage from which has the potential to influence the lagg communities. However, in recent years this has been successfully mitigated against by the construction of a new wetland prior to the drainage water leaving the quarry (Alistair Headley, personal communication). The SSSI is common land and was grazed up until the 2001 foot and mouth outbreak.

The bog itself consists of hummocks of Hare's-tail Cottongrass, Purple Moor-grass and Deergrass, with locally Heather and Bilberry. The hollows contain a range of *Sphagnum* species. The most abundant are *S. fallax, S. magellanicum* and *S. papillosum,* with *S. cuspidatum* in the pools. Flowering plants in the hollows include Bog Asphodel, Common Cottongrass, Cranberry, Cross-leaved Heath and Round-leaved Sundew, together with less common plants such as Bog Rosemary and White-beaked Sedge (*Rhyncospora alba*). The abundance of Purple Moor-grass also may be indicative of some nutrient enrichment as well as some drying of the bog surface. There is evidence of trees, notably Downy Birch, beginning to invade the bog surface. This is a similar situation to that observed at Tarn Moss, which may also be a response to the partial desiccation of the bog surface. Current management proposals seek to remove the invading trees and to increase the wetness of the bog surface so that the water table is within 10 cm of the peat surface for 95 per cent of the year. Raising the water table in the former peat cuttings using peat dams will hopefully help to achieve this.

FIG 151. Lagg on the margin of the Swarth Moor raised bog. Kingcups (*Caltha palustris*) in the foreground, with a distant view of Pen-y-ghent.

The vegetation in and around the lagg pools contains the stonewort *Chara vulgaris*, Lesser Bulrush (*Typha angustifolia*), Mare's-tail (*Hippuris vulgaris*), Bottle Sedge, Marsh Cinquefoil and Least Bur-reed (*Sparganium natans*) with willow carr, predominantly Grey Willow with some Downy Birch, established around the edges (Fig. 151). The somewhat drier areas of fen contain a range of common wetland herbs including Cuckooflower, Marsh Valerian, Marsh Thistle, Marsh Violet (*Viola palustris*), Ragged-Robin, Sneezewort (*Achillea ptarmica*) and Water Mint (*Mentha aquatica*). Grass, rush and sedge species in the fen community include the tussock-forming Tufted Hair-grass (*Deschampsia cespitosa*), Carnation, Common and Star Sedges, and Sharp-flowered Rush (*Juncus acutiflorus*).

Swarth Moor is noted for the presence of the native White-clawed Crayfish in its water courses and the first recorded population of Great Crested Newts (*Triturus cristatus*) in the National Park. It contains four other amphibian species: Common Frog (*Rana temporaria*), Common Toad (*Bufo bufo*), Smooth Newt (*Lissotriton vulgaris*) and Palmate Newt (*L. helveticus*), as well as the Common Lizard (*Zootoca vivipara*). It is also noted for a number of scarce or uncommon insects including the beetles *Ancistronycha abdominalis* and *Notiophilus aquaticus*, the click beetle *Ampedus balteatus*, the hoverfly *Criorhina floccosa*, the sawfly *Trichiosoma lucorum* and the bumblebee *Bombus jonellus*. Larvae of six species of Odonata have also been recorded here, including the hawker dragonflies *Libellula depressa* and *L. quadrimaculata* (A. D. Headley, personal communication). It is also noted for Marsh Violets, which support an important population of the Small Pearl-bordered Fritillary.

SEMER WATER

Semer Water is a shallow lake in Raydale extending to 31 hectares, but with a mean depth of less than 1 metre (Fig. 152). It is the remains of a much larger lake formed behind a terminal moraine at the end of the Devensian glaciation. Largely this is the result of sediments brought into the lake basin since that time by the Crooks Beck at its southern end. Chiverell and colleagues (2008) showed that *c.*2 metres of sediment had accumulated in the centre of the lake during the last 550 years alone, much of it sandy sediments with a carbonate content that rarely exceeded 3 per cent. They also demonstrated anthropogenic effects in the sediments from as far back as the Mesolithic to modern times.

A vegetation study of Semer Water recorded previous attempts over many years to drain the marsh which partially fills the lake basin at its southwestern end by constructing dykes and ditches (Ingram *et al.*, 1959). In particular the

FIG 152. Semer Water in Raydale. The foreground shows part of the beach exposed when the water level was lowered in 1938.

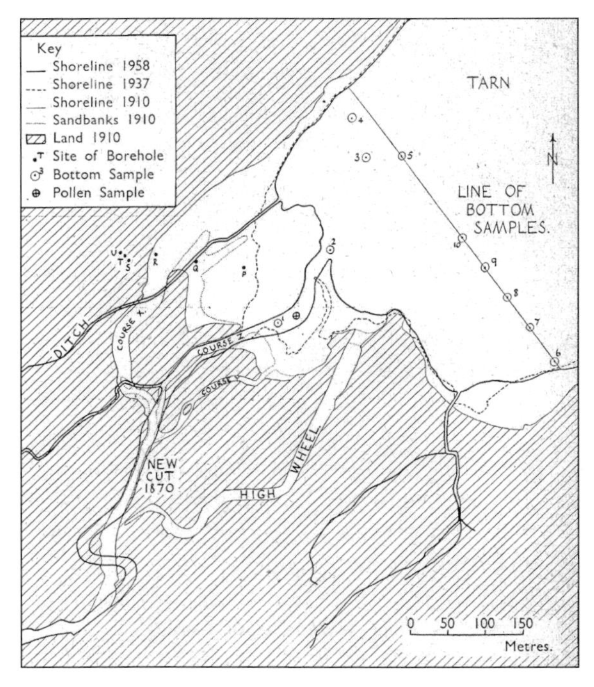

FIG 153. A map showing changes in the shoreline at the western end of Semer Water as the result of past drainage activities and lowering of the water level in 1938. Reproduced from Ingram *et al.* (1959).

New Cut dug in 1870 caused the main inflow stream to follow a new course. By 1910 this had become silted up, causing the inflow to form its present channel (Fig. 153). But by 1937 the owner, Mr Outhwaite, realised that drainage by digging further ditches in an attempt to increase the area of agricultural land in Raydale would be ineffective unless the lake water level was artificially lowered. This he achieved in 1937 with support from the then Ministry of Agriculture by deepening the outflow along Low Wheel at its northern end into the River Bain, reducing the lake height by 55 cm. The net result of this was to expose an area at the southwestern end of the lake which is now fen, and which forms part of the Yorkshire Wildlife Trust reserve. Semer Water and its surrounding wetlands are an SSSI.

Semer Water's shallow nature and the surrounding agricultural land within its catchment make it potentially sensitive to eutrophication. It is a mesotrophic lake of rather poor water quality with a phytoplankton assemblage characteristic of rich waters including *Asterionella*, *Ceratium* and *Pediastrum* species (Fryer, 1993) and is potentially capable of producing algal blooms. The latter may have been responsible for a fish kill in 2005. The Semer Water and Upper Lune Catchment Partnership was established in 2009 to encourage catchment-sensitive farming in parts of the Dales. In the case of Semer Water this is designed to improve the present unfavourable condition of the lake. The partnership provides some grant aid and, in addition, farmers in the catchment have been encouraged to enter Higher Level Stewardship schemes in an attempt to reduce nutrient enrichment.

Although the lake is fed in part by lime-rich water it does not show marl formation, and the open-water flora is poor. *Chara* species are absent, and the largest green algae present, but at low abundance, are brittleworts (*Nitella flexilis* agg.). Canadian Waterweed, which was introduced at some point in the past, and was frequent by 1970, may well have been replaced recently by another introduced plant, Nuttall's Waterweed (*Elodea nuttallii*), which may be an indicator of nutrient enrichment. Red Pondweed (*Potamogeton alpinus*) is the only conspicuous native plant in the open water community. Mudwort (*Limosella aquatica*), another native plant, but far from conspicuous, is exposed on the shore margins, as is the Needle Spike-rush (*Eleocharis acicularis*).

Reedswamp communities occur on the lake margins and on Crooks Beck, with Common Club-rush (*Schoenoplectus lacustris*) and Bottle Sedge among the emergent plants and Yellow Water-lily (*Nuphar lutea*) in the deeper water. Willow carr occurs near the outflow of the River Bain (Fig. 154), and also together with Alder on the banks of Crooks Beck. The willow species include Bay Willow (*Salix pentandra*), but there are also many hybrids. The Greater Tussock-sedge (*Carex paniculata*) is a prominent feature of the vegetation within the carr woodland,

FIG 154. Carr woodland on the edge of Semer Water near the source of the River Bain.

allowing the establishment of seedlings of trees and other plants on the tussocks above the winter water table. Fen vegetation together with swamp occupies some 3 hectares and includes a sedge fen community in which Bottle Sedge and Bladder-sedge (*Carex vesicaria*) are prominent, together with a small bed of Common Reed and Reed Canary-grass (*Phalaris arundinacea*). There are also areas of Bogbean swamp. The surrounding damp fields contain common wetland plants including Marsh-marigold, Ragged-Robin and Water Forget-me-not, with Soft-rush (*Juncus effusus*) prominent in the permanent pastures.

Semer Water SSSI supports populations of a large number of mayfly species. These include the stream species *Baetis rhodani* and *Habrophlebia fusca*. It is also known to support the rare large cladoceran *Leptodora kindti* and the native White-clawed Crayfish. Geoffrey Fryer concluded that Semer Water, with 68 or 69 species, had the richest crustacean fauna of all the Yorkshire waters he sampled (Fryer, 1993). The lake supports a fishery including Brown Trout, Perch and Roach (*Rutilus rutilus*).

SMALL TARNS

There are around 100 small tarns scattered across the Dales, usually on high moorland over the Grassington Grit. There are also small dams associated with the old lead industry, such as Blea Beck Dams on Grassington Moor. None of these water bodies extends to much more than 2 hectares in surface area, and many are shallow. Fountains Fell Tarn is perhaps the best studied and may be representative of many of the small high-moorland water bodies. It is surrounded by blanket peat and has no permanent outflow. The input of water from precipitation and run-off from the surrounding peatland is matched by evaporation and slow percolation into the underlying gritstone strata. Woof & Jackson (1988) measured the water chemistry on three occasions over 12 months in the 1980s. The water was strongly acidic (pH 3.92–4.25) with very low concentrations of calcium (0.7–1.0 parts per million). Drainage from the surrounding peat results in a water rich in humic compounds which contribute to the acidity. Allan Pentecost (personal communication) has recorded only a very sparse phytoplankton in the tarn, although a frequent alga in the littoral zone was *Tribonema bobmycinum*.

The combination of these characteristics is probably typical of the other dystrophic water bodies. Their shallow nature and altitude results in prolonged periods of freezing in winter, and few plants colonise them apart from the encroachment of marginal vegetation. One interesting plant found in several of these tarns by Allan Pentecost, but not so far in Fountains Fell Tarn, is the red alga *Batrachospermum atrum*. Geoffrey Fryer (1993) studied both the water chemistry and the crustacean faunas of many of these moorland tarns including Fountains Fell, Oughtershaw, Coverdale and Hunter's Hole Tarns. All were strongly acidic (pH *c*.4.0) and none of these contained more than six crustacean species, with Fountains Fell and Coverdale Tarns supporting only two. The maximum number he recorded in any of the 33 tarns he sampled was 11 species. This contrasts with his observations at Great Close Mire pool at Malham, where he recorded 24 species in the highly calcareous water (pH *c*.8.0). Among the species recorded in the moorland tarns were *Acanthocyclops vernalis* (found in 15 of the 33 tarns), *Bosmina longispina* (an open water species) and *Chydorus sphaericus*.

CONCLUDING REMARKS

Malham Tarn is a jewel, if not the jewel, of the National Park. The lake and its surrounding mires have been intensively studied over many years, and particularly since the establishment of the field centre there in 1948. This has not been without its downside, as for example Clunas & Shorrock (1990) record the increase in visitors and students adversely affecting some breeding bird species. The biodiversity in this area of about 100 hectares is probably now better known and documented than anywhere else in the National Park, if not any similar area in the UK. Lakes in Britain have been influenced by human populations over millennia, perhaps most markedly in recent centuries, both directly and indirectly. Malham Tarn and Semer Water have both, for example, been influenced directly by modification of their water levels, leading to effects both on the lakes themselves and on their surrounding wetlands. Malham Tarn has also had a long recorded history of management as a fishery. But probably at least as important are the indirect effects of human activities caused by polluting the air and by land-use changes in their catchments leading to changes in the water quality entering the lakes. Changes in the catchment have had a more severe effect at Semer Water, where marked eutrophication has occurred, resulting in changes in the lake's biodiversity. But even at Malham Tarn increases in nutrients entering the lake have been observed since the 1940s, and are now being closely monitored. This points to the present need to manage activities very carefully within the catchment to halt and, if possible, to reverse any tendency to eutrophication, with its probable resultant biodiversity loss. This need is not lost on National Trust staff.

CHAPTER 10

Rivers and Caves

Becks and rivers have helped to sustain human populations in the Dales for millennia, and in recent centuries have also provided a source of power and water for the local industries, notably for lead mining and smelting, but also for textile manufacture and corn milling. Today they also provide one of the major attractions for visitors, both for angling and for other forms of recreation. For many visitors the larger waterfalls are amongst the major draws, none more so than Aysgarth Falls on the Ure (Fig. 155), where the beauty of

FIG 155. The major tourist attraction of Aysgarth Falls. A view across the Lower Falls, with the River Ure in spate.

the waterfalls can be admired in juxtaposition with part of the Dale's industrial history. Just above the Upper Falls, on the southern bank of the river, stands Yore Mill, built in 1784 as a textile mill. Wensleydale is particularly rich in waterfalls. The more notable examples besides the Upper, Middle and Lower Falls at Aysgarth are Whitfield Force above Askrigg, and Cotter Force and Hardraw Force near Hawes. The last of these is the highest of the single-drop falls, where the Hardraw Beck plunges 28 metres over most of one cyclothem of Yoredale rocks.

Waterfalls are notable features of other dales too, including those at Keld and Kisdon in Swaledale, and Thornton Force at the head of the Ingleton Waterfalls Walk. Other spectacular attractions are the Strid in lower Wharfedale, where, between Barden and Bolton Abbey, the river has cut into a strong bed of Millstone Grit forming a narrow channel of deep swirl pools, and Cautley Spout in the Howgills, a cascade of falls with a broken drop of 180 metres. But the Dales also boast England's highest unbroken waterfall, albeit underground, where Fell Beck plunges 100 metres onto the floor of Gaping Gill Cave on Ingleborough.

The rivers Ribble, Swale, Ure and Wharfe now occupy the glaciated troughs which are the major dales today. These rivers and their tributaries originate where impermeable rocks or glacial deposits impede drainage, and many have their origins in the Yoredale series of rocks where water draining through the strata reaches impervious shale bands causing water to flow to, and over, the surface. Limestone is permeable, and this is perhaps most easily observed in the southern dales where the extensive pavements are the result of water eroding joints and fractures in the Great Scar Limestone, and where becks suddenly disappear into the first encountered eroded joint, forming potholes such as Gaping Gill on Ingleborough and Hunt Pot on Pen-y-ghent.

This propensity for underground drainage has produced dry valleys and regions within other valleys, where the river flows below the surface in karst conduits for part of the year. For example the River Skirfare in Littondale does not flow above ground for as much as 3.5 kilometres in dry weather. Similarly Kingsdale is dry between Kingsdale Head and Keld Head where the River Twiss emerges (Fig. 156). Neighbouring Chapel-le-Dale is also dry above the God's Bridge resurgence except in times of flood. In contrast, the River Ribble and the River Wharfe flow continuously except in parts of the latter's upper valley, Langstrothdale, where it sometimes sinks in places in dry conditions. This physical and temporal discontinuity between the headwaters and the stream further down is an important feature of many rivers in karst landscapes.

Erosion below ground, by water sinking through the joints and fractures in the rock, has produced complex patterns of flow through the limestone beds, and in places large cave systems have been created. This complexity of flow is perhaps

FIG 156. Keld Head resurgence in Kingsdale, the major source of the River Twiss.

best illustrated in the Three Counties system, which may start in Barbondale and probably ends in Chapel-le-Dale. It has been physically explored from Boundary Pot in Easegill to Large Pot in Masongill, but there are known hydrological connections to Aygill Cavern in Barbondale in the west, and from Large Pot to Keld Head and King Pot in East Kingsdale. A connection from East Kingsdale to Chapel-le-Dale via Dale Barn Cave is very likely. The Three Counties system is currently the 27th longest physically explored cave system in the world, with a length of 90 kilometres, and full exploration should establish it as the world's eleventh longest. With a depth of 257 metres, it is also the second deepest in the United Kingdom, after Ogof Ffynnon Ddu in south Wales (Allen, 2012).

Water flowing underground, and through the caves systems, provides the link between the surface river systems and the caves beneath, and is thus a major conduit for organisms to colonise the latter. Many caves have ancient origins, and some of the most ancient are now dry. A good example of the latter is the Victoria Cave in Ribblesdale (Fig. 157), in which flowstones have been dated to over 600,000 years ago (Lundberg *et al.*, 2010).

FIG 157. The enlarged entrance to Victoria Cave. The photograph is taken from rubble deposited as the result of excavations in the cave from the nineteenth century onwards.

FIG 158. River Cover, Coverdale, one of many examples of stretches of rivers in the Dales with wooded banks. The woods in this photograph contain both native lime species (*Tilia cordata* and *T. platyphyllos*).

Rivers can originate from the outflow of lakes or tarns in catchments such as the River Bain flowing out of Semer Water. But in the National Park many becks have their origins in springs where groundwater derived from rainfall within the catchment reaches the surface, or from resurgences where water flowing through cave systems emerges above ground. Outflows from major resurgences and springs erode the ground surface to form stream channels, which grow in size as the channels merge within the catchment. The riparian zone, consisting of the bank side and closely surrounding vegetation along the stream channel, forms the boundary between aquatic and terrestrial systems. The riparian zone has considerable importance for the stream biota. For instance, riparian vegetation provides a vital source of energy for aquatic organisms in the form of leaf litter and other organic detritus. This is perhaps most readily appreciated where the river banks are colonised by deciduous trees, as is the case in many parts of the Dales (Fig. 158). Primary production in streams by algae, bryophytes and higher plants, although important to some invertebrate species, provides only a small proportion of the food resource. Plant litter is the major basis of river food webs, and it becomes increasingly attractive to invertebrate shredder species once colonised by aquatic hyphomycete fungi.

WATER CHEMISTRY

Water chemistry has a major effect on the biota of running waters, as it does on lake systems. As we have seen in the previous chapter, water emanating from the Carboniferous limestone has a high pH (> 7) and may be saturated with calcium bicarbonate. Conversely, streams originating below blanket bogs on the Millstone Grit are poorly buffered, have very low concentrations of calcium and other important cations, and are very acidic (pH < 5). They frequently contain humic compounds and suspended peat particles derived from the blanket mires, which stain the water.

Human activities within catchments can also influence water chemistry. Farming can result in appreciable nutrient enrichment and increase sediment loads, as can sewage outfalls. Afforestation with conifers can lead to stream acidification in catchments with poorly buffered soils. But water chemistry can also be influenced by activities far outside catchments, as evidenced by the acidification of fresh waters caused by the deposition of atmospheric pollutants. The EU Water Framework Directive adopted in 2000 requires all inland waters to achieve 'good ecological status' by 2015, and has been the major driver to improve water quality in both lakes and rivers. In practice, however, water quality has been affected by human activities over centuries, and may not be easily reversible over such a short timescale. This is shown by catchments where the blanket peat has been heavily contaminated with lead, as is the case in the Dales. In the Peak District, Rothwell *et al.* (2008) showed that lead output from water draining a catchment containing extensive blanket mires was an order of magnitude higher than its current input from the atmosphere, and that there was a strong coupling between peat erosion and mobilisation of lead into the fluvial system. They concluded that peat soils were likely to remain a source of lead contamination of fresh waters well into the future.

Water emerging from springs has a fairly constant temperature throughout the year, often approximating to that of the mean annual air temperature of the region. Water temperature is important because on the one hand it determines the oxygen content and its availability to heterotrophic organisms, and on the other it determines their oxygen demand. The oxygen concentration in pure water is reduced by approximately a third as the temperature rises from 5 °C to 25 °C, whereas respiration can increase by 10 per cent or more for every degree rise. As a general rule the shallow, turbulent waters of upland streams have the highest oxygen content. This decreases downstream as the ambient temperatures increase, and the turbulence decreases as the river deepens, partly a consequence of the decrease in the ratio of surface area to volume. All the becks in the National Park show markedly turbulent flows, as do many stretches of the larger rivers, particularly during periods of heavy rainfall. But as we have seen, parts of some rivers do not flow during dry periods, and here, where pools persist and temperature rises, oxygen supply may become depleted. Another feature of turbulent flow is that many becks have beds composed of boulders and large stones with little sedimentation of finer material.

BECKS AND RIVERS

Beck is the name generally given to small upland streams in northern England, although the distinction between becks and rivers as named on a map can sometimes be hard to draw. Becks are shallow and often exhibit strongly turbulent flow over steep gradients throughout their lengths, whereas the rivers in the larger Dales have at least some regions on shallow gradients away from waterfalls and rapids. Here, in deeper pools, some fine sediment accumulates. The physical nature of the stream bed is important for the biota. In fast-flowing becks the bed may be largely composed of bedrock and boulders, with the organisms largely confined to marginal areas away from the strongest current. The rivers also contain exposures of bedrock, as for example seen very prominently on the upper Wharfe, but they also contain areas of relatively quiet flow where sands and gravels are deposited. The latter are important for fish reproduction. Salmonid species in particular spawn in redds, areas they essentially dig in gravel beds which can be up to 50 centimetres in depth in the case of Salmon. However, redds cannot be created if the substrate is too coarse, and if it is too fine or becomes silted, eggs and fry fail to survive. All becks and rivers provide an essentially unidirectional water flow, although boulders and rocks divert the current and provide local eddies. The flow is fastest at the surface, and slowest nearest the bed as the result of frictional drag. Fish are able to swim against the current, but the vast majority of river organisms need to exploit the relatively still water around rocks and close to the stream bed, or risk being carried away downstream. This risk is greatest during spate events following heavy rainfall, a strong feature of upland catchments in high-rainfall areas such as the Dales. It is under such conditions that becks disappearing into potholes can carry many aquatic organisms into the caves below.

Few detailed ecological studies of running fresh waters in the Dales have been published, although the River Wharfe was the subject of an early investigation organised by the Yorkshire Naturalists' Union Research Committee in 1926–27 (Pearsall, 1930). This involved studies of water chemistry, phytoplankton and invertebrate fauna at various sites along the river, only one of which, Grassington Bridge, falls within the National Park. Here Percival & Whitehead (1930) recorded more than 80 species of invertebrates over an 18-month period, with Olive Upright mayfly (*Rhithrogena semicolorata*) the most abundant invertebrate where the current was rapid, largely being replaced by False March Brown mayfly (*Ecdyonurus venosus*) in conditions of quieter flow. However, when egg-sized stones in midstream were sampled on 17 March 1927, and larger immovable stones on 18 August 1926, the caddisfly *Agapetus fuscipes* was the most abundant species, making up 47 per cent of all invertebrates on the larger stones. These workers also noted that the crustacean *Gammarus pulex* was scarce at Grassington relative to the sites they sampled outside the area that is now in the National Park. A later study of the Wharfe in mid and upper Wharfedale (Andrews, 1988) reported that caddisfly larvae were present in good numbers except at sites where drainage from blanket peat resulted in acid water; 68 species were recorded in total.

A much more recent multidisciplinary study arose from a Malham Research Seminar in 2001, when the late Oliver Gilbert suggested that a detailed investigation of Cowside Beck, a tributary of the River Skirfare, would be rewarding (Fig. 159). The subsequent study resulted in a report published by the Field Studies Council (Gilbert *et al.*, 2006). Figure 160 shows a map of the

FIG 159. The valley containing Cowside Beck, near its confluence with the River Skirfare at Arncliffe.

Cowside Beck catchment. The catchment includes, to the north, Darnbrook Beck with its tributaries rising on Fountains Fell and Darnbrook Fell, and, to the south, Upper Cowside Beck with tributaries located in Tennant Gill and Thoragill. The watercourses are in a natural state, not affected by appreciable water abstraction, canalisation or dams, and much of the catchment is covered in semi-natural vegetation with relatively small amounts of improved grassland. The watercourses show several specialised features including stretches of beck with intermittent flow, cold springs (with temperatures as low as 6.6 °C) and tufa deposits. But there is a major contrast in water chemistry between the northern tributaries which arise on Fountains and Darnbrook Fells, which are strongly acidic as the result of drainage from the blanket mires over Millstone Grit, and the calcareous southern tributaries, which include two fine examples of watercourses depositing tufa. The former tributaries have a pH 4.2–4.6, and have sodium as the major metallic cation, with low calcium concentrations (0.4–0.8 milligrams per litre). The latter have a pH > 7.0 with calcium as the dominant cation, and with most measurements of this element between 40 and 80 milligrams per litre.

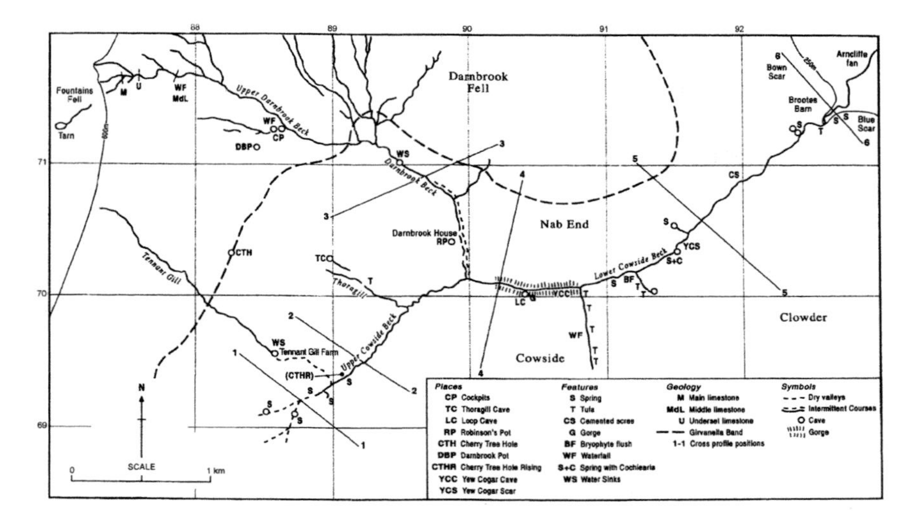

FIG 160. A map of the Darnbrook and Cowside Beck catchments, showing some of the geological and geomorphological features together with place names featuring in Gilbert *et al.* (2006).

Cold-water springs provide a potential refuge for species which were much more widespread following the Devensian glaciation. The flatworm *Crenobia alpina* is one such glacial relic found in these Cowside springs, which are also home to several cold-water diatoms including *Caloneis alpestris*, *Diatoma hiemale* and *Meridion circulare*. Large exposures of tufa are dominated by the mosses *Palustriella commutata* and *Platyhypnidium riparioides*, but several other bryophyte species are also common, including *Didymodon tophaceus*, *Hymenostylium recurvirostrum* and *Jungermannia atrovirens*.

Bryophytes are the dominant plants in the beck system. The acid headwaters of Darnbrook Beck are colonised by the leafy liverwort *Scapania undulata* and the moss *Racomitrium aciculare*, but further down, as the influence of the underlying limestones on stream chemistry becomes apparent, the community becomes more diverse. The Cowside Beck channel has a higher bryophyte cover and is in places choked by vigorous mat-forming mosses. There is a zonation within the beck, with *Platyhypnidium riparioides* in the deeper sections under water for most of the year and *Brachythecium rivulare* abundant above the summer water level. Parts of the Upper Cowside and Lower Darnbrook water courses are dry for prolonged periods during the summer as the water flows underground, and here the moss assemblage, adapted to both prolonged desiccation and submergence, is dominated by *Cinclidotus fontinaloides*, but both *Hygrohypnum luridum* and *Schistidium rivulare* are prominent in the community. The luxuriance of moss growth restricts the lichen flora, but the latter includes rare species such as *Eiglera flavida*, *Staurothele bacilligera* and *Thelidium fontigenum*. The richest lichen assemblages occur where the greatest areas of exposed limestone are found.

Mosses and liverworts provide shelter for other organisms. Diatoms for example grow abundantly as epiphytes in bryophyte mats and cushions, and many invertebrate species rely on these structures for cover. The invertebrate fauna is typical of fast-flowing streams with beds predominantly composed of large stones and exposed rocks. Mayflies such as *Ecdyonurus torrentis*, caddisflies such as *Glossosoma conformis* and stoneflies such as *Dinocras cephalotes* are important components of the fauna, as are Diptera species, notably the chironomids. A montane species of mayfly, *Ameletus inopinatus*, was found in considerable numbers in Upper Darnbrook, a first record for the headwaters of the River Wharfe, and the caddisfly *Melamophylax mucoreus*, known in Britain previously only from Malham Tarn and Darnbrook Beck, was found in Thoragill Beck. The freshwater shrimp *Gammarus pulex* is absent from the most acidic waters but common and widespread elsewhere. The invertebrate fauna provides the food source for birds such as the Dipper (*Cinclus cinclus*), and for fish. Brown Trout (*Salmo trutta*) occur all along Cowside Beck, and lower Cowside contains Bullheads (*Cottus gobio*) also feeding on the invertebrate fauna.

In regions where the becks are dry during the summer months, desiccation eliminates the nymphs of mayflies, stoneflies, caddisflies, many Diptera and *Gammarus pulex*, and the species able to survive are those with resistant egg stages or those such as flatworms and true worms which can burrow down into the substrate.

The Wharfe in upper Wharfedale (Fig. 161), above the confluence with the Skirfare, has some of the characteristics of both the small becks and the larger Dales rivers, although Pearsall (1930) considered that 'Above Grassington, the river is practically a mountain stream.' Its headwaters drain areas of forest plantation and blanket peat. Peat and humic compounds in the water stain the river, a fact exacerbated by previous land management. Between the 1960s and 1980s approximately 17 square kilometres of bog were gripped, much of this on Oughtershaw Moss, though the process has to some extent been reversed in the last few years by extensive grip blocking. The headwater stream channel has characteristics of many becks, with steep gradients and large limestone bedrock or boulder steps with pools behind them. In the wide valley bottom the gradient is much less steep, and the river bed has a series of cobble steps separated sometimes by deep pools in which silt accumulates, and gravel bed sections with

FIG 161. The River Wharfe at Yockenthwaite.

pools and riffles, and exposed gravel bars. Much of this valley-bottom section, from Buckden Bridge to just south of Kettlewell, was declared an SSSI in 1985 because of its contrasting upland and lowland character. Between Kettlewell and Grassington the Wharfe falls only 31 metres and flows through the broad valley in a channel which has not changed appreciably in the last two hundred years. However, there has been much change in the past, and much earlier it was a braided river. In this section Howard *et al.* (2000) identified four earlier river terraces, the first two of which relate to the late Devensian and early Holocene when braided flows occurred. A third terrace began to be formed in about 600 CE when fine-grained material began to be deposited, perhaps as the result of agricultural activities in the catchment. The fourth terrace began to be deposited in the eleventh century, perhaps resulting from woodland clearance related to the expansion of sheep grazing. The current terrace was initiated between the fifteenth and seventeenth centuries.

This pattern of steep gradients from the headwaters and much lower gradients in the wider U-shaped valley bottoms is repeated in other dales. For instance, the Swale near its headwaters flows in a narrow channel down a steep gradient over several waterfalls in which the bedrock is exposed until it reaches the wide valley-bottom floodplain (Fig. 162). Flash floods occur frequently in upper Swaledale, carrying large amounts of sediment into the Dale. For example Pounder (1989) records a particularly large event in 1883 when the river at Keld rose *c.*9.4 metres and deposited an estimated 1,000 tonnes of sediment per acre in some areas in the dale bottom. Dennis *et al.* (2003) record another serious flooding event in the autumn of 2000, which caused the most serious floods in the Vale of York since 1947. This produced widespread channel and slope erosion, including in the areas of old lead mining activity, causing for example high metal concentrations in the Swale tributaries of Gunnerside, Barney and Arkle Becks, all of which contained old smelt and grinding mills as well as mines. Very high metal concentrations in the Swale flood sediments resulted, posing a potential risk to agriculture. In the eighteenth and nineteenth centuries in particular, lead mining would have affected both the floodplain and the organisms in the river. Many mining and processing techniques utilised water, and the waste was discharged directly into the nearest water course. Thus Whittaker (1823) recorded that mining was:

FIG 162. The River Swale near Keld, where it cascades through a narrow rocky river channel.

> *detrimental to the spawn by impregnating the water with filth, poisonous minerals and particles of lead. This for so many miles in its descent so pollutes and discolours the river [Swale] with its thick dirty mud ...*

Flooding of villages, towns and cities many miles downstream of river headwaters in recent years has resulted in increased attention being paid to land management in upland catchments, and in particular to the question of how to slow water movement. This is part of the incentive to block grips on blanket mires in an attempt to restore natural drainage. But part of the problem lies further downstream, where rivers have been subjected to management practices designed to limit flooding in the Dales. These have involved isolating the river from its natural floodplain by building walls and flood banks near to the river channel. Other activities have included channel realignment, gravel removal and channel deepening. These practices have been employed within that region of the River Wharfe that is now an SSSI. The most recent assessment by Natural England showed the SSSI to be in unfavourable condition, and led to a proposed aim to restore the river to a near natural condition over the next fifty years. The achievement of this aim involves a plan to allow natural movement of the channel within a narrow riparian strip and to increase the connection between the river and its floodplain, which contains wet grassland, meadows, fens and areas of carr woodland. If this is achieved, water would be released more slowly while allowing for a diverse river bed suitable for fish populations and a rich invertebrate fauna for them to feed on.

The river flora in the Dales, like that of the smaller becks, is dominated by bryophytes, probably largely as a result of the incidence of flash flooding, but the filamentous red alga *Lemanaea fluviatilis* is also conspicuous in the community. There are several common bryophyte species in both communities, including *Chiloscyphus polyanthos, Cinclidotus fontinaloides, Hygroamblystegium fluviatile, Fontinalis antipyretica* and *Platyhypnidium riparioides,* but the National Park is particularly noted for one rare endemic moss, restricted in Britain to Thornton and Twisleton Glens, *Thamnobrium cataractarum,* the Yorkshire Feather-moss. Remarkably, this moss was first recorded as recently as 1991 in an area much visited by bryologists over many years (Hodgetts & Blockeel, 1992). In 2005 Nick Hodgetts undertook a detailed survey of its distribution for the National Park Authority. He showed that the moss is frequent to abundant along a 1-kilometre stretch of the River Doe, where it grows on near-vertical rock faces submerged in a zone 7–25 cm below the summer-flow water level in a swiftly flowing current. The difficulty of accessing the habitat may account for the moss remaining undiscovered for so many years. It occupies a zone above which are two more distinct zones: the first dominated by *Cinclidotus fontinaloides* and *Platyhypnidium riparioides*, and the second by *Thamnium alopecurum* (Yorkshire Dales National Park Authority, 2006).

Mosses have the ability to accumulate metals from their environment, and they can be used to demonstrate pollution in rivers. In the Swale and in the Arkle Beck, Wehr & Whitton (1983) showed that *Platyhypnidium riparioides* accumulated large amounts of heavy metals, with possible consequences for invertebrate herbivores. Although the Swale and the Arkle Beck are the most affected by heavy metals, rivers in other dales close to historical mining sites, for example the Wharfe, also show some contamination.

In the river systems, as the gradients fall, slower flows and less turbulence allow sediment to accumulate. This sediment supports the stonewort *Chara vulgaris*, and pondweeds including Red Pondweed (*Potamogeton alpinus*) and Broad-leaved Pondweed (*P. natans*). With more sluggish flows, both in the main river and in tributary streams across the floodplain, other species colonise banks and wet hollows, including Common Reed (*Phragmites australis*), Canary-grass (*Phalaris arundinacea*) and a number of sedge species including Bottle Sedge (*Carex rostrata*) (Fig. 163) and Lesser Pond Sedge (*C. acutiformis*). The Northern Spike-rush (*Eleocharis austriaca*) is a rare plant found in this situation in Wharfedale, while in damp areas of the floodplain set back from the river, Northern Hawk's-beard (*Crepis mollis*) occurs.

FIG 163. Bottle Sedge (*Carex rostrata*), a plant of swamps and wet hollows in floodplains.

The native White-clawed Crayfish (*Austropotamobius pallipes*) was once widely distributed in all the main river systems in the Dales (Fig. 164). Now the American Signal Crayfish (*Pacificastus leniusculus*) (Fig. 165) is established at sites in all these systems, and the native crayfish has been eliminated or its populations markedly reduced. In the Ribble the demise of the latter throughout much of the river system was caused by an outbreak in 2001 of the crayfish plague fungus introduced by the invading American species (Peay *et. al.*, 2009). But not all invading Signal Crayfish populations carry the fungus, and in both the Wharfe and the Ure populations of the

FIG 164. The native White-clawed Crayfish (*Austropotamobius pallipes*), once widely distributed in all the main river systems. (Linda Pitkin)

FIG 165. American Signal Crayfish (*Pacifastacus leniusculus*), larger than the native species, and sometimes a carrier of the crayfish plague fungus. (Malcolm Schuyl)

two species occur together. Signal Crayfish were stocked into a trout farm at Kilnsey in Wharfedale in 1983. Bubb *et al.* (2005) recorded colonisation of the river by the crayfish after its first record in 1990 (Fig. 166). By 2003 Signal Crayfish were found 23.3 kilometres downstream of Kilnsey and 4.6 kilometres upstream, as well as 6.3 kilometres upstream in the Skirfare. These workers also observed a more rapid downstream spread of the Signal Crayfish in the Ure after their first arrival in 1997. Even in the absence of the crayfish plague, however, the larger American species competes successfully with the native crayfish for shelter and possibly also for food, and numbers of the latter decline.

The major Dales rivers are important fisheries for salmonids including Brown Trout, Sea Trout, Atlantic Salmon (*Salmo salar*) and Grayling (*Thymallus thymallus*), and further down river also for coarse fish. The possibility that the establishment of large populations of Signal Crayfish may affect the fisheries has been a subject

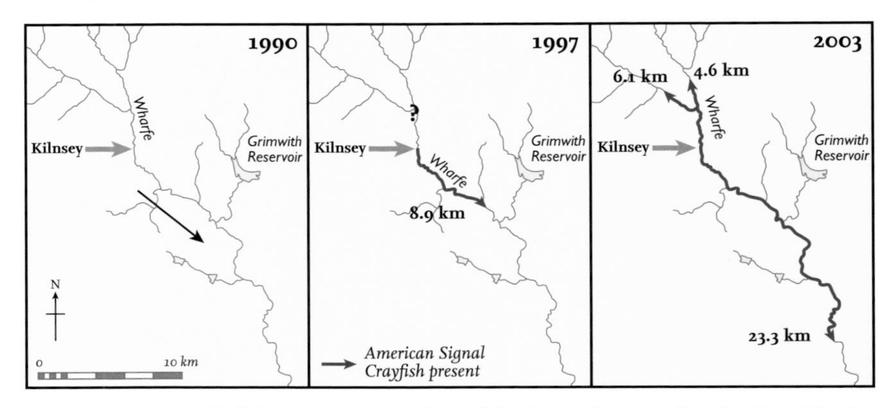

FIG 166. The spread of the American Signal Crayfish after its first record in the River Wharfe at Kilnsey in 1990. Reproduced from Bubb *et al.* (2005).

of concern. In a study in the River Wharfe, Bubb *et al.* (2009) showed that both species of crayfish were dominant over Bullheads at shelter sites, with the non-native Signal Crayfish being the more aggressive. They showed that there was a negative association between densities of Signal Crayfish and Bullheads, with Bullhead numbers being high where both crayfish species were absent or where the native species was present at low densities. Some of the headwater streams in the Ribble catchment escaped the plague, and on one of these, Bookill Gill Beck, a tributary of Long Preston Beck, an illegal introduction of 4–12 individuals of apparently plague-free Signal Crayfish was made at one location in 1995 (Peay *et al.*, 2009). By 2008 they were found 3.4 kilometres downstream and 0.6 kilometres upstream of the point of introduction. Peay and her co-workers found that there was a strong negative correlation between the abundance of Signal Crayfish in the beck and the density of Brown Trout, suggesting that invading populations of the Crayfish can have a negative effect on the recruitment of Brown Trout (Fig. 167). These workers also showed that Bullheads were absent from at least 1.7 kilometres of stream invaded by Signal Crayfish where they had previously co-existed with the native species. The crustacean *Gammarus pulex* is a major food source for Brown Trout, and it is possible that competition from high Signal Crayfish populations for this food source may be a factor affecting trout abundance.

Considerable effort is now being expended to improve the water quality of Dales rivers through the work of the Environment Agency, Natural England and bodies such as the Eden Rivers, Lune Rivers, Ribble Rivers and Ure Salmon Trusts, assisted by government initiatives such as the Catchment Restoration

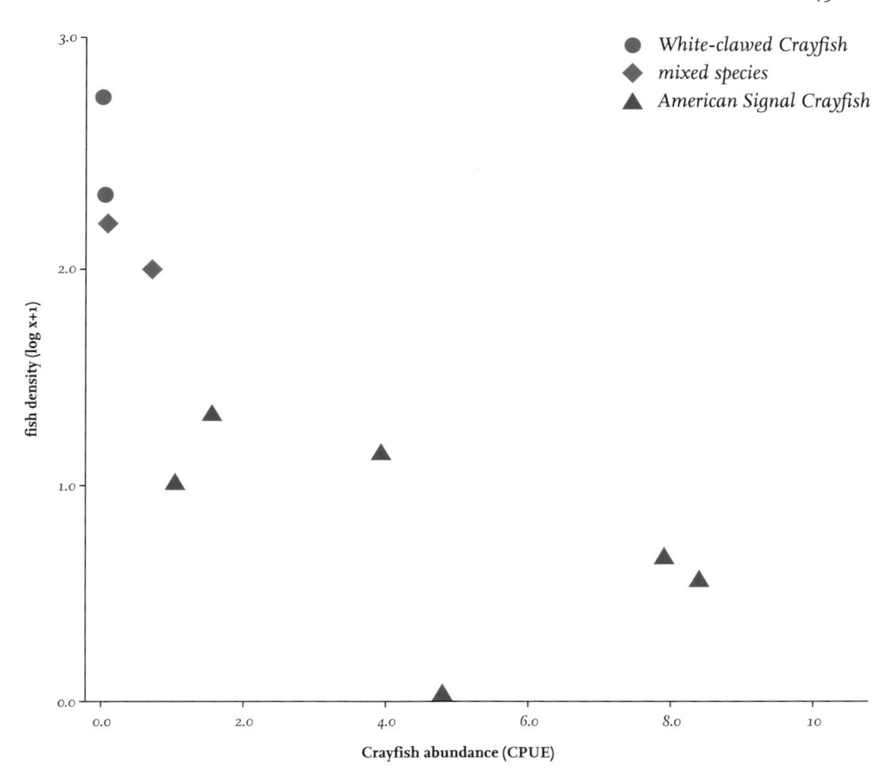

FIG 167. Correlation between total density of fish (per 100 m^2) in Bookill Gill Beck and abundance of crayfish. Reproduced from Peay *et al.* (2009).

Fund. Within the National Park much of this effort is aimed at increasing fish populations, particularly those of the salmonid species, Salmon and Brown Trout. The Ouse, into which the Nidd, Swale, Ure and Wharfe drain, was an important Salmon river up until the early part of twentieth century, but poor water quality, particularly in the tidal Ouse and Humber, caused a dramatic decline in the fishery. An improvement in water quality from the 1970s onwards resulted in a marked increase in Salmon numbers from the 1990s, with densities of juvenile fish at some sites on the Ure similar to those of the best UK rivers (Ure Salmon Trust). However, a study of the Wharfe in 1996 and 1997 failed to record the presence of Salmon (Hopkins, 1998).

Salmon spawn in the late autumn and early winter in redds created in shallow gravel. In January 2001, David Bamford mapped Salmon redds on the Ure for the Environment Agency. Within the National Park he recorded spawning sites in the main river and also in Bishopdale Beck and Walen Beck. The eggs hatch in the spring, and the hatchlings or alevins remain in the gravel until they have absorbed their yolk sacs. The Salmon fry leave the gravel, and become parr after their first winter. After spending between one and three further winters in the river, they develop into smolt and undertake a spring migration to the sea. Brown Trout also create redds, and much conservation work is designed to optimise successful breeding sites for both fish species. For example, the Ure Salmon Trust has carried out extensive work on Bishopdale Beck, near Aysgarth, fencing both sides of the river for 3 kilometres to exclude dairy cattle, while installing solar-powered livestock drinking troughs. Fencing the river banks against livestock and reconstruction of eroding banks has been carried out on other becks and rivers, in part to limit sedimentation in the river gravels, including in upper Wharfedale (Fig. 168). Sedimentation in the river gravels can interfere with both spawning and fry development.

FIG 168. The banks of the River Wharfe near Yockenthwaite, fenced to protect against bank erosion caused by cattle and sheep grazing.

Salmon are not the only migratory salmonid species. On some rivers, such as the Lune, Sea Trout are also keenly sought after by anglers, who are well aware that these fish tend to run the rivers at night. Sea Trout and Brown Trout are in fact the same species, and in most rivers the former are largely the female component of the population whereas the latter make up the majority of the male spawning fish. Female fish feeding at sea get larger and produce more eggs than those that stay in the river. The latter put a smaller proportion of their body weight into eggs and do not breed every year. Salmon and Sea Trout differ in that after spawning over 80 per cent of Salmon die, whereas a smaller proportion of Sea Trout die, and many may spawn several times.

Other fish, apart from salmonids, also spend part of their lives at sea. For example the River Eden contains all three British species of lamprey, jawless cartilaginous fish somewhat resembling eels, two of which, Sea Lamprey (*Petromyzon marinus*) and River Lamprey (*Lampetra fluviatilis*), migrate to sea before returning to the river to spawn. The third species, Brook Lamprey (*L. planeri*), remains in fresh water throughout its life. Lamprey spawn in river gravels, and the eggs hatch to produce larvae, the so-called ammocoetes, which burrow into the sediment leaving just their mouthparts exposed. They spend several years in the sediments, filter-feeding on microorganisms and detritus, before metamorphosing into adults, and, in the case of Sea and River Lampreys, then migrating to sea. Probably all three species were once common in the Dales, but recent records are rather scarce. Hopkins (1998) recorded lamprey ammocoetes at two sites on the Wharfe, Linton Stepping Stones and near Appletreewick, where he also recorded Brown Trout, Grayling and the common small fish: Bullheads, Stone Loaches (*Barbatula barbatula*) and Minnows (*Phoxinus phoxinus*). The lamprey species was probably Brook Lamprey, but it is difficult to distinguish the species at the larval stage.

For salmonid species in particular, and also perhaps more recently for the lampreys, the importance of retaining the connectivity between the estuaries and the river headwaters in the very smallest becks has long been recognised as a major part of conservation measures, along with improving water quality throughout the river catchment. In recent years there has been increasing emphasis on removing manmade barriers, even small ones, and where possible installing suitable passes to help fish returning from the sea to reach their spawning grounds.

CAVES

As becks sink below ground or descend into potholes they provide not only the means by which caves form, but also the source from which they can become colonised by aquatic organisms. If one assumes that successive glacial periods would have eliminated all animals in the cave systems, then inflow in streams during the Post-glacial period must have provided one important way in which the current cave fauna has been established. Other colonisation routes include accidental falling into sink holes and access through cave openings. This history of glaciation is probably the reason for the paucity of cave specialists amongst the Dales fauna. These species are known as troglobionts, but in addition Sket (2008) recognises three other categories of cave animals. These are: (1) species which essentially maintain populations on the surface, but can also maintain permanent subterranean populations; (2) species which spend part of their life underground, but feed or breed above ground, or both; and (3) species which are perhaps found accidently underground, but are unable to maintain permanent populations there.

There are many cave systems in the Dales, some of them very extensive, some ancient and now devoid of the streams which formed them, but many still with water flowing through them towards a resurgence. Proudlove (2013) estimated that of about 2,000 known caves in the Dales, fewer than 5 per cent have been sampled for their existing biodiversity since Hazelton and Glennie first made records of animals in Ingleborough Cave and Marble Steps Pot in 1938, and that nearly a third of all records came from only seven caves. This suggests that there is still much to be discovered. There are also many artificial caves resulting from mining activities in the eighteenth and nineteenth centuries, few of which have had their fauna documented. These contrast in age with natural caves, which are many thousands of years old. Although both cavers and miners may have inadvertently introduced some organisms underground, this is likely to have been much more significant to the biodiversity of busy mines, where, for example, new shafts would have been devoid of animals. However, the faunas of caves and mines have many species in common, although mines, not surprisingly given their origins, have fewer aquatic species (Proudlove, 2013).

There are very few troglobionts in British caves and none so far recorded from mines. Two species are known from the Dales, both aquatics: the minute crustacean *Antrobathynella stammeri* and the coleopteran *Hydroporus ferrugineus.* The former species has been recorded in three Dales caves (Great Douk, Scoska and White Scar) and is also known from the hyporheic zone of the River Skirfare (Stubbington *et al.*, 2008). The hyporheic zone is the region beneath and adjacent to rivers where surface water and groundwater mix. The origin of *A. stammeri* in the Dales, and elsewhere in northern England and Scotland, has been the subject of some speculation because it has poor powers of dispersal, which may suggest that it survived the Devensian period in sub-glacial refugia (Proudlove *et al.*, 2003). *Hydroporus ferrugineus* is a water beetle known only from Gaping Gill.

A total of over 210 species of invertebrates have been identified in Dales caves, of which insects represent by far the largest group (65 per cent), and within the insects, the Diptera are the most commonly recorded (Proudlove, 2013). Rather more than a third of all the invertebrates recorded are species which occur on the surface, but are able to maintain permanent subterranean populations. These include many species of mites and springtails, but also some oligochaete worms. Of the last group of species, Piearce (1975) observed the earthworms *Allolobophora chlorotica* and *Aporrectodea rosea* uncharacteristically crawling on the surface of sediments in Ingleborough Cave. Unpigmented green earthworm (*A. chlorotica*) populations occur in Robinson's Pot in the Cowside Beck valley, and in Ingleborough Cave. Spiders make up an important part of the fauna, and there are four species which are able to maintain permanent subterranean populations. The majority of these occur in the threshold region, where some light penetrates the cave or mine entrance, but the small money spider *Porrhomma convexum* is able to flourish in total darkness.

One of the most commonly recorded invertebrates is the freshwater shrimp *Gammarus pulex* (Fig. 169), which drifts into caves and may maintain discrete populations there. Piearce (1975) observed a depigmented population of this species in the Ingleborough Cave and suggested that this, and other similar populations, might differ genetically from those in the becks and rivers. Cave individuals of this species are also smaller than those found above ground.

FIG 169. The freshwater shrimp *Gammarus pulex* is common in Dales rivers, including in caves, where it may show depigmented forms. (Alex Hyde)

About 60 per cent of all the invertebrate species found in Dales caves are unable to maintain permanent populations there, occurring as the result of accidental entry. This is also true of the only commonly recorded aquatic vertebrate species, Brown Trout and Bullhead. Brown Trout in the caves, like the freshwater shrimp, often appear pale, but this is thought to be a plastic response to the environment rather than a genetic change. It is supposed that the fish would regain a darker colour if flushed from a resurgence (Proudlove, 2013). In contrast, Bullheads in Dales caves remain darkly coloured.

A feature of many caves and mines with aerial entrances is that they provide hibernation sites for some animal species and roosts for others. Hibernation sites exist for several moth species including Herald Moth (*Scoliopteryx libatrix*), Tissue Moth (*Triphosa dubitata*) and Winter Moth (*Opherophtera brumata*), but the Dales caves are better known for their use by bats. Eight species of bats are widespread in the Dales (Altringham & Glover, 2013), and most of these use caves. Males use caves both for roosting in summer and for hibernation in winter, whereas for females caves are only hibernation sites. But caves provide sites for another important biological event in late summer and early autumn. Several bat species exhibit the phenomenon of swarming, when the animals chase each other inside and outside caves. Figure 170 shows the distribution of caves investigated by Glover & Altringham (2008) in a study of swarming in the Dales. They showed that this activity peaked between mid-August and mid-September. Of the 53 cave sites investigated, over 60 per cent were used, with swarming activity favouring those caves carrying less water. The resident five swarming species were Brandt's Bat (*Myotis brandtii*), Brown Long-eared Bat (*Plecotus auritus*), Daubenton's Bat (*Myotis daubentonii*) (Fig. 171), Natterer's Bat (*Myotis nattereri*) and Whiskered Bat (*Myotis mystacinus*), and all five were found at most sites. Swarming involves large numbers of bats and plays an important role in the reproduction of those species which show this phenomenon. Many chases lead to copulation, and one function of this behaviour is to prevent inbreeding in small local populations. Rivers et *al.* (2005) showed that all the populations of Natterer's Bats which they studied showed high gene diversity, and this would not have been the case if mating occurred in the small summer colonies, typically containing only 10–30 individuals. These workers concluded that all mating must occur at the swarming sites.

Bat populations in Wharfedale, including Daubenton's, Natterer's and Common Pipistrelle (*Pipistrellus pipistrellus*), are amongst the best studied anywhere, thanks to the work of John Altringham and his colleagues (see e.g. Warren *et al.*, 2000; Senior *et al.*, 2005). Among their many findings is the fact that bat species prefer sections of the upper Wharfe, between Kettlewell and Yockenthwaite, with smooth water surfaces and trees on both banks. Two possible

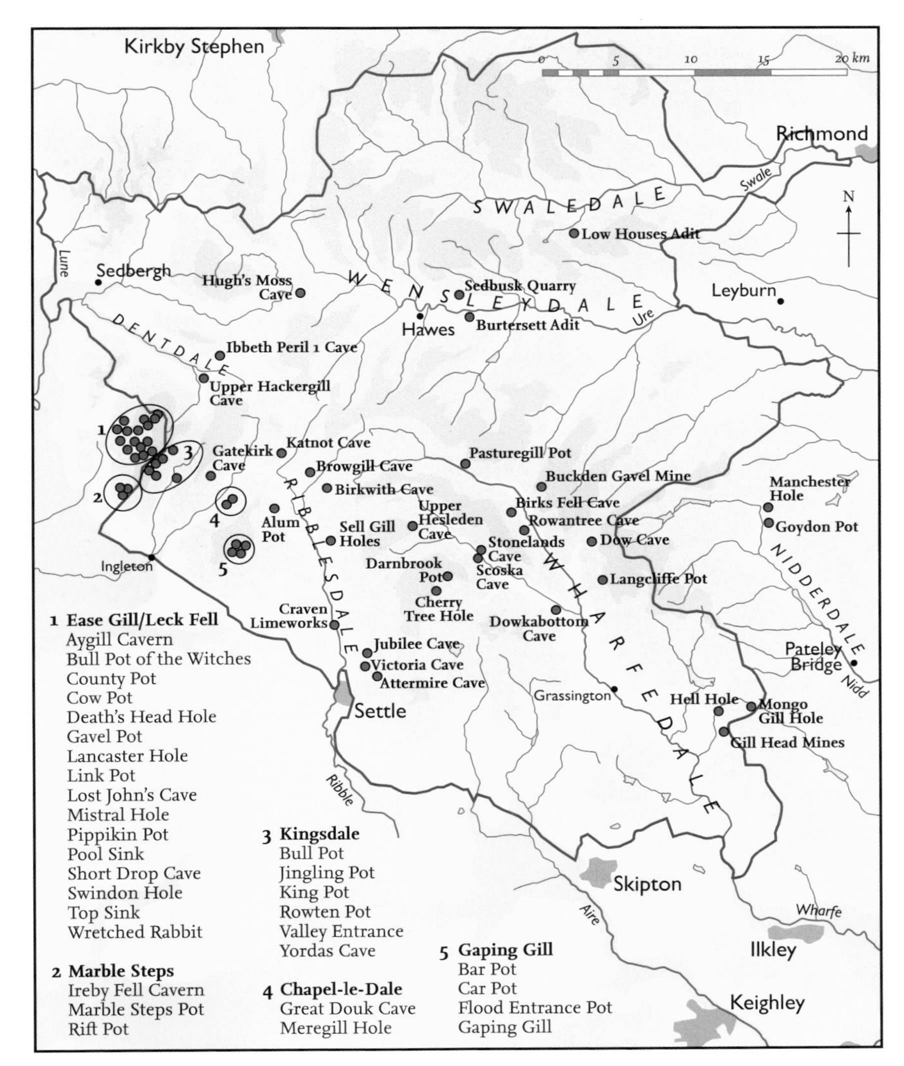

FIG 170. A map of the many caves and mines in the Dales that were investigated in a study of bat swarming behaviour. Adapted from Glover & Altringham (2008).

reasons for this are greater insect densities and low river noise, which would reduce interference with the bats' echo-location.

Their detailed studies of Daubenton's Bat showed that in summer it roosts, and has its nursery colonies, in crevices in bridges or holes in trees by the river

FIG 171. Daubenton's Bat (*Myotis daubentoni*). This species feeds mostly over smooth-flowing water, and is widespread in the Dales. (Dale Sutton)

over which it feeds, prior to dispersing to cave or mine swarming sites. But these workers also showed an interesting difference in the distribution of male and female bats along the river. When bats were captured and ringed along the upper Wharfe, from just north of Buckden to a kilometre south of its junction with the Skirfare, only one out of 127 bats caught between April and November was a female. But further downstream, on the stretch of the river from below the Skirfare junction to just south Grassington, 64 out of a total of 108 bats caught in this period were female (Fig. 172). In this 20-kilometre stretch from Buckden, the river falls from 250 to 150 metres above sea level and widens from 3–10 metres to over 20 metres, becoming smoother with fewer stretches of fast-flowing water. A possible reason for the difference in distribution of the sexes is that upstream the narrower river and cooler air temperatures might not supply the abundant and regular insect food required by nursing females, since the critical temperature for insect flight is reached on fewer nights. This difference in distribution suggests that dominant males and/or females exclude the majority of males from the better foraging sites close to nursery roosts. Many males are thus forced to use suboptimal and more distant foraging sites, where they have to work harder for their food.

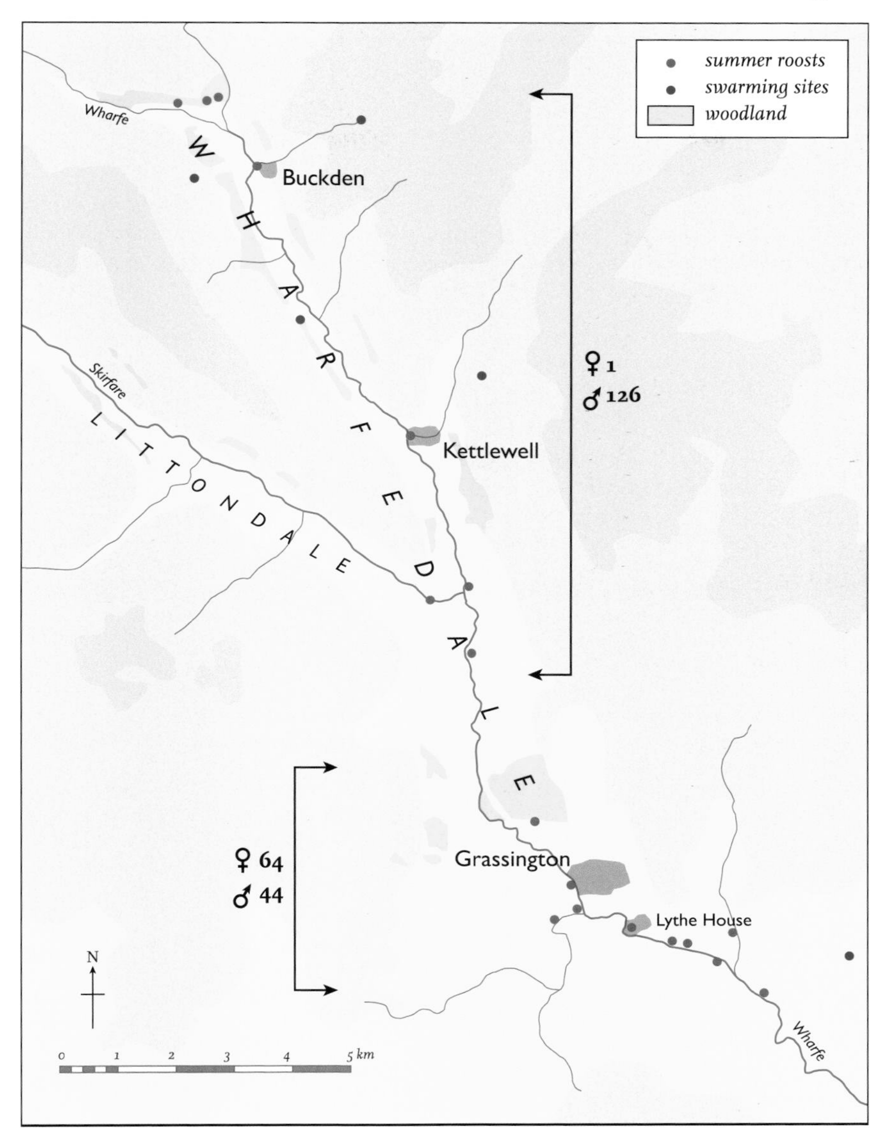

FIG 172. A map of the River Wharfe study site together with the results of the distribution of the sexes of Daubenton's Bat along the river, from Senior *et al.* (2005). The figures refer to the number of bats caught and ringed from roosts and foraging sites during the summer months.

In a continuation of their studies on the Wharfe, but this time over a 40-kilometre stretch extending to just outside the National Park, and over a larger altitudinal range, John Altringham and his co-workers were able to suggest that the environment and its effect on resources determines both social structure and mating pattern in Daubenton's Bats (Angell *et al.*, 2013). They showed that high-altitude roosts (> 200 metres) were composed almost exclusively of males whereas low-altitude roosts (< 100 metres) contained almost equal numbers of females and juveniles, with few adult males. Roosts at intermediate altitude contained almost equal numbers of males and females with a small proportion of juveniles. Using molecular genetics techniques, they showed that offspring in low-altitude female-dominated roosts had a very high probability of being fathered by bats caught at swarming and hibernation sites. They concluded that females usually exclude males from nursery roosts near good foraging sites. But in more marginal habitat at higher altitude, where males and females are both present, there was a high probability of offspring being fathered by these males. Although they found that most offspring were fathered during autumn swarming, in more marginal habitats the breeding success of a small proportion of males was improved by living with females in nursery roosts in late summer.

Scoska Cave in Littondale has been studied for its invertebrate and bat fauna, but its flora has also been investigated. Allan Pentecost and Z. Zhang (2001) examined plant distribution in relation to light penetration within the cave (Fig. 173). The cave has a straight passage entrance, 3–4 metres wide, following a near-horizontal bedding plane in the Great Scar Limestone. The roof is 2 metres high and follows a higher bedding plane. Gildersbank Sike emerges near the cave entrance. A total of 59 taxa were recorded in the cave, comprising 4 algae, 3 lichens, 47 bryophytes, 4 ferns and one flowering plant, the Opposite-leaved Golden-saxifrage (*Chrysosplenium oppositifolium*). Cover as well as species diversity was dominated by bryophytes. The greatest numbers of species (16) were found 0–4 and 10–15 metres into the cave, but species diversity declined rapidly after 15 metres with declining light penetration, and beyond 20 metres only two cyanobacteria (blue-green algae) were recorded: *Schizothrix* at 27 metres and *Gloeocapsa* at 34 metres. No algae were observed beyond 34 metres. Of the three lichen species, *Lepraria incana* was the most common, found to a depth of 17 metres. The commonest bryophyte was *Thamnobryum alopecurum*, which was one of three moss species found deepest into the cave, the other species being *Amblystegium serpens* and *Fissidens dubius*.

Today not all deep caves remain in perpetual total darkness. Three show caves, Ingleborough Cave, Stump Cross Caverns and White Scar Cave, have fixed lighting. This has resulted in the development of a biofilm on the rock surfaces

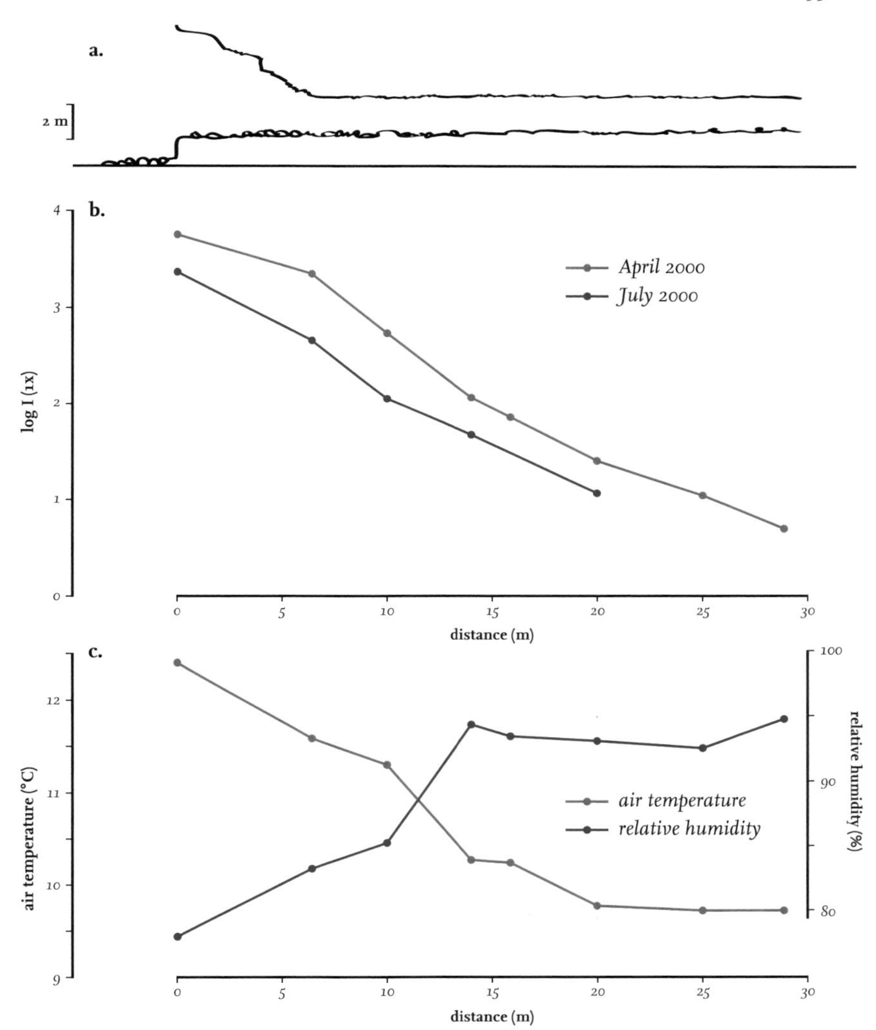

FIG 173. Morphometric and climatic data for the entrance passage to Scoska Cave, Littondale: (a) cave profile, showing rock-strewn passage and flat cave roof; (b) photosynthetically available radiation in April and July 2000; (c) air temperature and relative humidity. Reproduced from Pentecost & Zhang (2001).

in the vicinity of the lights where the temperature and relative humidity of the air as well as the light intensity are locally altered. In this microclimate a so-called lampenflora has developed. Pentecost (2010) investigated the 'lamp floras' of these three Dales show caves, and recorded 30 taxa in total: 18 cyanobacteria, 6 diatoms, 4 bryophytes, one coccoid green alga and one fern. The most conspicuous of the moss species was *Eucladium verticillatum*, and the other taxa identified to species level were *Crataneuron filicinum* and *Fissidens taxifolius*. The fern, Brittle Bladder-fern (*Cystopteris fragilis*), was only observed as gametophytes. It will be interesting to observe to what extent these communities have reached a steady state or whether a slow succession occurs over time, given that fixed lighting in the caves is fairly recent in origin.

CONCLUDING REMARKS

Running waters provide a major attraction for present-day visitors to the Dales, both above and below ground. In the past they have been important to the area's economy as a source of power and water for the lead and textile industries. Today they help to sustain the local tourist economy both as amenity attractions in their own right and by supporting fisheries. They also continue to provide vital water resources for the agricultural industry. In the past the various demands placed on the river systems have sometimes resulted in marked reductions in water quality, in terms of both chemical composition and sediment load, and this has been to the marked detriment to the biota. Today, the Water Framework Directive is continuing to drive improvements in water quality which are helping to reverse former declines in biodiversity, but in areas despoiled by lead mining and smelting this may prove to be a very slow process.

This chapter has largely concentrated on the running fresh waters themselves, but it is worth noting that present-day attempts to improve water quality, by restoring the connectivity between the rivers and their floodplains, have another potentially important ecological outcome. Enhancement of the riparian zone helps to increase connectivity through the Dales not only for the watercourses themselves but also by providing improved corridors by which, for example, some terrestrial animals can move through a landscape of fragmented habitats. Connectivity through the landscape is of major importance to conservation and the maintenance of biodiversity, and is highlighted again in the following chapters.

CHAPTER 11

The Changing Dales – Birds

In 2000, the publication of *Nature in the Dales: a Biodiversity Action Plan for the Yorkshire Dales National Park* was a modern landmark in nature conservation for the region. In the same year Ian Court, species officer for the National Park Authority, published *Birds of Conservation Concern in the Yorkshire Dales National Park*. In this he listed 50 species, of which 27 were on the red list of high conservation concern. If this list could have been shown to naturalists familiar with the Dales and their villages at any time in the first four decades of the twentieth century, they would almost certainly have been amazed. The presence on that list of then familiar and common species around the villages, such as Song Thrush (*Turdus philomelos*), Common Blackbird (*Turdus merula*), Common Starling (*Sturnus vulgaris*), Barn Swallow (*Hirundo rustica*) and Dunnock (*Prunella modularis*) would have been quite incredible to them, as would Northern Lapwing (*Vanellus vanellus*), Common Snipe (*Gallinago gallinago*), Corncrake (*Crex crex*) and Yellow Wagtail (*Motacilla flava*) from the damp pastures and hay meadows. Perhaps the only unsurprising part of the list, from their point of view, would have been the birds of prey, long persecuted by gamekeepers on the grouse moors, including Hen Harrier (*Circus cyaneus*), Peregrine Falcon (*Falco peregrinus*) and Common Buzzard (*Buteo buteo*). Equally those naturalists would have been surprised by the species unknown or rare in the Dales before the second half of the century which are now common. Collared Dove (*Streptopelia decaocto*), a bird that originated in Asia and spread northwest across Europe, reaching the Dales in 1968, is now very common. Nuthatch (*Sitta europaea*), once largely confined to the southern half of England, first bred in Malham Tarn Woods in 1971 (Clunas & Shorrock, 1990), and is now common in the National Park. In recent years Siskin (*Carduelis spinus*) numbers have increased, perhaps as the result of conifer plantations reaching maturity, and Goldfinch (*C. carduelis*) numbers have also increased, reflecting a national upward trend. Feral flocks of Canada (*Branta canadensis*) and Greylag (*Anser anser*) geese are widespread, and the Common Merganser or Goosander (*Mergus merganser*) is present on many rivers.

The long-term recording systems developed by the British Trust for Ornithology (BTO), the Common Birds Census established in the 1960s, and, with some years of overlap, succeeded by the Breeding Birds Survey in 1994, provide a wealth of data to indicate population trends both nationally and regionally. Understanding the factors causing these trends, and any regional variation in them, is key to developing successful conservation measures, but is not always easy. Changes in the populations of some bird species can sometimes be readily interpreted in terms of changes in land-use management or increased predation. For example, the loss of the Corncrake as a breeding bird in the Dales by the 1960s is very probably related to drainage of meadows and pastures, and the increased mechanisation of grass harvesting in the twentieth century, combined with earlier cutting of meadows, particularly for silage, but also for hay. Similarly the loss of Moorhen (*Gallinula chloropus*) from some river valleys including the Ribble can be related to predation from the release of American Mink (*Neovison vison*).

But changes in the populations of other species cannot be so readily interpreted, and this is particularly true of many migratory birds. The Cuckoo (*Cuculus canorus*) is a good case in point. There has been a marked decrease in this species in Britain and northwest Europe in recent decades, including, for example, its virtual disappearance from parts of Craven. Populations of its major host in the Pennines, Meadow Pipit (*Anthus pratensis*), may be somewhat reduced, although the species is still common, but the Cuckoo also appears to be declining in other English regions such as the Fens where the Reed Warbler (*Acrocephalus scirpaceus*) is its main host, and still abundant. Although a decrease in the Cuckoo's preferred food source in Britain, hairy caterpillars, may be one potential cause of at least some of the decline, particularly in poor summers, other likely causes are the difficulties related to the migratory journey, and habitat and other changes on the wintering grounds in sub-Saharan Africa.

In 2011 five young male Cuckoos from Norfolk were fitted with GPS devices by the BTO, allowing their migratory journeys to be followed. This was repeated in 2012 when twelve more male Cuckoos were fitted with these devices, including five from Wales and five from Scotland, and by 2014 a total of 31 birds had been tagged. A key initial finding is that the birds follow different routes across Europe and the Sahel to a similar region in central Africa. This may suggest perhaps that the wintering grounds provide the key to understanding the decline, but losses on migration were also significant, and the small number of birds followed so far makes any generalisation difficult. One bird showed markedly different migratory routes to and from the same area within the Congo in the three years, and each individual may have its own preferred strategy and route, which may differ markedly from that of other birds. Remarkable findings of the BTO study include the fact that migrations to and from central Africa are very different in duration, four and two months respectively, and that more than half of the British birds have left Britain by the end of June. Birds may spend as little as 15 per cent of their time each year in this country, pointing to the potential importance of conservation measures elsewhere.

Several other migratory birds which breed in the Dales and over-fly the Sahel are also in serious decline. These include Tree Pipit (*Anthus trivialis*), Common Whitethroat (*Sylvia communis*), Willow Warbler (*Phylloscopus trochilus*), Wood Warbler (*P. sibilatrix*) and Whinchat (*Saxicola rubetra*). With several of these species it is not yet possible to tell whether the causes of the decrease are to be found on the migration routes or on the wintering grounds, although Hulme & Cresswell (2012) concluded that in the case of Whinchats, population decline was unlikely to be caused by availability of suitable habitat in West Africa.

However, not all migratory birds have shown year-on-year declines. Sand Martins (*Riparia riparia*) showed a marked slump in 1984, but their numbers in the Dales have now recovered (Brian Shorrock, personal communication), and Chiffchaffs (*Phylloscopus collybita*) have increased. The increase in Chiffchaffs may be related to the fact that many birds are now wintering in southern Spain rather than in Africa. Some are also wintering in southern England.

Clearly local biodiversity action plans can have no effect on problems encountered by migratory species outside the Dales. Nor, except in the case of a few pest species such as the American Mink, can these plans include measures to markedly influence predation rates. Instead they are mainly aimed at trying to maximise the reproductive success of each species through optimising land-use management, and as such they are very valuable conservation tools.

BIRDS OF MOORLAND AND UPLAND GRASSLANDS

The mosaic of Heather (*Calluna vulgaris*) moor, blanket bog, rocky slopes and upland grassland provides important breeding areas for a number of species still common in the Dales including Meadow Pipit, Skylark (*Alauda arvensis*) and Northern Wheatear (*Oenanthe oenanthe*) (Fig. 174). But these habitats also provide important breeding sites for less common species such as Golden Plover (*Pluvialis apricaria*), Dunlin (*Calidris alpina*), Merlin (*Falco columbarius*), Twite (*Carduelis

FIG 174. Northern Wheatear (*Oenanthe oenanthe*). This summer migrant is still common in the Dales, nesting amongst the rocks, boulders and walls of upland pastures. (Andy Sanday)

flavirostris), Ring Ouzel (*Turdus torquatus*) and Black Grouse (*Tetrao tetrix*). Several of these latter species have been in serious decline and have been the subject of research to identify its causes.

Ring Ouzels are thought to have declined in the United Kingdom during the twentieth century, including a 58 per cent decrease in breeding bird population between 1988–91 and 1999 (Fig. 175). This contrasts with the apparent stability of continental European populations in the same period. There is some overlap in wintering areas between continental and UK breeding birds, which suggests that at least part of the observed decline must relate to breeding success. The only detailed study of the bird in the Dales was undertaken by the late Ian Appleyard in the Grassington area over a 15-year period from 1978 in which he identified the territories of 353 pairs. He recorded that the birds preferred to nest near a prominent landscape feature such as a rock outcrop or a steep gulley rather than on open Heather moor. Nests in one area were as close as 140–200 metres apart, but could be up to 500 metres apart in less favourable habitats. He found that nest predation was usually *c.*20 per cent at his study site, but in one year was much higher (62 per cent), and that appreciable numbers of pairs would lay double clutches, up to 73 per cent in one year. Predation was lower when and where the activity of gamekeepers was greater. Appleyard did not identify any marked decline in his study area, and in fact he observed that occupied territories increased in the second half of the period. However, the Yorkshire Dales Upland Bird Study Group (2006) lists a later survey of the same population which suggests a possible reduction in subsequent years, although differences in survey effort may complicate this conclusion.

FIG 175. Ring Ouzel (*Turdus torquatus*). This species was the subject of a detailed study in the Grassington area by Ian Appleyard over 15 years from 1978. (Markus Varesuo)

In a study in the Moorfoot Hills, southeast Scotland, Sim *et al.* (2007) examined Ring Ouzel breeding occupancy in 1998–2000 in an area which had been previously surveyed between 1952 and 1985. Breeding sites identified in the earlier survey were classified as either occupied or deserted in the later one, and the vegetation cover in the area during the later survey was determined from satellite images. They concluded that occupied breeding sites were more likely to have either Heather or a grass–Heather mosaic within 100 metres than potentially available but unoccupied ones. They suggested that the latter sites might have lacked sufficient Heather cover for nesting, and that desertion of sites might relate to the loss of cover from this dwarf shrub. Heather decline occurred widely in the uplands with increased sheep grazing during the latter half of the twentieth century, and the reduction in grazing pressure this century should therefore result in increased Heather cover and help to reverse the decline in Ring Ouzel populations. However, the authors point out that the association between successful nesting sites and heather cover may result from the contraction of birds into favoured sites as the population declines for other reasons, such as changes in the abundance of food items. Further studies by these workers showed that juvenile Ring Ouzels appear to require access to short-grass habitats where they feed on earthworms in the early summer, but also access in late summer to dwarf-shrub communities where they feed on Bilberries (*Vaccinium myrtillus*) and Crowberries (*Empetrum nigrum*) (Sim *et al.* 2005, 2013). They suggest that annual survival is partly mediated by the availability of juniper (*Juniperus* species) berries in the Moroccan wintering areas, which might be adversely affected by increase in grazing pressure and firewood collection.

The Black Grouse is another species which has undergone a marked reduction in its range in Britain during the twentieth century, having virtually disappeared from many southern counties (Fig. 176). Its main stronghold is in Scotland, but its English population is now largely confined to the northern Pennines. In continental Europe it is essentially a species of the forest edge, but in the Dales, where there is a paucity of woodland and scrub, it is a bird favouring the mosaic of Heather moorland and rough, damp grassland, including hay meadows.

Black Grouse employ a lek mating system in which usually between five and ten displaying males (blackcocks) gather and hold territories in an open area of short grass or heathland. Females (greyhens) are attracted to mate by the display, particularly to bigger blackcocks which have longer tails, show more vigorous displays, and often occupy the central territory within the lek. During the period immediately after the establishment of alien conifer plantations in the mid-twentieth century, Black Grouse numbers temporarily increased, and as many as 150 displaying males were observed at one site (Mather, 1974). The increase was short-lived as a dense tree cover was established in these plantations. Leks continued to be lost elsewhere, including one recorded by P. F. Holmes at Kirkby Malham. By 1999, a survey of the whole National Park revealed a very low minimum total of only 48 lekking males (Court, 2000).

The adult Black Grouse feed on a variety of plants, but the chicks, in their first few weeks, require a diet rich in invertebrates, which they find in damp

FIG 176. Black Grouse (*Tetrao tetrix*). Only 48 lekking males were observed in the whole National Park in 1999, but since then populations may be responding to a reduction in grazing pressure on moorland and other conservation measures. (Des Ongi)

habitats such as flushes within the grassland and moorland. Thus drainage as part of agricultural improvement since the Second World War is one factor which may have led to a decrease in breeding success and hence population decline. Similarly, increased grazing pressure during this period, leading to a marked reduction in dwarf shrub cover and shorter grassland swards, may have made the birds more susceptible to predation. The birds favour vegetation with a canopy at roughly knee height, which provides cover from raptors. Baines (1996) compared Black Grouse populations on 20 moors in northern England and southern Scotland with different sheep-grazing pressures. Although the plant species did not differ between the moors, breeding success and density were higher where the sheep density was lower. Heavily grazed moors supported fewer insects, which may have reduced the survival of young chicks. Calladine *et al.* (2002) monitored Black Grouse breeding success at 20 sites over a five-year period. Ten sites were selected where grazing had been reduced between one and five years before observations commenced to < 1.1 sheep per hectare in summer and < 0.5 in winter. Each site was paired with another site at which sheep density was twice the summer and three times the winter density on the grazing-reduced plots. On average, the number of displaying males increased by 4.6 per cent a year over the period at sites with reduced grazing, and the proportion of females retaining broods during late chick-rearing was significantly greater (54 per cent as against 32 per cent at the sites with higher grazing pressure). Although these observations covered only five years, the data suggest that reduction in grazing pressure may be beneficial to Black Grouse populations in the longer term.

Although Black Grouse is regarded as a game bird, most shooting estates show a positive interest in its conservation. The North Pennine Black Grouse Recovery Project, covering an area from Wensleydale north to the Scottish border, was instigated in 1996, and since then most estates in the area have tried to avoid shooting the bird. Accidental shooting does occur, particularly of greyhens, but Warren *et al.* (2011) estimated the annual losses to be 1 per cent of the post-breeding populations. Lekking males increased from 773 in 1998 to 1,070 in 2007, but breeding success varied from year to year, being particularly poor in summers with a cold wet June, when only 0.3 chicks per hen were raised, markedly below the 1.2 chicks needed to sustain the population.

The activities of gamekeepers in removing predators of ground-nesting birds such as Foxes (*Vulpes vulpes*), Stoats (*Mustela erminea*) and Carrion Crows (*Corvus corone*) is likely to have a beneficial effect on Black Grouse populations. The encouragement of landowners to plant small areas of gill woodland with native trees is also likely to create more of the woodland-edge communities favoured by the birds. This, combined with a reduction in grazing pressure to encourage the growth of Heather and other dwarf shrubs, and the blocking of grips and other drainage channels to create more wetland areas suitable for young chicks, is likely to optimise the habitat to meet the birds' requirements. Black Grouse also feed on seed in hay meadows in winter, and here the reversion to later cutting dates and hay rather than silage production is also likely to be favourable to the birds.

The Twite is another bird which has undergone a serious decline in recent decades, and is red-listed in the UK Birds of Conservation Concern (Gregory *et al.*, 2012) (Fig. 177). The Yorkshire Dales Upland Bird Study Group Report for 1992–2004 recorded between 53 and 59 pairs. This was probably a considerable underestimate, given that the group's survey was principally designed to record breeding waders. However, there has been a considerable decline since then, though a small breeding population still exists. Twite is a bird which nests in Heather or Bracken (*Pteridium aquilinum*) on the moorland edge and also in limestone screes, but requires a succession of grassland seed sources to raise its young. Typically the Twite produce two broods each season, and foraging to feed the nestlings may take the birds several kilometres from the nest. In the southern Pennines at least important seed sources are dandelions (*Taraxacum* species) in spring, Common Sorrel (*Rumex acetosa*) in summer and Autumn Hawkbit (*Scorzoneroides autumnalis*) and thistles in late summer and early

FIG 177. Twite (*Carduelis flavirostris*). Only a small breeding population of this finch survives in the Dales. (David Kjaer)

autumn (Langston *et al.* 2006). A factor in the reduction in Twite numbers may be the general failure to successfully raise a second brood, possibly as a result of a paucity of seed sources. Intensification of agriculture is often seen as the major cause of the decline. Increased stocking rates lead to a reduction in the height of vegetation and the loss of Heather, with adverse effects on nesting sites, increasing disturbance and possibly also predation. Increased grazing pressure also leads to a reduction in flowering and seed set. The increased use of herbicides to control weeds, and importantly the change from hay to silage production, markedly reduces seed availability to the birds. If these are the factors causing the decline, then the move to less intensive farming encouraged by Higher Level Stewardship schemes should help to reverse it.

The blanket mires and damp areas close to the moorland tarns are important areas for breeding Golden Plover (Fig. 178) and Dunlin. The Yorkshire Dales Upland Bird Study Group, reviewing breeding bird records for 1992–2004, estimated that there were between 169 and 188 pairs of Dunlin in the National Park, with much higher numbers of Golden Plover (1,286–1,436 pairs). Another study, based on surveys in 1981, 1991, 2001 and 2002, suggested that for North Yorkshire as a whole Dunlin had declined by 56 per cent and Golden Plover by 28 per cent over the period (Sim *et al.*, 2005). The many potential causes of such declines might include habitat loss and disturbance. Yalden & Yalden (1989)

FIG 178. Golden Plover (*Pluvialis apricaria*). The breeding population in the Pennines is susceptible to disturbance and moorland drainage. (Dickie Duckett)

showed that Golden Plover were susceptible to disturbance in the southern Pennines, particularly by walkers with dogs, and areas with much human activity were avoided by the birds. Such disturbance is also likely to increase losses from predation. Moorland drainage has almost certainly had a negative effect on populations of both species. In a study of the status of Golden Plover and Dunlin in upper Wharfedale, Bell (1979) showed that one drainage scheme alone could have resulted in the loss of 20 per cent of the Dunlin population in the area. Drainage leads to the partial drying out of the peat surface, a phenomenon which will occur more often and more extensively if summers become warmer. Golden Plover chicks feed on adult craneflies (*Tipula* species), but if the surface peat dries, the larvae may be killed. In the southern Pennines, Pearce-Higgins & Yalden (2004) showed that chicks survived better in years when adult craneflies were abundant. In a later study, Pearce-Higgins *et al.* (2010) reported that breeding numbers of Golden Plover were correlated with August temperatures almost two years earlier. When the mean August temperature was less than 18 °C, breeding numbers in the next but one spring increased, whereas the reverse was found when the August temperature exceeded this figure and craneflies were less abundant. If August temperatures continue to increase as climate-change models suggest, then a drier peat surface leading to fewer adult craneflies may well lead to poorer reproductive success of this species in the Dales, and possibly to its eventual loss as a breeding bird.

Whilst disturbance is likely to continue to be a potentially important factor in some areas, particularly close to the Pennine Way and Coast-to-Coast footpaths, the reversal of drainage in attempts to re-wet the mire surfaces is likely to be beneficial to the breeding success of both Dunlin and Golden Plover, and to some extent reverse any effects of increased summer temperature on their food supply. Predation also affects the breeding birds, and there is some evidence that breeding success is greater on or close to grouse moors where there is active control of potential predators such as Foxes, mustelids and Carrion Crows.

Such predator control most probably accounts for the scarcity of raptors such as Hen Harriers and Peregrine Falcons (Fig. 179) on moors within the National Park. Court *et al.* (2004a), in an analysis of Peregrine Falcon breeding data between 1978 and 2002, showed that on grouse moors only 34 per cent of occupied nests successfully fledged young, whereas on land at least 2 kilometres from grouse moors, 76 per cent of occupied nests were successful. In Britain as a whole, Newton (2013) concluded that 'ongoing illegal killing is unequivocally limiting the numbers and distributions of some [raptor] species'.

The most successful moorland raptor is the Merlin (Fig. 180). A national survey in the 1990s estimated a population of 60–80 breeding pairs in the Dales

FIG 179. Peregrine Falcon (*Falco peregrinus*). In the National Park the breeding success of this raptor is lower on grouse moors than in suitable habitats elsewhere. (Chris O'Reilly)

FIG 180. Merlin (*Falco columbarius*). Merlin populations in the National Park appear to be stable or increasing after a long-term decline. (David Kjaer)

(Rebecca & Bainbridge, 1998). A later survey by Ewing *et al.* (2011) suggested a modest decline since 1993–94 in breeding pairs in both Scotland and England, although this intensive survey did not include the Dales. Detailed studies by the Yorkshire Dales Upland Bird Study Group (2006) and Wright (2005) suggest that populations are currently stable or increasing following a long-term decline. Wright speculated that this long-term decline may have been the result of a reduction in its major moorland prey species in his study area, the Meadow Pipit. There is recent anecdotal evidence at Merlin nests that Meadow Pipits are becoming less common prey items (Ian Court, personal communication), but if so, this does not seem to have affected the bird's reproductive success over the period 1992–2004 in the Dales as a whole. The Upland Bird Study Group recorded that breeding attempts were made at 95 per cent of occupied sites, of which 80 per cent successfully fledged young with a mean of 3.45 young fledged per successful nesting attempt; this compares favourably with what has been observed in other regions.

In a study in Wales, Colin Bibby (1986) suggested that habitat is key to the conservation of Merlin populations, and that successfully occupied sites had greater Heather and Bracken cover and less grass moorland. In fact it is likely that moorland managed for grouse will favour Merlins, in terms of both vegetation cover and predator control. The reduction in sheep grazing pressure in this century, and the subsequent recovery of Heather cover more widely in the Dales, is likely also to favour Merlins.

BIRDS OF DAMP PASTURES AND MEADOWS

Naturalists who remember the Dales in the 1950s and 1960s recall with pleasure that the Yellow Wagtail (Fig. 181) was a colourful summer visitor to many meadows and damp pastures. Today it is rare. In both 1966 and 1977 the BTO's Common Birds Census identified 17 territorial males on the Malham Tarn estate. In 2012, and for many years previously, there were none (Brian Shorrock, personal communication). David Hill, a Swaledale farmer, records, 'When we came here in '95 there were yellow wagtails in the fields ... they have completely vanished in the last eight to ten years' (in Gamble & St Pierre, 2010). The BTO lists the long-term population trend for this species in the UK as one of rapid decline since the early 1980s. It is a priority species in the UK Biodiversity Action Plan, not least because the UK has almost the entire population of the *flavissima* race of this species.

In 2000, a survey of 10 areas in the National Park located a total of only 25 Yellow Wagtail pairs. In the Dales, they mostly nest in hay meadows. Peak fledging

FIG 181. Yellow Wagtail (*Motacilla flava*). This species was once a colourful summer visitor to meadows and damp pastures, but is now rare. (Tony Hamblin)

FIG 182. Corncrake (*Crex crex*). Corncrakes were once common in the meadows and damp pastures of the Yorkshire Dales, but are not thought to have bred in the National Park since the 1960s. (Andy Sands)

date is in the last week of June, and in most years all chicks are fledged by the end of the month, but in cold, wet springs nesting may be delayed. Another characteristic of the species is that the birds are site-faithful in breeding, which makes them vulnerable to change in agricultural practices. The major changes during the second half of the twentieth century were silage replacing hay in many areas, and a tendency towards earlier cutting dates where hay remained the major grass crop. The early cutting dates, particularly in silage production, are markedly detrimental to the breeding success of the birds. With the reintroduction of late cutting regimes as part of agri-environment schemes there is evidence of some recovery in bird numbers (Gamble & St Pierre, 2010).

Naturalists with even longer memories recall that the Corncrake (Fig. 182) was fairly common in the Dales. In the 1960s, I asked my father-in-law, who farmed in south Westmorland, fairly close to the Dales, when he had last heard a Corncrake.

It was clear from his answer that it had been such a familiar bird before the Second World War that he was surprised he had not noticed it disappearing. Utley (1936) provides evidence for the former abundance and decline of the bird in Wensleydale as follows:

> *The most notable absentee [in 1936] has been the Corncrake. On but two occasions did I hear the bird, once at Haygarth near Cauldron Snout and once at Wensley. During normal years, near the latter locality, scarce a summer evening would pass without the note of the Corncrake being heard.*

Brian Shorrock recorded birds nesting near Horton-in-Ribblesdale in 1950 and 1957, and there are breeding records from the Sedbergh area in the 1960s (Mather, 1986), but it was subsequently lost as a breeding bird. The probable cause of its decline during the twentieth century was the progressive introduction of mechanisation into hay harvesting, but now the increasing number of meadows with late cutting regimes may perhaps provide opportunities for it to become established as a breeding bird once again. It is regularly recorded on passage, and it may have bred at one site in the Dales in 2002 (Ian Court, personal communication). There is evidence of a partial recovery in its core breeding areas in Scotland, from 446 singing males in 1993 to 1,040 in 2004 (O'Brien *et al.* 2006).

In spring, the tumbling display flights of male Lapwings are one of the most familiar sights in many dales. However, Lapwing shows one of the steepest downward trends of all birds across Europe as a whole, and national surveys in England and Wales showed a 49 per cent population decrease between 1987 and 1998. The decline in northeast England was smaller (15 per cent), and although there are no data for the Dales, it is very likely that there has been some reduction in numbers in recent decades. Chick mortality is thought to be the major determinant of population decline nationally, with habitat loss through drainage and changes in agricultural practice as the major cause. The Yorkshire Dales Upland Bird Study Group survey between 1992 and 1995 estimated that there were between 2,636 and 2,942 pairs in moorland survey areas, but this was an underestimate for the Park as a whole because lowland areas were not included. A later survey of enclosed upland fields undertaken by the National Park Authority and the Royal Society for the Protection of Birds (RSPB) in 2000 produced an estimate of 889–1,591 breeding pairs.

Lapwing is not the only wader to have suffered a large decline in breeding numbers in England and Wales in recent decades. BTO surveys between 1982 and 2002 revealed a 62 per cent decrease in Common Snipe and a 29 per cent decrease in Common Redshank (*Tringa totanus*) in wet meadows, and a 39 per cent decrease in Curlew (*Numenius arquata*). Although there are no long-term data for the Dales over this period, it is likely that there has been some decline (see e.g. Sim *et al.*, 2005). Although these species nest on moorland as well as on enclosed grassland, changes in agricultural practice in the latter habitat alone may have caused some decline. In a study carried out both in the Eden valley and in Teesdale, Baines (1988, 1989) showed that agricultural improvement in the form of drainage and inorganic fertiliser applications, and in some cases reseeding, resulted in the virtual disappearance of Snipe, and a marked reduction in the proportion of fields used by Curlew, Lapwing and Redshank, and in their densities. Breeding densities of Curlew were reduced from 10 pairs to 1 pair per square kilometre following agricultural improvement. The change from hay to silage is also likely to have had a detrimental effect on breeding success. However, a survey of enclosed upland grassland in the National Park in 2000 gave fairly wide estimates for the number of breeding pairs of Snipe (245–745), Redshank (83–301) and Curlew (1,106–1,527). These data, taken together with data from the Yorkshire Dales Upland Bird Study Group (2006), suggest that, at the turn of this century at least, the Dales remained an important breeding area for these species. Since then, the situation is likely to have improved following the uptake of agri-environment schemes covering moorland, enclosed pastures and meadows in many areas. David Baines also found that not all waders declined as a result of agricultural improvements. Oystercatchers (*Haematopus ostralegus*) started to nest on improved grasslands in areas where they had not bred previously, and for example in 2012 three pairs attempted to breed on the top of roadside walls on Malham Moor (Brian Shorrock, personal communication).

BIRDS OF LAKES, RIVERS AND MIRES

One of the more remarkable changes in the second half of the twentieth century was the arrival of the Goosander as a breeding bird (Fig. 183). It was first recorded as a breeding bird in England in 1941 in Northumberland, and Brian Shorrock first recorded it in Craven in 1977. It is now a familiar sight on many rivers in spring and summer across northern England. Goosanders typically eat small fish, between 8 and 15 cm in length, and their main prey species include Brown Trout (*Salmo trutta*), Salmon (*Salmo salar*) parr, Eels (*Anguilla anguilla*) and Minnows (*Phoxinus phoxinus*) (Meek & Little, 1977). The fact that Salmon and Trout are important prey species brings potential conflict with fishery interests, particularly where the birds are found at high densities. Goosanders are highly mobile except when their broods are young, which makes them hard to drive off, and, as a protected species, the birds can be shot only under licence.

FIG 183. Goosander (*Mergus merganser*). Goosanders were first recorded breeding in Craven in 1977. (Richard Steel)

FIG 184. Wigeon (*Anas penelope*). Wigeon were first recorded as breeding in the Yorkshire Dales in 1955, and have been recorded in the breeding season at 15 different sites since 1992. (Paul Hobson)

Eurasian Wigeon (*Anas penelope*) (Fig. 184) is another important addition to the National Park's breeding birds. It first bred in Scotland in 1834 and in England (Cumbria) in 1903 (Cabot, 2009). It was first recorded as breeding in the Yorkshire Dales in 1955, although Nelson (1907) recorded an adult bird with young on Malham Tarn half a century earlier. The total UK breeding population remains small, and was estimated in 1997 at between 300 and 500 pairs. A survey by the Yorkshire Dales Upland Bird Study Group in 2003 revealed a minimum of 16 pairs at seven sites, with breeding at a minimum of four of those sites. Nine breeding pairs were present at one site in 2004, and a minimum of two females successfully produced chicks. The study group has recorded Wigeon in the breeding season at 15 different sites since 1992, but many of these are isolated small moorland tarns, making for difficulty in regularly recording quantitative data, and thus firmly to determine population trends. However, interestingly one of the sites is Grimwith Reservoir, which extends to 1.47 square kilometres. Despite the fact that many of the sites are isolated, disturbance may still represent a threat to successful breeding at Grimwith and some other locations. There is some evidence of population decline from the 30-plus breeding pairs of the early 1990s (Court *et al.*, 2004b).

The Coot (*Fulica atra*) (Fig. 185) is a very familiar bird on lakes and ponds throughout the British Isles. One of the most remarkable recorded changes in bird populations is the very recent decline of Coot on Malham Tarn (Table 4). Numbers recorded each month crashed in January 2011 to nine from a maximum of 300 in the two preceding years, and have remained at even lower maximum figures (five and four) in 2012 and 2013 (Shorrock & Sutton, 2014). In 2011 one or two pairs attempted to breed, but none was successful (Shorrock & Sutton, 2012). Over the period from 1947 to 1959, Holmes (1960) recorded between four and seven pairs on the tarn, and winter maxima between 150 and 240 birds. Shorrock & Sutton (2014) recorded a less sudden and smaller decline in Pochard (*Aythya ferina*), but no similar decrease was observed in the numbers of other waterfowl including Wigeon and Teal (*Anas crecca*). If anything Tufted Duck (*Aythya fuligula*)

TABLE 4. Coot numbers (monthly counts) on Malham Tarn. From Shorrock & Sutton (2012).

Year	*Jan*	*Feb*	*Mar*	*Apr*	*May*	*Jun*	*Jul*	*Aug*	*Sep*	*Oct*	*Nov*	*Dec*
2009	150	60	50	40	15	16	18	100	250	300	300	300
2010	10	32	35	25	26	26	45	200	300	150	70	10
2011	9	8	6	3	3	1	2	4	0	2	2	1

showed a small increase in total numbers in 2010 and 2011, but in both years no breeding attempts were observed. This contrasts with the earlier studies of Holmes (1960), who recorded between 6 and 10 pairs, and Williamson (1968), who recorded 12 pairs. Tufted Duck were once uncommon winter visitors, and were first recorded as a breeding bird in Britain from Malham in 1849.

The cause of the sudden dramatic reduction in Coot numbers is difficult to explain. There are no recent records or sightings of Mink at Malham Tarn, but Otters (*Lutra lutra*) reached the tarn in 2009 for the first time in many years, and are known to take waterfowl, although this has been assumed to be only a small part of their diet (*c.*5 per cent). However, a recent study on Shapwick Heath in Somerset showed that bird feathers were found in 41 per cent of all Otter spraints (de la Hey, 2008). Coot feathers were recorded more frequently than any other species, but Moorhen, Little Grebe (*Tachybaptus ruficollis*), Mallard (*Anas platyrhyncos*), Pintail (*Anas acuta*), Teal, Water Rail (*Rallus aquaticus*) and even Cormorant (*Phalacrocorax carbo*) were also recorded. A recent study of Otter diet at Malham by Emily Alderton covering the period from December 2011 to June 2013, and after the decline in Coot numbers, showed no evidence of Coot predation, but both Mallard and Tufted Duck feathers were found in Otter spraints. However, bird feathers were only found in 12 per cent of the 166 spraints examined during this period.

FIG 185. Coot (*Fulica atra*). Coot populations on Malham Tarn have declined remarkably in recent years. (Nick Upton)

Otter predation might explain the poor performance of Great Crested Grebe (*Podiceps cristatus*) and Moorhen, which were also near to extinction as breeding birds on the Tarn in 2011, and might provide some deterrence for Coot; but it is hard to see this as the only cause of the decline in this species, particularly because several other waterfowl appear not to be affected, including the predated Tufted Duck. It is also difficult to see that such a sudden change could result from an equally rapid change in the availability of their major food source, submerged aquatic plants. It will be interesting to see how long the low Coot numbers persist into the future.

Canada Geese have become increasingly common as a breeding bird in the Dales, as they have in many parts of the country in recent decades. The birds were first introduced into Britain by King Charles II in 1665, but remained scarce until the second half of the twentieth century (Cabot, 2009), during which time they have achieved pest status such that they can now be controlled under licence. Nests are controlled around Malham Tarn, but occasional broods are produced, and the only such brood in 2011 was predated by a Fox or an Otter; the only attempt in 2013 was unsuccessful (Shorrock & Sutton, 2012, 2014).

The Common Sandpiper (*Actitis hypoleucos*) is a species characteristic of lake shores and the stony edges of upland rivers, but it is another species in decline. Detailed studies in the Peak District over many years by Derek Yalden and his collaborators revealed a decline from 20–22 pairs in 1968–1972 down to 12 pairs in 1989 in their study area (Dougall *et al.* 2010). These workers compared the performance of the bird in the Peak District, on the periphery of its breeding range in Britain, with its performance at a more central location of its breeding range in the Scottish Borders. They showed that adult survival and breeding success were similar in the two locations, but far more potential recruits to the population returned to the Scottish Borders. This might suggest that in the southern Pennines fewer birds returned from Africa in spring, but the cause of the decline is still not entirely established. Although there are no detailed figures for the Dales as a whole, it is probable that the species is in decline in the National Park. Several surveys in the period 1960–89 recorded annually between four and eight pairs in the Malham district, but in 1992 Brian Shorrock recorded only two pairs. By 2011 there were none, and only three sightings of single birds on passage were made along the tarn's shoreline in 2011 (Shorrock & Sutton, 2012).

Two other characteristic species of fast-flowing becks, the Dipper (*Cinclus cinclus*) and the Grey Wagtail (*Motacilla cinerea*), are probably also in some decline. Nationally Dipper populations have fluctuated in recent decades but with an overall downward trend, and Grey Wagtails have declined recently too (BTO Bird Trends: www.bto.org/about-birds/birdtrends/2012). In Wales, some of this decline in Dipper numbers has been attributed to the acidification of streams caused by atmospheric pollution and conifer plantations in their catchments (Ormerod *et al.*, 1986). In a study in southwest Scotland, Vickery (1991) showed that the breeding density of Dippers was lower, and territories were significantly longer, along streams of low pH and steep gradients compared to less acid streams. She found that invertebrate families important to Dippers, such as caddis larvae (Tricoptera) and mayfly nymphs (Ephemeroptera), were scarce in low pH streams. In contrast, stream pH was not an important correlate of the distribution or the density of Common Sandpipers or Grey Wagtails. Ormerod & Tyler (1991) showed that, in contrast to Dippers, aquatic insects made up a minority of a Grey Wagtail's diet (9–33 per cent), and that adult Diptera were the most common prey. They also showed that Grey Wagtails favoured riparian shingle for foraging; insect abundance in this habitat was not affected by stream acidification and, in contrast to the Dipper, there was no correlation between Grey Wagtail density and stream acidification. Both the Welsh and Scottish studies were in soft-water areas, but in the Dales most fresh waters are hard, the becks being strongly influenced by drainage from the Carboniferous limestone and, with one or two exceptions, there is no acidifying effect from large coniferous plantations in their catchments. Thus any decline in Dipper or Grey Wagtail populations is unlikely to be the result of stream acidification, and the cause or causes must be sought elsewhere.

WOODLAND BIRDS

Some birds of woodland, parkland and scrub have shown remarkable increases nationally in recent decades, including Collared Dove, Goldfinch, Wood Pigeon (*Columba palumbus*), Jackdaw (*Corvus monedula*), Nuthatch and Great Spotted Woodpecker (*Dendrocopos major*). But many other species such as Marsh Tit (*Poecile palustris*), Spotted Flycatcher (*Muscicapa striata*), Pied Flycatcher (*Ficedula hypoleuca*), and Wood Warbler are in strong decline, and these national trends are apparent in the breeding bird populations within the National Park.

It is easy to understand the increases in birds such as the Collared Dove and Nuthatch, which extended their ranges in Britain during the second half of the twentieth century, but it is more difficult to understand increases in birds long resident in the Dales. Possible causes might include abundance and availability of food sources, availability of nesting sites and changes in interspecific competition. Birds that visit gardens, such as Great Spotted Woodpeckers, which first bred in Malham Tarn Woods in 2001 (Brian Shorrock, personal communication) and Nuthatches (Fig. 186), may perhaps be favoured by an increasing availability of food in recent decades, particularly in the form of nuts put out by people, reducing winter mortality. However, in the case of the Great Spotted Woodpecker other factors may also be at work, including the decline since the 1980s of the Common Starling, a bird on the amber list of species of medium conservation concern. A study in Hertfordshire found that up until the 1980s, when Starling numbers were high, nest-site interference was a significant cause of delayed breeding and nest failure in Great Spotted Woodpeckers, which may have affected their population and habitat distribution (Smith, 2005). The decline in Starling numbers since the 1980s was associated with the increased breeding success and population growth of the woodpecker.

Marsh Tits have declined as a breeding bird in the Dales in recent years. In the past, Brian Shorrock recorded as many as four breeding pairs in Malham Tarn Woods, and Holmes (1960) recorded that it was the most common tit in these woods in 1948, but it last bred there in 1970. It is now thought to be absent as a breeding bird from the Settle area. Siriwardena (2006) used a long-term data set (1965–2000) to show that the decline of Marsh Tits in Britain was similar in woodland and on farmland. The study revealed no evidence of increased predation or competition from other species as factors in the decline, and no evidence of an increase in nest failure rates or a decline in breeding success: conclusions supported by a later study of Broughton *et al.* (2011). Siriwardena

FIG 186. Nuthatch (*Sitta europaea*). This species extended its range northward in Britain during the twentieth century and is now commonly attracted to gardens in the Dales by winter supplies of nuts. (Roger Powell)

concluded that the decline was most likely to be caused by woodland habitats becoming less suitable for the birds, with increased grazing by deer, reducing woodland understoreys, and the lack of availability of dead wood being two possible factors. Another possible factor is that, although Marsh Tits have a similar diet to other tits in summer, they are less likely to visit bird feeders and to join multi-species roving flocks, perhaps resulting in increased winter mortality. The recent efforts to increase deciduous woodland cover in the Dales are likely in the longer term to benefit Marsh Tits and other woodland birds.

Many of the declining woodland birds are long-distance migrants wintering in Africa south of the Sahara, and for these species, depending on the cause or causes of the declines, habitat management strategies designed to increase breeding success may or may not help to reverse the declines. The UK population of Pied Flycatchers has decreased strongly since at least 1990. Goodenough and colleagues (2009) examined potential causes of the decline during the period 1990–2004, including breeding performance, weather patterns on the wintering grounds and on migration, and possible impacts of climate change on spring temperatures. They concluded that decreased breeding performance was contributing to the decline, but other factors were more important. Pied Flycatchers (Fig. 187) readily use nest boxes, which, when optimally placed, can be used to increase breeding success, particularly when combined with habitat management to increase their larval food supply; but this would not halt the decline. A similar conclusion was drawn in the case of Spotted Flycatchers, for which the 1965–96 census data show similar declines across all the regions of the UK and all the major habitats in which the birds occur (Freeman & Crick,

FIG 187. Pied Flycatcher (*Ficedula hypoleuca*). This species is still found in Dales woodland, but is in decline across the UK. (Mark Hamblin)

2003). Nest records show that nesting success was not the cause of the decline, and a more likely cause was the fall in survival of fledged birds prior to the next breeding season: this suggests adverse factors operating on migration or in the wintering area. But it is not always easy to identify any one causal factor. An example of the latter is the decline in Redstart (*Phoenicurus phoenicurus*) populations in the late 1960s and early 1970s, which was correlated with severe drought conditions in the Sahel wintering area (Marchant *et al.*, 1990). The recovery in this familiar Dales woodland bird (Fig. 188) from the mid-1970s to the late 1990s was associated with increased breeding success, as measured by numbers of fledglings per breeding attempt. This is another bird which should benefit from the increase in deciduous woodland in the Dales.

Hewson & Noble (2009) reviewed the population trends of breeding British woodland birds over a 32-year period from 1967. Collared Doves and Wood Pigeons were among the 12 species which showed increases, but 17 species showed significant declines, including Whitethroats, Willow Warblers and Wood Warblers; changes reflected in the Dales too. Between 1989 and 1999 it was the species wintering in the humid tropics which showed the greatest declines. Again habitat degradation in the wintering areas and problems associated with the migratory journey itself are the most likely causes, although difficult to separate. However, another possibility relates to the milder British winters and earlier springs of the 1990s and early 2000s adversely impacting on some long-distance migrants. Species that advanced their spring migration during this period did not decline, whereas those that did continued to decline. In the latter species, earlier springs potentially cause an asynchrony between the availability of insect

FIG 188. Redstart (*Phoenicurus phoenicurus*). Redstart populations should benefit in time from the increase in deciduous woodland in the National Park. (Dave Pressland)

food and the birds' ability to utilise this resource. It will be interesting to see whether the return to colder winters and later springs of recent years has any effect on summer migrants.

CONCLUDING REMARKS

Looking back on the past 60 years or so, it is hard not to be pessimistic about breeding bird populations in the Dales. Admittedly there have been gains such as Collared Dove, Goosander and Wigeon, but many more species have been in serious decline for at least part of this time, and there have been losses too. In addition, short-term aims as part of the biodiversity action plans have not always been met. For example the aim to have a breeding population of five pairs of Hen Harriers in the National Park by 2007 has not been achieved. No successful breeding attempt has been observed in recent years, and a bird found shot on a Dales moor in 2012 is evidence of continued illegal persecution.

However, it is perhaps too easy to be pessimistic. The decline in several species is probably less severe in the Dales than in many other areas, and in the case of the long-distance migrants, there is much effort locally, nationally and internationally to understand, and if possible remedy, the causes of the declines. Local conservation measures elsewhere in England have produced rapid results; for example, newly created wetland at Lakenheath in Suffolk produced large increases in breeding pairs of several summer migrants within 10 years, with Reed Warblers increasing from 6 to 780 pairs, Sedge Warblers (*Acrocephalus schoenobaenus*) from 7 to 150 pairs, Common Whitethroats from 10 to 76 pairs and Grasshopper Warblers (*Locustella naevia*) from 0 to 10 pairs (see Newton, 2010, for this and other examples).

Rapid responses to changes in management are very encouraging, but biodiversity action plans are still very recent in terms of ecological timescales, so that insufficient time has elapsed to see fully the effects of the considerable efforts to implement *Nature in the Dales* over the last 10–15 years. For example, the planting of new areas of deciduous forest in this time period will take many years to achieve the full ecological benefits. But efforts to enhance existing habitats and land use already appear to be having positive effects on for example Black Grouse and Yellow Wagtail populations in at least some areas of the National Park. The re-wetting of mire surfaces and reduction in grazing pressure, as seen in some of the Higher Level Stewardship schemes, may take much longer for the full ecological effects to be realised. Certainly there has never been greater effort to conserve and enhance bird populations in the Dales than there is today.

CHAPTER 12

The Changing Dales – Mammals, Moths and Butterflies

A long history of animal populations in the Dales, their rises and falls, is preserved in the form of bones in caves dating back at least as far as 440,000 years ago (O'Connor & Lord, 2013). The Victoria Cave near Settle, close to the Middle Craven Fault, has been famous for its bone archive since a campaign of excavations was made there from 1870 to 1878. These and later excavations have revealed animal bones dating back before the end of the last or Ipswichian interglacial period, > 115,000 years ago (Gilmour *et al.*, 2007). This interglacial fauna assemblage contains some species still found in the Dales today, including Roe Deer (*Capreolus capreolus*), Red Deer (*Cervus elaphus*) and Red Fox (*Vulpes vulpes*), but also species such as Lion (*Panthera leo*), Hippopotamus (*Hippopotamus amphibius*), Spotted Hyena (*Crocuta crocuta*) and Narrow-nosed Rhinoceros (*Stephanorhinus hemitoechus*) more reminiscent of the African savanna fauna of the present day. Besides the Narrow-nosed Rhinoceros, other now extinct species found in these deposits include mammoth (*Mammuthus* species), Bison (*Bison priscus*) and Giant Deer (*Megaloceros giganteus*) as well as species present in the Holocene, but now lost from the British fauna, most notably Brown Bear (*Ursos arctos*). A somewhat similar interglacial assemblage was also recorded at Raygill fissure, southwest of Skipton, in the late nineteenth century which included the extinct Straight-tusked Elephant (*Palaeoloxodon antiquus*). The pattern which emerges from these deposits is of a fauna of large browsers and grazers together with their associated predators existing in a mosaic of habitats, and in an environment cooling towards the end of the interglacial.

As the climate deteriorated, it oscillated between increasingly cold stadials and warmer interstadials. In one of these warmer interludes evidence from the pollen preserved in flowstones from Lancaster Hole shows that Ash (*Fraxinus excelsior*) and oak (*Quercus* species) were present within the vicinity of Morecambe Bay as late as *c.*84,000 years ago (Caseldine *et al.*, 2008). However, animal bones recorded in Stump Cross Caverns, between Wharfedale and Nidderdale, show that by *c.*80,000 years ago a markedly different fauna was established from that present in the Last Interglacial. Gone are many of the large herbivores (except Bison) and their predators, to be replaced by species of the taiga and tundra such as Reindeer (*Rangifer tarandus*), Wolf (*Canis lupus*) and Wolverine (*Gulo gulo*). This has been attributed to an abrupt change during the cold stadial between 92,000 and 84,000 years ago (Currant & Jacobi, 2001) when Britain was still isolated from the continent to the southeast. However, O'Connor & Lord (2013), using evidence from Stump Cross, suggest that it was a staggered process when long periods of snow cover filtered out the Last Interglacial mammals one by one. From *c.*60,000 years ago sea level was sufficiently low to establish a land bridge allowing, during milder interstadials, the Eurasian Mammoth Steppe fauna to colonise Britain. Evidence from further south in England at this period, such as at Wretton and Coston in Norfolk, shows Bison as the major animal in the deposits, but Wolf, Arctic Fox (*Vulpes lagopus*), Reindeer, Woolly Mammoth (*Mammuthus primigenius*), and Woolly Rhinoceros (*Coelodonta antiquitatis*) were also present as well as Brown Bear, Wild Horse (*Equus ferus*) and Red Deer (Yalden, 1999). The Dales caves so far provide little evidence for this Mammoth Steppe fauna, apart from a possible Woolly Rhinoceros tooth found in Ingleborough Cave.

There is no evidence from the caves of animals present in the Dales during the Devensian Glacial Maximum, between 26,000 and 18,000 years ago, when all of the area is now thought to have been entombed in ice. However, evidence suggests that at least some areas were ice-free as early as *c.*17,000 years ago (Telfer *et al.*, 2009; Vincent *et al.*, 2011) when perhaps recolonisation by plants and animals began. But some animals did not return. Yalden (1999) concludes that there is no convincing evidence of Woolly Rhinoceros and Bison returning to Britain after the Devensian glaciation maximum. Carnivores which did not return include Spotted Hyena and Lion, but Brown Bear, Lynx, Wolf and Red and Arctic Foxes did. Rapid climate warming began at the beginning of the Late-glacial, *c.*15,000 years ago; shortly after this time a record of the fauna is again found in the caves. Radiocarbon dating of these remains demonstrates the presence of Brown Bears as early as *c.*14,700 years ago in both the Kinsey and Victoria Caves, and a little later in this interstadial at Sewell's and Conistone Dib Caves. The cave remains do not reflect the fauna of the period as a whole, but largely the lives of large predators of the period living in the Dales. Bears and Wolves used caves as dens, and the former also as hibernation sites. Thus the palaeontology largely reflects these animals and their prey species, which included Reindeer, Aurochs (*Bos primigenius*) and Wild Horse. Although human hunters first began to visit the Dales, perhaps only seasonally, during the Late-glacial, there is no evidence from the record of that period that they used the caves. But from then onwards the presence of hunters began to influence both plant and animal communities, and progressively, during the Holocene, came to dominate bone deposition in the caves.

Some of the deposits have resulted from the caves, or areas within them, acting as pitfall traps, and perhaps none more remarkable than the Cupcake shaft on Leck Fell. Among the remains here are a complete skull of a Wild Boar (*Sus scrofa*) (Fig. 189) as well as Aurochs and Wolf bones dated to *c.*9,300 years ago. As well as the bones of large animals, some caves contain deposits of small animal bones, the so-called 'frog earths', associated with Neolithic and Bronze Age activity. Frog (*Rana temporaria*) and Common Toad (*Bufo bufo*) bones predominate in this assemblage in Kinsey Cave, but bones of small mammals including the Hazel Dormouse (*Muscardinus avellanarius*) also occur (O'Connor & Lord, 2013). These workers also report the abundance of Water Vole (*Arvicola amphibius*) remains, indicating that this species was widespread across the Dales into the post-Roman period, and speculate that the present-day restriction of this

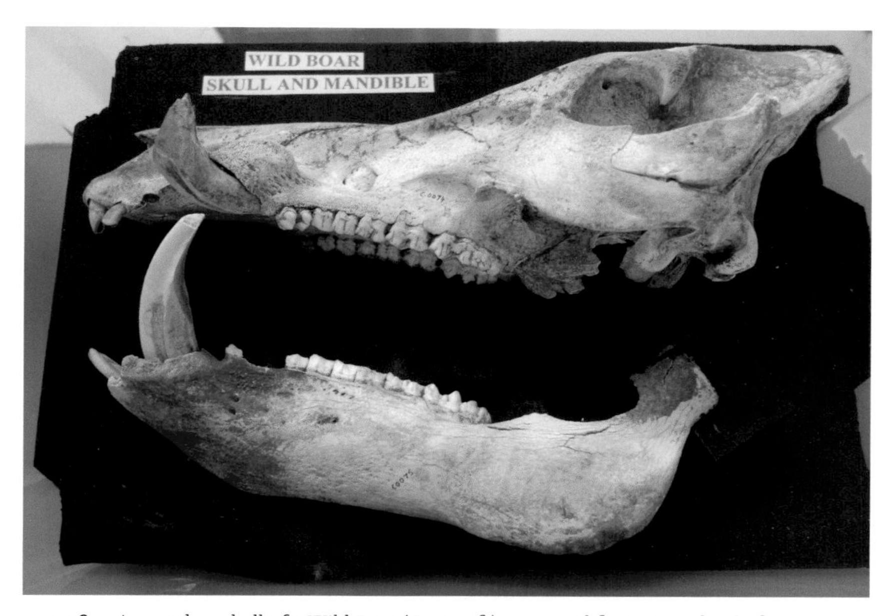

FIG 189. A complete skull of a Wild Boar (*Sus scrofa*) recovered from Cupcake shaft on Leck Fell.

species to aquatic habitats is due to competition from feral Rabbit (*Oryctolagus cuniculus*) populations. One of the puzzles of the historic small mammal remains within caves is the paucity of bat bones, even in those now used as roosting sites. O'Connor & Lord suggest that this may be because, before human excavations increased the size of caves and cave openings, many were unsuitable for bats.

From the Mesolithic period (10,000–5,800 years ago) onwards, during which Britain became an island, evidence for human activity in the Dales increases and that for some large mammals declines. For example, evidence of Brown Bears using caves is confined to the beginning of this period, and at the end, and in the early Neolithic period that followed, domestic cow and sheep bones appear. The earliest evidence for sheep in Britain comes from bones in Berkshire dated to 5,365 years ago (Clutton-Brock, 1989). A human and an Aurochs skull are recorded from North End Pot, dated *c.*5,000 years ago (Lynch *et al.*, 2008). Other animal bones found in this deposit include Wolf, Red Deer and Black Grouse (*Tetrao tetrix*) as well as small pigs and a dog. But evidence for the presence of large wild carnivores in the Dales continued into the late Bronze Age, with Lynx bones from Sewell's Cave dated to 997–833 BCE and 813–569 BCE (Lord *et al.*, 2007).

Increasingly, from the Neolithic period onwards, with the continued destruction of the forest cover and the need to protect domestic livestock from predation, the large carnivores were hunted, and their days were effectively numbered. The establishment of deer forests and chases following the Norman Conquest added to the need for their persecution, but at least the Wolf survived as a potent threat to livestock into the early fourteenth century in northern England, as recorded by payments to guard cattle against them (Shaw, 1956) and by the infield wall construction at the sheep farm at Winskill in Craven. However, it was not only the large carnivores which were persecuted. The Elk (*Alces alces*) had been hunted to extinction in the Mesolithic, but progressively in the Neolithic more herbivores such as the Aurochs, European Beaver (*Castor fiber*) and Wild Boar began to suffer a similar fate. Wild Boar, which had been much prized in the Norman hunting forests and parks, survived the longest of these, becoming extinct in Britain at the end of the sixteenth century. The Auroch was extinct by Roman times, but the Beaver survived until the end of the twelfth century (Yalden, 1999). Domestic cattle, sheep, pigs and goats came into Britain with the Neolithic farmers (Yalden, 1999) and became the major agents of human land management in the Dales away from the deer forests and parks. Humans and their grazing animals had progressively become the ecosystem engineers, replacing Bear, Lynx and Wolf as the top predator, and, with advancing technology from at least the eighteenth century onwards, increasingly able to influence, both directly and indirectly, animal populations.

MAMMALS

There is perhaps no better example of human influence on animal populations and ecosystem processes than following the introduction of alien mammal species. In Chapter 4 we saw the example of the effects of introduced Grey Squirrels (*Sciurus carolinensis*) on the native Reds (*S. vulgaris*), but there are other examples too, and none more noticeable than the Rabbit. Rabbits were introduced into Britain as food by the Normans (Yalden, 1999), and as late as the nineteenth century were farmed all over Yorkshire. Inevitably animals escaped from the farmed warrens and became established in the wild, a process aided by their classification as game, reaching peak densities of 10–50 per hectare (Malam, 1985a). For example, in the 1930s there are reports of high densities of Rabbits on limestone pavements, where they helped to suppress woody plant encroachment both there and in surrounding grassland. The illegal introduction of the pox virus *Myxomatosis cuniiculi* into Sussex in 1953, and its subsequent spread across the country, resulted in the death of 95 per cent of the UK Rabbit population by 1955. The immediate effects on the vegetation were to encourage flowering, increase sward cover and allow woody plant establishment in areas with light grazing pressure from domestic livestock. There was also an immediate sharp decline in Buzzard (*Buteo buteo*) populations as a result of the removal of its major prey item (see e.g. Newton, 2013), and in the Rabbit's principal mammalian predator, the Stoat (*Mustela erminea*). Colin Howes (personal communication) records that a gamekeeper in Littondale reported trapping about 60 Stoats a year before 1955 when myxomatosis reached the dale, but only about 10 per year in the period immediately following. One unpredicted effect of the eradication of Rabbits from the mid-1950s to the 1960s was a large increase in Weasel (*Mustela nivalis*) numbers. This was partly the result of an increase in grassland rodents as Rabbit grazing pressure was removed, and also of the removal of competition from Stoats for food and denning sites. The number of Weasels trapped on an estate in Wensleydale rose from 17 per year in the 1940s to 31 in 1969. The ratio of Weasels to Stoats trapped on the estate was 0.38 : 1 pre-myxomatosis, rising to 3.4 : 1 in its immediate aftermath (Howes, personal communication).

The Rabbit population slowly recovered after myxomatosis, so much so that as part of the Limestone Country Project, 2002–08, designed to increase the species diversity on 11,000 hectares in the south of the National Park, Rabbit control was once again necessary as part of the measures designed to relieve grazing pressure. Stoats and Weasels, however, seem to be in long-term decline (Howes, personal communication). Today, evidence of Rabbit damage is perhaps most easily observed in some areas adjacent to large shooting estates where predator control measures relieve one constraint on Rabbit population growth.

Predator control by gamekeepers and farmers must have been responsible for the restriction and, in some cases, the further demise of carnivores from the late eighteenth century onwards. Langley & Yalden (1977) concluded that the nineteenth-century decline in both Pine Martens (*Martes martes*) (Fig. 190) and Wild Cats (*Felis sylvestris*) in Britain was not caused by a change in woodland cover; the loss of forest cover occurred before reductions in these carnivores were observed. Wild Cats became extinct in northern England early in the nineteenth century. Reviewing the historical evidence for Pine Marten habitat in Cumbria, Webster (2001) concluded that 'Despite the apparent modern view that woodland is absolutely important for Pine Martens, Cumbrian populations survived successfully for many generations in highly fragmented habitats.' He also noted that, at the end of the eighteenth century, Polecats (*Mustela putorius*) were much more numerous than Pine Martens in the county, and that in 1794, the churchwardens of Kendal Parish Church paid out for four Pine Martens and 173 Polecats under pest control measures. It is likely that this reflected the

FIG 190. Pine Marten (*Martes martes*). Nineteenth-century records for this species exist for the Dales and reliable recent records require confirmation. (Laurie Campbell)

position in the nearby western dales at least, and that Polecats were always much more numerous than Pine Martens there. Howes (1980, 1985b) records that the Polecat was widespread throughout Yorkshire in the nineteenth century, but had been lost by 1928. Similarly Howes (1985a) records that Pine Martens were once widespread in both upland and lowland areas throughout the county, but the range of this native mammal contracted markedly during the nineteenth century owing to the attention of gamekeepers. There are records of this species in the 1880s from Sedbergh, Deepdale-in-Craven and Ingleborough, with odd reports into the early years of the twentieth century. More recent evidence includes two reliable reports in the last decade which are yet to be confirmed as definitive records (Ian Court, personal communication). However, since the species was given full protection in 1988, it is perhaps possible that it may be very slowly re-establishing itself in the Dales once again.

The position with Polecats (Fig. 191) is a little more complicated. Ferrets (*Mustela putorius furo*) were derived from them, possibly from Spanish animals, and were subsequently introduced into Britain (Yalden, 1999). Some of these animals will have escaped and established themselves as feral breeding

FIG 191. Polecat (*Mustela putorius*). Nine Polecat records from the Dales were made between 2005 and 2012. (Paul Hobson)

populations. However, another source of Polecats in the Dales results from a reintroduction programme in Cumbria from 1978 onwards. Initially at least these were Polecat × Ferret hybrids (Howes, 2013), but from the early 1980s onwards pure Polecats of Welsh origin were released. Colin Howes lists nine Polecat records from the Dales between 2005 and 2012, including a freshly dead animal with many of the features of a Polecat found by Ian Court near Kettlewell in 2012. Subsequent close investigation suggested that this may have been a Polecat × Ferret hybrid, which casts some doubt on sight-only records. Ian suggests (personal communication) that some Polecat records at least may be the result of successive generations of wild Ferrets gaining more and more features of pure Polecats. However, in a survey of the Cumbrian population, Birks & Kitchener (1999) recorded that although many animals appeared to be Polecat × Ferret hybrids, these animals were becoming scarcer in the population, with the majority now conforming to the Welsh Polecat phenotype, and this is possibly the situation in the Dales today. But a full assessment requires a detailed genetical study. The most recent detailed study of British populations using DNA technology revealed extensive past hybridisation between the two forms, with introgression mediated by crosses between male Polecats and female Ferrets whose offspring backcrossed with Polecats (Costa *et al.*, 2013). The hybrids were most frequently found outside Wales, particularly on the eastern margin of the Polecat's range expansion, which would include the Yorkshire Dales.

The Otter (*Lutra lutra*) is another example of a predator which has undergone considerable population change in the last two hundred years. Otters (Fig. 192) have been hunted in Yorkshire since at least the late fifteenth century, when their pelts were apparently valued at 3 shillings each; and later, in the mid-eighteenth century, a Mr Whitaker of Auckley was alleged to have received up to one guinea per pelt (Howes, 1976). Despite this financial incentive, the Otter population in England was large until the mid-eighteenth century, but, with the rise of large estates and the increased availability of reliable firearms, Otters were increasingly hunted both for fishery protection and for sport (White *et al.*, 2003). However, in some cases, hunting for sport may have helped Otter populations to survive because of the vested interest of the huntsmen in conserving their quarry and its habitat (Yalden, 1999). In south and west Yorkshire at least, from the late eighteenth into the early nineteenth century, escalating persecution, the growth of the industrial towns and pollution events were responsible for a series of sudden crashes in the Otter population, and Howes records that by 1859 Otters were very rare in the trout streams around Kirklees. Probably Otter populations in the Dales, away from the rivers grossly polluted by the lead industry, fared better at this period despite persecution.

FIG 192. European Otter (*Lutra lutra*). Otters are being observed in all the major catchments with confirmed breeding on the River Ure. (Paul Hobson)

However, the population collapse, which began in England as a whole in the late 1950s, and in Yorkshire in the 1960s (Howes, 1985c), was not simply from continued persecution or habitat loss and pollution associated with towns and cities, but also from a new source of pollutants derived in the main from agriculture. Organochlorine and organophosphate pesticides entering the rivers, from sources such as crop spraying and sheep dips, and accumulating up the aquatic food web, were thought to be major causes of this collapse. Attempts to reverse the situation began in the 1970s, with legal protection of the Otter from 1978, a ban on pesticide use and an emphasis on improving water quality. The severity of the situation in England as a whole can be judged from the first Otter survey, undertaken between 1977 and 1979 (Lenton *et al.*, 1980). Otter numbers are difficult to establish, and the survey was based on signs of Otter activity, especially on their spraints, prominent markers of their territories. In the survey, 2,940 sites were surveyed throughout England, but signs of Otters were observed at only 170 of these (5.8 per cent). The only significant populations were in the Southwest and along the Welsh border, with small fragmentary populations in northern England. This survey has now been repeated four times (Crawford, 2010), and the results for the same 2,940 sites are shown in Table 5.

In Yorkshire, only four of 226 sites (*c.*2 per cent) were occupied at the time of the first survey, rising to *c.*62 per cent in the latest one. The Yorkshire figures have been influenced to some extent by reintroductions, which will have speeded up the recovery on the North York Moors. Woodroffe (1994) recorded that Otters were rare in the Derwent and Esk catchments. Between 1990 and 1993, 21 wild-born Otters were released into the Derwent catchment and four into the Esk (White *et al.*, 2003). There is no recorded evidence of this occurring in the Dales, but there are recent reports of Otters being observed in all the major catchments, with confirmed reports of breeding on the Ure near Bainbridge and Hawes (Ian Court, personal communication). An ongoing study of Otter diet at Malham Tarn by Emily Alderton has shown Bullheads (*Cottus gobio*) as the major prey item, followed by small Brown Trout (*Salmo trutta*) and amphibians, and some evidence of bird predation.

TABLE 5. Surveys of site occupation by Otters in England, 1977–2010.

Years	*1977–79*	*1984–86*	*1991–94*	*2000–02*	*2009–10*
% occupied sites	5.8	9.6	23.4	36.3	58.8

FIG 193. American Mink (*Neovison vison*). Mink probably became established in the Dales in the late 1960s or early 1970s. (Derek Middleton)

During the second half of the twentieth century, populations of a new predator, American Mink (*Neovison vison*), became established on British river systems (Fig. 193). The Mink was introduced into Britain in 1929 when it was farmed for fur. A rapid increase in Mink farms occurred after the Second World War, reaching a peak of over 700, of which over 70 were in Yorkshire (Malam, 1985b). Inevitably escapes occurred, and perhaps also some deliberate releases, so that by the 1950s populations were established along some river systems. By the mid-1980s Mink were being regularly caught on all the major rivers in the Dales. In contrast to Otters, Mink, although closely tied to riverine habitats, are more generalist predators, taking a range of small mammal species (Bonesi & Macdonald, 2004) as well as fish and birds. Mink probably first became established in the Dales in the late 1960s and early 1970s, and there is evidence for their arrival causing the demise of breeding populations of birds such as the Moorhen (*Gallinula chloropus*) in Ribblesdale in that period (Brian Shorrock, personal communication).

FIG 194. European Water Vole (*Arvicola amphibius*). Water Vole remains are abundant in the cave record, but the species is now very rare in the Dales, or even completely absent, probably because of the presence of Mink. (Derek Middleton)

Water Voles, despite their abundance in the cave record, are now very rare in the Dales, if present at all (Fig. 194). There have been unconfirmed sightings in the headwaters of some rivers in recent years, and in the middle of the last century Taylor (1956) remarked that they 'could still be haunting the less rapid streams throughout the county.' However, Hazelwood (1971) was amongst the first to record their decline in numbers, noting that Water Voles were 'completely missing from long stretches of our streams'. Although there is no detailed study in the Dales linking Mink invasion to the demise of Water Vole populations, the results of investigations in the North York Moors National Park are likely to be directly applicable. John Lawton's research group at the University of York studied both the behaviour and the habitat requirements of the voles, as well as the effects of Mink predation (Woodroffe *et al.*, 1990; Lawton & Woodroffe, 1991). Using radio-tracking and direct observation, they showed that the voles spent most of their time within 2 metres of the rivers, and core population sites had a high percentage of grass (usually > 70 per cent) within this region and steep bank angles (> 35 degrees). Steep banks are favoured because the voles construct extensive burrows at a number of levels. Grass is the major food source, and used for nesting material. These workers also found that voles favoured sites where the bank-side vegetation was highly layered, giving protection from avian predators. Across 38 sites on five rivers they observed an inverse correlation between average Mink activity and average Water Vole activity, implying that Mink depress vole

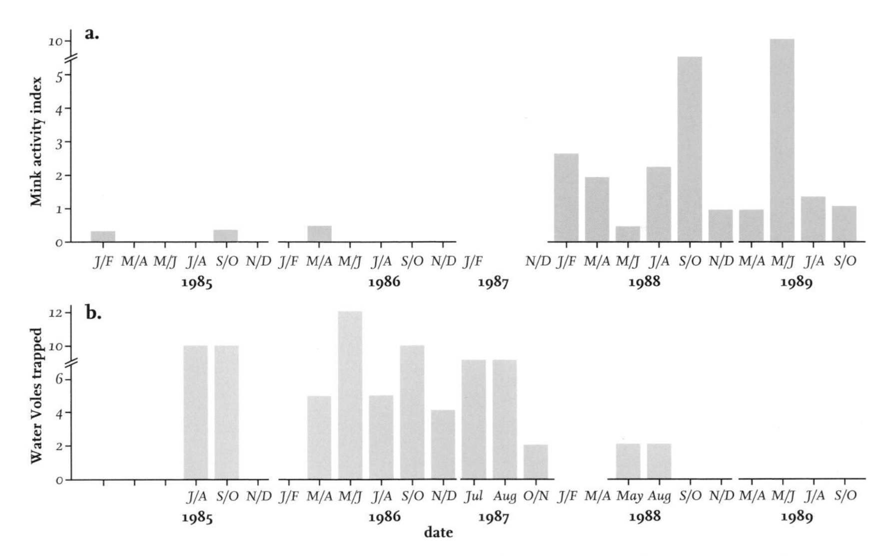

FIG 195. The increase in Mink and concomitant decline in Water Voles at a site on the River Esk, North Yorkshire: (a) bimonthly mink activity indices 1985–89; (b) Water Voles trapped during 1985–89 with constant trapping effort throughout the period. From Lawton & Woodroffe (1991).

numbers. This is demonstrated in Fig. 195, from one of their core sites on the River Esk. They also showed that five out of eight radio-tracked Water Voles were known or suspected to have been killed by Mink. The general conclusion from this study was that 'by reducing population size, and fragmenting Water Vole colonies, Mink pose a serious long-term threat to the survival of Water Voles on British rivers.'

During the period of Mink spread through England, Otters had been eliminated from many river systems. Otters are larger than Mink and better adapted to exploit aquatic resources. Part of the Otter recovery programme included reintroductions, and one such was used by Bonesi & Macdonald (2004) to study the effects of the release of Otters on a population of Mink in the upper Thames catchment. They showed that Otters were associated with a significant and rapid reduction in Mink in one area which was not observed in a control area where no Otters had been introduced. They concluded that, in similar lowland rivers at least, 'European Otter will not eliminate the American Mink, but that Otters are able to reduce Mink densities to about half that they are able to attain in their absence.' Thus, if these results are capable of being translated to upland catchments, it is possible that Otters may reduce Mink to densities low enough to allow Water Vole populations to survive. Attempts are made to control Mink directly, but the return of Otters to the Dales provides a biological control on Mink numbers, which should aid any future efforts to establish Water Vole populations.

Deer have been hunted in the Dales ever since humans first set foot there, and both native species, Red and Roe, were probably numerous and widespread in Yorkshire during medieval times. The former species, the largest British land mammal, was particularly prized in the Norman hunting forests. The wild Red Deer of Langstrothdale and Wharfedale were hunted by the Percy family and subsequently by the Cliffords of Skipton, but became extinct during the latter part of the seventeenth century (Mitchell, 1985a), a process probably repeated in the northern dales, and in England as a whole, with perhaps one or two exceptions such as at Martindale in the Lake District (Yalden, 1999). By the late nineteenth century Red Deer in Yorkshire were largely confined to parks and little more than semi-domesticated (Clark & Roebuck, 1881). But during the Second World War, when many country estates were occupied by the military, opportunities for escape occurred, and by the later decades of the twentieth century the deer were patchily distributed across Yorkshire (Mitchell, 1985a).

Roe Deer are the commonest deer in the Dales today, and the species most likely to be seen (Fig. 196), but this species was also extinct in England by the end of the eighteenth century (Yalden, 1999), being reintroduced from Scotland and Germany to sites in Dorset and Norfolk during the nineteenth century. New populations in northern England probably resulted from southern Scotland as the population there expanded. Mitchell (1985b) states that nineteenth- and early-twentieth-century records of the species in Yorkshire were sparse, and that by 1950 there was again an assertion that there were no Roe Deer in the county. Almost certainly this was incorrect, but a combination of new woodland plantations and an improvement in food supply following myxomatosis meant that colonisation of the Pennine dales was under way by the late 1960s. By 1983, Mitchell records that up to three deer, two does and one buck, were regularly seen on Malham Tarn fens, and there are other records of a similar date from Lawkland Moss, Austwick and Helwith Moss, Ribblesdale. Today Roe Deer are still regularly seen on the Malham fens and elsewhere where there is sufficient cover for them during the day and little disturbance.

In addition to the native species, at least three species of introduced deer may rarely be encountered in the National Park. Fallow Deer (*Dama dama*) were present in previous interglacials, but did not recolonise Britain in the Holocene. The deer were probably introduced in Norman times, and were an important species of the royal hunting forests. A census of 1538–39 gave *c.*600 head in the Forest of Wensleydale, but by the eighteenth century the deer were thought

FIG 196. A Roe Deer buck (*Capreolus capreolus*). Roe Deer are the commonest deer in the Dales today. (Elliott Neep)

to be confined to deer parks on large estates (Mitchell, 1985c) from where they may have escaped in the twentieth century, particularly during war time. Sika Deer (*Cervus nippon*) were deliberately released from a paddock at Park Nook, Bolton-by-Bowland, in 1906 to provide hunting for buck hounds (Yalden, 1999) and became established in woodland in the Forest of Bowland, spreading to the Ribble Valley where they were first recorded on the edge of the National

Park in the 1980s (Mitchell, 1985d). As well as posing a problem for foresters, this species interbreeds with the Red Deer, threatening the survival of any native populations of the latter, including that at Martindale. Chinese Muntjac (*Muntiacus reevesi*) were introduced to Woburn Abbey in Bedfordshire in 1900, and during the 1920s local feral populations began to be established. The deer spread its range naturally, and probably also as the result of introductions by shooting interests. It was first recorded from the Dales in 2000 (Colin Howes, personal communication), and the latest Great British Deer Distribution Survey of the British Deer Society (www.bds.org.uk) shows a noticeable increase in northern England between 2007 and 2011. Howes (2014) records that it was first reported in northeast Yorkshire in 1999, with more recent records there in 2008 and 2011. All the evidence suggests that the species is becoming more widespread in the Dales and elsewhere in northeast England at the present time.

BUTTERFLIES AND MOTHS

Whereas the changes in some mammal populations can often be related to human persecution and/or introductions of alien species, effects on many insect populations are less likely to result from direct human interference. Admittedly large changes in land use over several millennia, with for example the almost complete removal of forests and their replacement by grasslands and heaths, has had a great influence on many insect communities, not least from effects on their food plants. But, compared with arable farming areas such as the Vale of York, in the Dales there has been relatively low use of insecticides and herbicides. The exceptions are pesticides used in animal husbandry which directly affect insect communities, notably those employed in worming drugs and sheep dips, and herbicides used to control weeds such as Stinging Nettles (*Urtica dioica*) which are also important insect food plants.

However, because of their potential mobility, changes in the distribution of some insects may be among the first observable animal responses to another result of human activity, namely anthropogenic climate change. Butterflies and moths are likely to be rewarding species to study in this regard, not least because there is a long history of collecting and recording Lepidoptera in the Dales. However, systematic attempts to record numbers are a fairly recent phenomenon. From 1968 the Rothamsted Insect Survey (RIS) established a network of 80 UK sites in which standardised light traps run by volunteers are used to monitor the larger macro-moths. One of these sites is at Malham Tarn. Systematic butterfly recording coordinated by Butterfly Conservation came later, in the first decade of the twenty-first century. This involved establishing transects through sites designed to sample evenly the habitat types and management activities. A belt 5 metres wide along a fixed transect usually 2–4 kilometres long is used, and the survey involves approximately weekly walks from the beginning of April to the end of September, ideally resulting in 26 counts per year. These transect walks are undertaken between 10:45 and 15:45 hours, and only when conditions are suitable for butterfly activity, which even within the Dales can vary from site to site.

There are currently seven transects operational in the Dales, of which three are shorter than the recommended 2–4 kilometres, and one of these, at Lower Winskill Farm, was established as recently as 2014. Ballowfield is the shortest, at 831 metres. It is a small grassland site near Carperby in Wensleydale which extends into the adjacent Ox Close SAC in an area of old lead mining, but which also includes an important woodland component. Craven Limeworks at Langcliffe in Ribblesdale contains calcareous grassland with adjacent broadleaved woodland. Swarth Moor further up Ribblesdale includes raised bog, fen and small areas of carr woodland. Scar Close in Chapel-le-Dale is an exposed area of sparsely wooded limestone pavement. The Lea Green – Bastow Wood transect in Wharfedale passes through limestone grassland and one of only two examples of Ash–Hazel wood pasture in the National Park. The last transect is at Yockenthwaite and includes limestone grassland and deciduous woodland.

Sites for the butterfly transects were selected with regard to populations of several Biodiversity Action Plan species, most notably Northern Brown Argus (*Aricia artaxerxes*) (Fig. 197), predominantly found on upland calcareous grassland where its larval food plant is Common Rock-rose (*Helianthemum nummularium*),

FIG 197. Northern Brown Argus (*Aricia artaxerxes*). This is a species of upland calcareous grassland whose larvae feed on Common Rock-rose (*Helianthemum nummularium*). (Peter Entwistle)

FIG 198. Small Pearl-bordered Fritillary (*Boloria selene*). The larvae of this butterfly feed on Violets, notably Marsh Violet (*Viola palustris*) and Common Dog-violet (*V. riviniana*). (Robert Thompson)

and Small Pearl-bordered Fritillary (*Boloria selene*) (Fig. 198), found in mires, damp grasslands and open areas of deciduous woodland where its larval food plants are violets, notably Marsh Violet (*Viola palustris*) and Common Dog-violet (*V. riviniana*). Thus the transect records reflect the butterfly populations at these sites, rather than those of the National Park as a whole. In 2012, one of the coolest and wettest summers of recent years, only 47 butterflies in total were recorded on the Ballowfield transect. The most common butterfly recorded across all six transects in that year was Ringlet (*Aphantopus hyperantus*), followed by Green-veined White (*Pieris napi*) and Meadow Brown (*Maniola jurtina*), but the totals for all three species amounted to only 1,021 individuals. The total number of individuals of these three species recorded in the warmer summer of 2013 was 1,891, with Ringlet again the most abundant species followed by Small Heath (*Coenonympha pamphilus*) and Common Blue (*Polyommatus icarus*). Green-veined White and Meadow Brown were only the fourth and fifth most abundant species in 2013 (Court, 2014). Reviewing the results from 2012 and earlier years, Court & Whitaker (2013) concluded that Northern Brown Argus numbers were greatly influenced by the weather and that no clear annual population trend could be determined for the Dales over the recording period, in contrast to the downward trend for the UK as a whole (Fig. 199). However, the population of Small Pearl-bordered Fritillary at Swarth Moor was stable, and Small Heath populations showed an increase between 2008 and 2011 (Fig. 200).

Populations of Dark Green Fritillary (*Argynnis aglaja*) are also monitored on the transects, notably at Lea Green – Bastow Wood and Scar Close, but two other Biodiversity Action Plan species, Wall Brown (*Lasiommata megera*) and White Letter Hairstreak (*Satyrium w-album*), have a very few, small populations

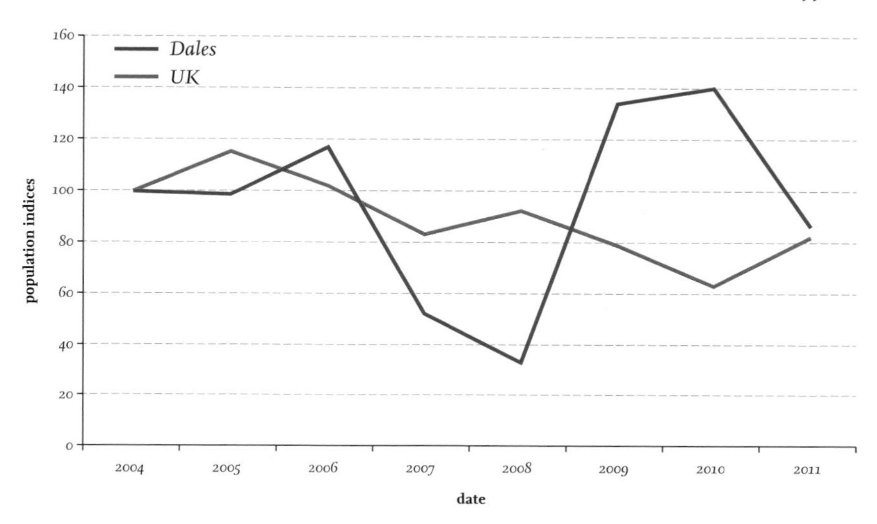

FIG 199. The population trend of Northern Brown Argus (*Aricia artaxerxes*) in the Yorkshire Dales National Park between 2004 and 2011 compared to the trend in the UK as a whole. From Court & Whitaker (2013).

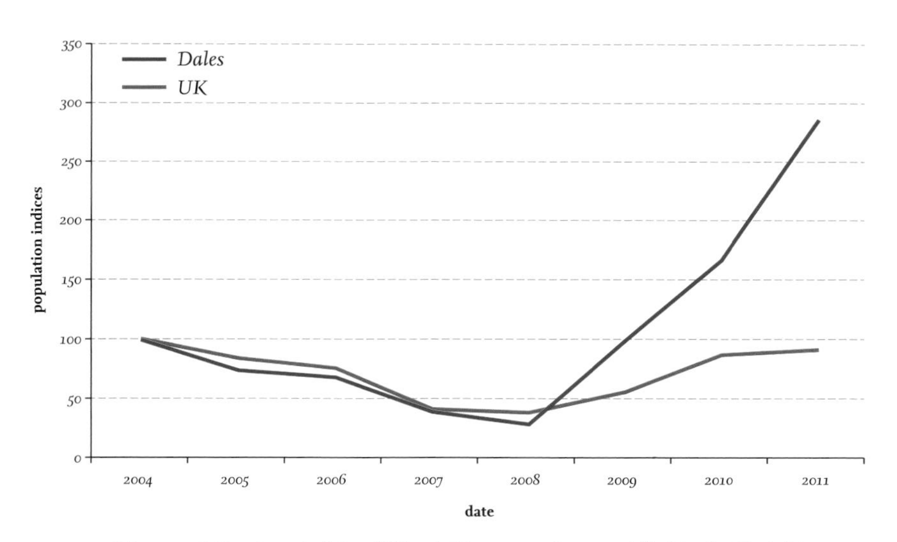

FIG 200. The population trend of Small Heath (*Coenonympha pamphilus*) in the Yorkshire Dales National Park between 2004 and 2011 compared to the trend in the UK as a whole. From Court & Whitaker (2013).

FIG 201. Dark Green Fritillary (*Argynnis aglaja*). The range of this butterfly has expanded in the National Park in the twenty-first century. (Malcolm Schuyl)

for which a monitoring programme is yet to be established. Terry Whitaker has made a detailed investigation of Dark Green Fritillary populations in the Dales (Whitaker, 2014) (Fig. 201). In 2000 this butterfly was rare, being known to breed at only one site, Scar Close, and up to 2003 it was recorded from less than 1 per cent of tetrads in Vice County 64 (mid-west Yorkshire). From 2003 onwards the range of this butterfly expanded eastward, so that by 2010 it was recorded from over 12 per cent of tetrads and breeding occurred at more than 12 locations. The main food plants for this species are Common Dog-violet, Marsh Violet and Hairy Violet (*Viola hirta*), and Whitaker ascribed this range expansion to pasture improvement following the foot and mouth epidemic of 2001, which resulted in a sudden reduction in grazing pressure.

Over time the butterfly transects and other detailed studies will allow longer-term trends in the abundance of both common and rarer species to be determined, but the situation with the moths is more problematic, given that there is only one operational RIS trap in the Dales, and all other trapping is not systematised (Charles Fletcher, personal communication). The recorded numbers of rarer species may be very small, making for difficulties of interpretation, such as distinguishing long-term population performance from annual fluctuations. And even at sites where regular records are made, years can elapse between records of rare species. For example, at Malham, the micro-moth *Acleris effractana* was recorded in 2004 and not again until Robin Sutton found it in 2013. This is a northern moth at or near the southern end of its distribution at Malham. Do the records represent a very small resident population, not effectively sampled every year, or are they rare vagrants? Another example is *Bryotropha galbanella*, for which all the records come from Scotland except for two from Malham, in 1958 and again in 2011 (Charles Fletcher, personal communication). There are several more micro-moth species which are much more common in Scotland, reaching their southern limit in the Dales. These include *Crambus ericella* and *Eana penziana*, whose larvae feed on Sheep's-fescue (*Festuca ovina*), and *Bryotropha boreella*, a species whose larvae feed on Heather (*Calluna vulgaris*).

There are examples amongst the rarer macro-moths too, including Chestnut-coloured Carpet (*Thera cognata*), which Terry Whitaker found in Juniper scrub at Moughton in 2013, the first county record since 1992. This moth was again found at Low Whita, Swaledale, in 2014 (Charles Fletcher, personal communication), but the present largely moribund status in the Dales of its food plant Juniper (*Juniperus communis*) because of *Phytophthora austrocedrae* infection must raise question about the survival of these populations. Yellow-ringed Carpet (*Entephria flavicinctata*), whose larvae feed on *Saxifraga* species, is another example of a species with a UK distribution largely based in Scotland. There are very few English records since 2000, although it had been recorded several times at Colt Park between 1990 and 1993. In 2013 Julian Clarke found larvae of the moth in plants of Mossy Saxifrage (*Saxifraga hypnoides*) at Dib Scar near Bastow Wood, which he bred out to confirm the identification. Larvae were again found there in this food plant in 2014 by Paul Millard (Charles Fletcher, personal communication). Heath Rivulet (*Perizoma minorata*) is another scarce species found in Grass and Bastow Woods with no recent records south of Yorkshire.

FIG 202. Cistus Forester (*Adscita geryon*). Sizeable populations of this moth occur in limestone grassland, notably in Wharfedale, where its larvae feed on Common Rock-rose (*Helianthemum nummularium*). (G. E. Hyde)

Species at the southern limit of their UK distributions in the Dales are potentially very susceptible to climatic warming. Whether species extending northwards in England and reaching the Dales are already responding to a warmer climate is less certain. Examples of these include the Dingy, Buff and Red-necked Footman (*Eilema griseola, E. depressa* and *Atolmis rubricollis*). An example of a long-established species in the Dales near its northern limit is Cistus Forester (*Adscita geryon*) (Fig. 202). Its larvae feed on the Common Rock-rose, and sizeable populations occur in limestone grassland, notably in Wharfedale. Common Rock-rose is the food plant of another rare moth, *Scythris fallacella*, found at Scar Close and at perhaps one or two other sites in the Dales, as well as on the Carboniferous limestone of neighbouring north Lancashire and Cumbria. Another limestone grassland moth, and perhaps the most important in the Dales, is the Least Minor (*Photedes captiuncula*). It feeds on the stems of Glaucous Sedge (*Carex flacca*), but the whole UK population is now virtually confined to the western Dales and parts of south Cumbria, where it appears to be holding its own (Charles Fletcher, personal communication).

There is no Environmental Change Network site in the Dales, the nearest being at Moor House in upper Teesdale. Morecroft *et al.* (2009) reviewed the data collected at the 12 terrestrial sites across the country constituting the network over the period 1993–2007. They showed at Moor House that two moths with northerly European distributions, Haworth's Minor (*Celaena haworthii*) and Blood Vein (*Timandra comae*) had declined significantly over this period. However, there is no clear evidence of a decline in Haworth's Minor in the Dales, from where there are plenty of recent records (Charles Fletcher, personal communication). At Moor House significant increases in both butterfly numbers and species richness were also recorded, suggesting that butterflies and moths were responding to a warmer climate here and perhaps also in the Pennines further south. A factor complicating this simple interpretation of these data is change in grazing pressure over the period affecting the insects' food plants such as Sheep's-fescue and Glaucous Sedge.

Although there is now increasing interest among professional scientists in systematic recording of biodiversity and environmental variables, Britain in the past has always relied heavily on expert amateur volunteers for this, and nowhere does this hold more true than in studies of butterfly and moth populations. This tradition continues in the Dales in terms of butterfly transect monitoring and

FIG 203. Tissue Moth (*Triphosa dubitata*). The larvae of this species feed on Buckthorn (*Rhamnus cathartica*) and the adults hibernate in caves. (Robert Thompson)

studies of individual species. Thus Paul Millard and his team are researching Barred Tooth-striped Moth (*Trichopteryx polycommata*) at its only known Yorkshire site in Grass Wood, where they have shown that the food plant is Wild Privet (*Ligustrum vulgare*) rather than Ash. Having gained a good insight into the moth's habitat requirements, they are improving it by selective felling and are searching for new sites in nearby woodland. In Littondale David Hodgson is researching another important species, the Tissue Moth (*Triphosa dubitata*) (Fig. 203). The food plant for this species is Buckthorn (*Rhamnus cathartica*), but so far no larvae have been found (Charles Fletcher, personal communication). This species overwinters as adults in caves, and in 2013 a record count of over 400 individuals was found in its major cave in Scoska Wood. These and other such studies are key to understanding the constraints on the present distribution of moths and butterflies, and in predicting how they may respond to a changing climate. It is only through long-term systematic recording by dedicated individuals that such change can readily be detected. Sometimes, however, well-meaning naturalists can get carried away with their enthusiasm, and two colonies of the Scotch Argus (*Erebia aethiops*) butterfly in Wharfedale are thought to result from recent unauthorised introductions.

CONCLUDING REMARKS

The cave records clearly show that major changes in the fauna have occurred since the beginning of the last interglacial period, over 120,000 years ago. Until the first human activity in the Dales began around 14,000 years ago, these changes can be readily interpreted in terms of response to major climatic changes. It is perhaps not easy to envisage large-scale changes in the landscape when the forests and their faunas advanced early in the Ipswichian interglacial as the climate warmed, only to retreat again into taiga and tundra as the climate deteriorated, finally to be entombed in ice. But at least the changes, which included the extinction of some species, can be interpreted without the complication of humans fragmenting the natural vegetation cover, influencing the freshwater systems, polluting the air and markedly affecting animal numbers and their distribution both directly and indirectly. This is not a luxury we can allow ourselves in the Holocene.

Detecting the response of animal communities to contemporary global change is not easy, given the many potential conflicting factors and the small perturbations of the climate which we have observed thus far. Even in interglacial times and early in the Holocene when major climate-driven changes occurred, although perhaps rapid in geological terms, these changes may still have been little detectable in the human life span of years. Today we have many accurate and long-term records of weather data in Britain as a whole from which we can accurately define both short-term variation and longer trends in the climate. We also have increasingly sophisticated and accurate models allowing us to predict the climate into the future. However, we are not so blessed with long records of animal population numbers, and for at least one good reason: because in many species they are not easy to quantify. The Yorkshire Naturalists' Union has records of what species were found in the Dales, where and when, going back into the nineteenth century, but interpreting these data in terms of, for example, population trends and their possible causes is not easy. Some of the best quantitative data come from annual records of predator control on large shooting estates, but even here numbers may reflect changes in the intensity and effectiveness of predator control measures rather than fluctuations in animal population size.

However, repeated records of a species' distribution within Britain allow us to make estimates of any range expansion, contraction or steady state, the best example of which from the Dales is Terry Whitaker's study of Dark Green Fritillary populations. More generally, Hickling *et al.* (2006) studied the distribution of a wide range of species with a southern and low-altitude distribution in Britain. The invertebrate species groups included dragonflies, damselflies, grasshoppers, lacewings, long-horn beetles, soldier beetles, spiders, woodlice, millipedes, harvestmen, amphibia and aquatic bugs. Vertebrate species were birds, freshwater fish and mammals. These workers compared the distribution of the species over two 11-year time periods with a 14-year gap period between them. Most of the early-period records occurred in the 1960s and 1970s, with the later records from 1985 to 2000. Of the 329 species analysed, 275 had shifted their range margin northwards by the later period, 52 southward, and 2 remained the same. The data also showed that 227 species shifted to a higher altitude and 102 to a lower; the mean increase in altitude was 25 metres. These data for Britain as a whole strongly suggest a response of species with a southern distribution to climatic amelioration, which we might expect to be mirrored to some extent at least in the Dales. In the case of the mammals, human interference and predation over the last three hundred years is the major cause of changes observed in the Dales fauna, and this has had major effects on other animal groups too. However, climate change from the second half of the twentieth century onwards cannot be ignored as an important factor influencing the distribution and abundance of animal species in the Dales, although we must also always be mindful of the potential complication of land-management changes in interpreting the data.

CHAPTER 13

Into the Future

As I hope has become apparent through the pages of this book, the Yorkshire Dales National Park, with its landscape and its natural history, provides a continuing major attraction for many visitors and naturalists, as well as for scientists who study the natural world. This attraction will hopefully extend far, far into the future. The Dales, along with many other parts of Yorkshire, have been blessed by a long history of dedicated studies, stretching back into the mid-nineteenth century, by members of the Yorkshire Naturalists' Union and the Yorkshire Geological Society, many of whom were and are experts in their fields of study. This work has been enhanced since the Second World War by the conservation efforts of the Yorkshire Wildlife Trust and the Yorkshire Dales National Park Authority, and at a more local level by a number of largely amateur societies which play an important part in documenting and conserving wildlife in their areas of interest. This largely Yorkshire-based effort has been augmented by records from members of specialist national societies such as the Botanical Society of the British Isles, the British Bryological Society, Butterfly Conservation, the British Trust for Ornithology and the Mammal Society, who have also made detailed investigations of plant and animal distributions in the area, and by the major conservation efforts of Natural England and its predecessor bodies. The end result is that the biodiversity of the Dales, and its history, may well be better known today than that of any comparable area in this country, and large areas of the National Park are now managed for conservation, including in both national and local nature reserves.

THE NATIONAL PARK

Today all National Park authorities are required to have a management plan, which has to be reviewed every five years. This is designed to provide the vision for the National Park – the way in which the authority sees the park developing over the five-year period, often combined with longer-term aspirations. The latest management plan for the Yorkshire Dales National Park focuses on the period 2013–18, but it also looks forward as far as the year 2040. In that longer-term vision it includes the following statements relevant to the natural environment:

By 2040 the Yorkshire Dales National Park will be:

- *A distinctive, living, working, cultural landscape that tells the ongoing story of generations of people interacting with their environment.*
- *Home to the finest variety of wildlife in England.*
- *Resilient and responsive to the impacts of climate change, storing more carbon each year than it produces.*
- *Providing an outstanding range of benefits for the nation based on its natural resources, landscape and cultural heritage, which underpin a flourishing local economy.*

These aspirations are supported by a series of objectives in the plan, and those directly relating to wildlife are as follows:

- *Support farmers and landowners to get 85% of the area covered by priority habitats into 'good condition' by 2016, and to get around 38% of Sites of Special Scientific Interest into 'favourable condition' by 2020, including all geological sites.*
- *Support farmers and landowners to increase the area of priority habitats, including creating at least 20 hectares of upland hay meadows by 2020.*
- *Support farmers and landowners to ensure that 50% of all ancient semi-natural woodland is in good condition or being well managed by 2018.*
- *Work with farmers and landowners to achieve and then maintain good ecological status for at least 60% of rivers and 33% of water bodies by 2022 by reducing diffuse pollution, restoring adjacent habitats and improving fish stock and range.*
- *Establish baseline population estimates for all monitorable priority species by 2016, and set targets to get the population of these species stable or increasing.*

- *Work with parish councils, local community groups and landowners to increase from 20 to 45 the number of sites that are being managed for nature by local community or volunteer groups by 2018.*
- *Help landowners and other organisations to manage invasive, non-native species by establishing which can be effectively managed, and mapping their distribution by 2018.*

In relation to the aspiration to increase both the resilience and responsiveness to climate change, the plan's objectives include the following:

- *Through the Yorkshire Peat Partnership, help farmers and landowners to restore more natural drainage that slows the flow of water, enhances biodiversity and reduces carbon emissions across a further 14,000 hectares of degraded peatland by 2018.*
- *Make semi-natural habitats more resilient and adaptable to the uncertainties of climate change and the risks from new pests and diseases by identifying priority sites by 2014, and helping farmers and landowners to 'buffer' or link together a number of the key gaps by 2018.*
- *Support farmers and landowners to create at least 400 hectares of new native woodland by 2020, to strengthen habitat networks, increase carbon storage and help to reduce flooding.*
- *Ensure that at least 66% of all woodland is in active management by 2018 and develop a locally based woodfuel initiative.*

Several at least of these objectives rely to a greater or lesser extent on a further key objective:

- *Support farmers and landowners to deliver a wide range of environmental benefits by maintaining at least 90% of the National Park in basic 'Environmental Stewardship' agreements and increasing the area covered by enhanced management agreements to at least 50% by 2017.*

Thus the continued commitment of central government to agri-environment schemes is vital.

Clearly, these are ambitious objectives, and they rely for their achievement on the commitment of many individuals, organisations and public bodies. To this end it is extremely helpful that the steering group which produced the plan included representatives from a wide range of interest groups including, from the natural environment standpoint, the Yorkshire Dales Farmer Network, the Dales Rural Estates Network, the Environment Agency, the Forestry Commission, Natural England and the National Park Authority. The National Park is unique in that nearly 30 per cent of its area is occupied by nationally and internationally important habitats, and therefore the success of conservation efforts to enhance the biodiversity and ecosystem services here is of much more than purely local interest.

Good progress with some of these objectives has already been achieved, including getting 88 per cent of priority habitats into 'good' condition, and demonstrating that 36 of the 46 monitorable Local Biodiversity Action Plan priority species were stable or increasing by 2013 (Yorkshire Dales National Park Authority, 2014). A total of 124 Local Biodiversity Action Plan priority species occur in the National Park, at least several of which are difficult to monitor effectively – for example, in the case of the fungi *Bovista paludosa* and *Mycena renati*, fruit bodies can be rare and may not appear regularly, sometimes not for many years at any one site. Efforts to increase the number of monitored species are in place, but encouraging landowners to maintain appropriate habitat management regimes is also vitally important.

The achievement of these objectives – against, in some cases, rather short time constraints – perhaps fails to consider another important fact, which is that in human terms, ecological processes can be extremely slow to produce observable effects. Perhaps nowhere is this more true than in the extensive areas of moorland, which cover 42 per cent of the National Park. The eroding blanket bogs which today cover much of the Pennine hills have been influenced by human activities over millennia, especially in the last three hundred years, and even as recently as the 1980s they have been subjected to artificial drainage. The result has been the destruction of the natural hydrology and the loss of, or marked reduction in, both plant and animal populations. Plans to increase carbon storage in the National Park depend largely on re-wetting the mire surfaces by blocking grips and re-profiling erosion gulleys to reverse previous drainage operations. The result of this will quickly be demonstrated in re-wetting of the mire surface, at least locally around the former grips, but vegetation change is much slower. In particular *Sphagnum* species, the major peat-forming plants, may take decades before they achieve anything like their former dominance, and reach rates of carbon storage comparable to those of more pristine mire systems. Even if grips were being blocked on a massive scale over very large areas, it is likely that some eroding blanket peats will continue to contaminate the becks. The bogs may also continue to be affected by pollution arising from the last three centuries of urban and industrial activities. Surface peat layers have high concentrations of metals, notably lead, from proximity to old mining and smelting areas, and, as has been demonstrated in the southern Pennines (Rothwell *et al.*, 2008), this source of lead contamination is likely also to affect water courses draining the mires for many years to come, albeit perhaps in reduced amounts over time.

LONG-TERM MONITORING

Demonstrating change in ecosystems is another challenge, and one at which the ecological community in Britain, until recent years, has been rather remiss. The Environmental Change Network (ECN) was only established as recently as 1992 in Britain, although there is a longer history of Long Term Ecological Research (LTER) sites in North America. Records only began to be collected from British terrestrial sites in 1993, and from aquatic sites in 1994. The ECN (co-ordinated by the Natural Environment Research Council's Centre for Ecology and Hydrology) collects, manages, analyses and interprets data from a network of sites across the UK, and is linked to both the International Long Term Research and Long Term Ecological Research – Europe networks. It monitors a range of environmental variables to identify natural and human-induced environmental changes with the aim of improving knowledge of the causes of change, and distinguishing long-term trends from short-term fluctuations, with an additional aim of predicting future changes.

There are no ECN monitoring sites in the Yorkshire Dales National Park, which, given its importance in terms of the natural environment and wildlife conservation, is unfortunate. The nearest terrestrial site is at Moor House in Teesdale. Eden Bridge at Temple Sowerby is the nearest aquatic site, and one influenced partly by water draining from the northwest of the National Park. However, by 2012, Natural England had established the Long-term Monitoring Network at 20 National Nature Reserves to complement and extend the ECN sites, with the intention of increasing the number of sites to 40 by 2014. At each site records of weather, air pollution (diffuse ammonia and wet precipitation), butterflies, birds, vegetation, soil and land-management activities are made. The data are fed into and managed by the ECN Data Centre. Two of these sites are located in the Yorkshire Dales National Park: Ingleborough, where the principal emphasis is on upland heaths and blanket bogs; and Malham, with emphasis on the raised bog and fen, calcareous grassland and broadleaved woodland. Baseline measurements at these sites include the establishment of permanent quadrats in the vegetation within which repeated observations can be used to assess vegetation change. Figure 204 shows one of the permanent quadrats being established at Malham on the fens and raised bog in July 2013. The use

FIG 204. Establishing permanent quadrats in the Malham Fens, July 2013, as part of Natural England's Long-term Monitoring Network. Colin Newlands (extreme right) directing the recording.

of permanent quadrats is a simple yet powerful way of quantifying vegetation change, but this technique has been used far too little by British plant ecologists in the past, and even more rarely in a coordinated way.

Although until recently sites in the Dales have not formed part of the national networks of environmental change sites, the area can boast some long-term records. Permanent quadrats as such may not have been much used by professional ecologists in the Dales, but perhaps the nearest equivalent is the remarkable record of Willie and Bob Jarman, father and son, in studying the performance of the Lady's Slipper Orchid (*Cypripedium calceolus*) over more than 30 years until 1967 at its last known site (see Chapter 5); this forms the basis of records still being made at the site to this day. The great amateur tradition of recording is still alive and well in the Dales. This is encouraged by local societies such as the Wharfedale Naturalists Society and the Yoredale Natural History Society as well as by the Yorkshire Naturalists' Union. It is also encouraged by national bodies such as the British Trust for Ornithology and Butterfly Conservation. Brian Shorrock is just one exemplar of this amateur tradition through his detailed studies over many years of bird populations at Malham and elsewhere in Craven.

EXTENDING THE NATIONAL PARK

In 2009, Natural England proposed extending the boundaries of both the Yorkshire Dales and Lake District National Parks, which amongst other changes would result in the two almost joining in the Lune Gorge. Following a period of public consultations, Orders to extend the National Parks were signed by the chair and chief executive of Natural England in 2012, and eventually resulted in a public inquiry in June 2013. The proposed extension would add 420 square kilometres to the Yorkshire Dales National Park, increasing it by *c.*20 per cent and taking in parts of Lancashire and the old county of Westmorland (Fig. 205). The proposed extension to the west includes Barbon, Middleton, Casterton and Leck Fells, the River Lune and part of Firbank Fell and other fells to the west of the river. To the north, the proposed extension would take in the northern half of the Howgill Fells including the northern slopes leading down to the upper Lune valley; part of the Orton Fells (Fig. 206); and Wild Boar Fell and Mallerstang. While some purists might object to the apparent incursion of the White Rose into other counties, from both a landscape and an ecological point of view it makes perfect sense. For example the old boundary of the National Park effectively split the rounded Howgill Fells into two along the old county boundary with Westmorland. But the Howgills form a discrete and continuous landscape formed predominantly of hard Silurian sandstones, today largely covered by acidic grassland with Bracken (*Pteridium aquilinum*)-dominated fellsides and some blanket bog on the rounded summits. The highest summit, the Calf, at 676 metres, currently falls outside the National Park, as do the deeply incised valleys draining northward to the Lune, noted for their fluvial geomorphology, which include Carlin Gill SSSI and Black Force. The traditionally managed hay meadows on the northern edge of the Howgill Fell extension include Bowder Head and Piper Hole Meadows SSSI. The SSSI contains 10 unimproved meadows and pastures, maintained as such by Juliet and Raven Frankland over many years up until their deaths. These meadows have strong affinities to the best of those in the Dales, and Piper Hole (Fig. 207) was made Cumbria's Coronation Meadow in 2013.

The proposed northern extension would include part of the Orton Fells encompassing an area of upland limestone with a lower-lying fringe of enclosed farmland. The upland limestone has extensive limestone pavements and, where there is some glacial drift cover, an interesting mosaic of moorland vegtatation. This part of the extension contains 10 SSSIs, amounting to 16 per cent of the land area. Among the most important is the Smardale National Nature Reserve, owned and managed by the Cumbria Wildlife Trust (Fig. 208). The reserve covers part of

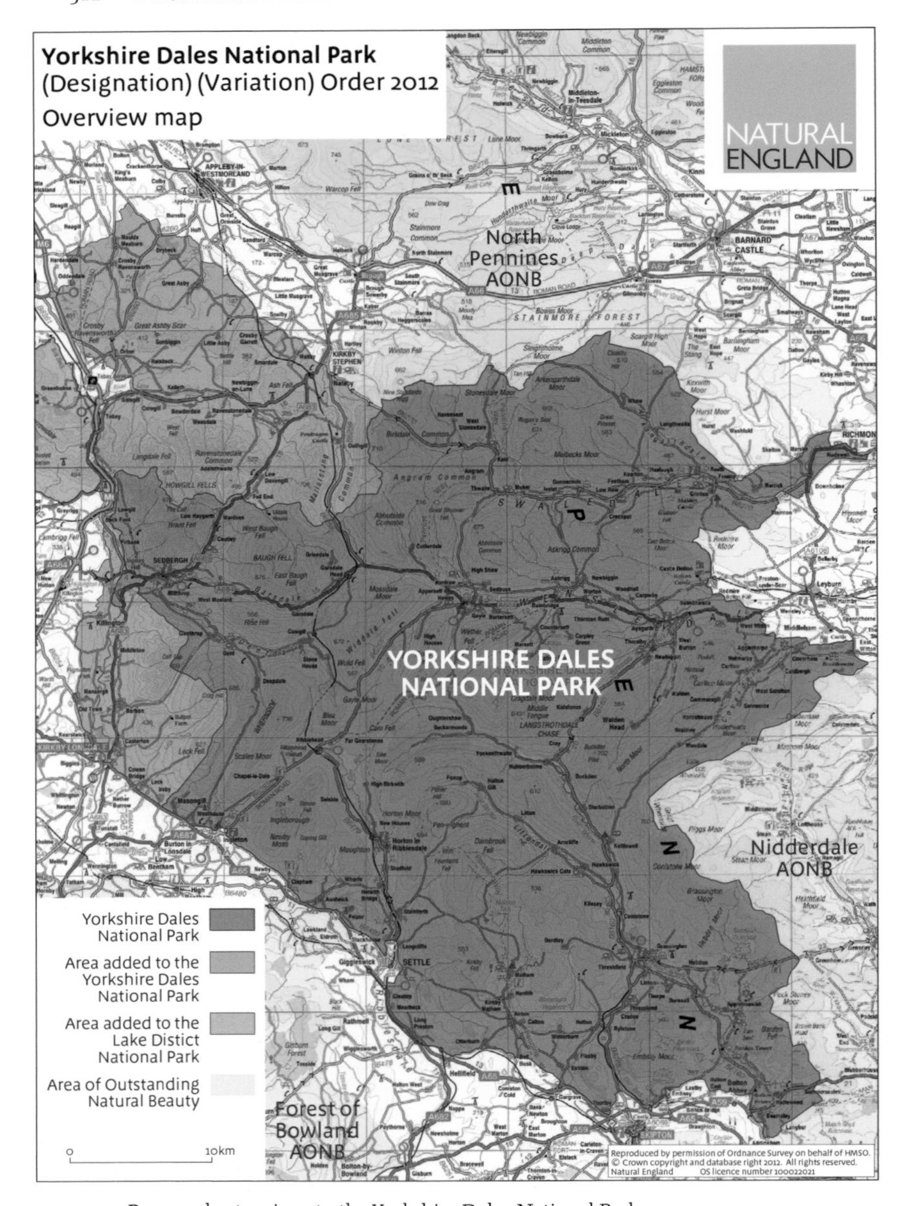

FIG 205. Proposed extensions to the Yorkshire Dales National Park.

FIG 206. A view of part of the proposed northern extension to the National Park, looking south from the Orton upland limestone across Tarn Moor and the upper Lune valley to the northern slopes of the Howgills.

FIG 207. An unimproved hay meadow, the Coronation Meadow at Piper Hole, Ravenstonedale, with the summit of Wild Boar Fell in the distance.

the disused Darlington-to-Tebay railway line including the Smardale viaduct. It contains a range of habitats including important Ash (*Fraxinus excelsior*) woodland and calcareous grassland established on the cuttings and embankments.

FIG 208. Deciduous woodland at Smardale NNR on the old Darlington-to-Tebay (Stainmore) railway line.

The reserve has a rich flora including both common woodland and grassland species. It is noted for orchid species including Fly (*Ophrys insectifera*), Frog (*Coeloglossum viride*), Bird's-nest (*Neottia nidus-avis*) and Greater Butterfly Orchids (*Platanthera chlorantha*); and a number of other uncommon plants including Bird's-foot Sedge (*Carex ornithopoda*), Common Wintergreen (*Pyrola minor*), Horseshoe Vetch (*Hippocrepis comosa*), Mountain Melick (*Melica nutans*) and Stone Bramble (*Rubus saxatilis*) together with tall herb species such as Wood Crane's-bill (*Geranium sylvaticum*), Melancholy Thistle (*Cirsium heterophyllum*) and Saw-wort (*Serratula tinctoria*). But it is also renowned for its Red Squirrel (*Sciurus vulgaris*) population, its breeding birds and its butterflies, most particularly being one of very few English sites of the Scotch Argus (*Erebia aethiops*) butterfly (Fig. 209). This butterfly was formerly known from Grass Wood in upper Wharfedale, but is long extinct there, although two unauthorised reintroductions have occurred recently. Other notable butterfly species are the Northern Brown Argus (*Aricia artaxerxes*), the Dark Green Fritillary (*Argynnis aglaja*) and the Dingy Skipper (*Erynnis tages*).

On the southern edge of the Orton Fells – once also famed for their species-rich meadows, alas now largely lost – occur some of the finest roadside-verge tall-herb communities in the North of England. These are also rich in orchids, and here are found Melancholy Thistle, Wood Cranes-bill, Water Avens (*Geum rivale*) and Great Burnet (*Sanguisorba officinalis*), all representative of the species-rich northern hay meadow community (MG3). The karst landscape of the Orton Fells includes the outstanding limestone pavements of the Great Asby Scar National Nature Reserve (Fig. 210), which is rich in ferns including Green Spleenwort

FIG 209. Scotch Argus (*Erebia aethiops*). This species occurs naturally at Smardale NNR, and has recently been subject to unauthorised introduction at Grass Wood, Wharfedale. (Niall Benvie)

FIG 210. The limestone pavements of Great Asby Scar NNR, looking east across the Eden valley to the northern Pennines.

(*Asplenium trichomanes-ramosum*), Limestone Fern (*Gymnocarpium robertianum*) and Rigid Buckler-fern (*Dryopteris submontana*). Among the rare plants of the fragmentary pavements and rocky grassland on the Orton limestone ridges are Baneberry (*Actaea spicata*), Dwarf Milkwort (*Polygala amarella*), Hutchinsia (*Hornungia petraea*, at its northernmost site in Britain), Rare Spring-sedge (*Carex ericetorum*) and Spring Cinquefoil (*Potentilla tabernaemontani*). Immediately to the south and below the NNR lies an area with obvious affinities to Malham Tarn and its associated fens: this is Sunbiggin Tarn, another marl lake which is linked to a smaller fen-enclosed water body, Cow Dub Tarn (Fig. 211).

To the west of these water bodies, Tarn Moor occupies a shallow valley in glacial drift, and is rich in tufa springs and mire communities with similarities to those found at Great Close and Ha Mires at Malham. Here the calcareous springs and damp calcareous grassland are rich in Bird's-eye Primroses (*Primula farinosa*), Northern Marsh-orchids (*Dactylorhiza purpurella*), Common Butterwort (*Pinguicula vulgaris*), Marsh Valerian (*Valeriana dioica*), Grass-of-Parnassus (*Parnassia palustris*) and many sedges and brown mosses; these contrast with small hummocks composed of calcifuge vegetation including *Sphagnum* species, Cross-leaved heath (*Erica tetralix*) and Round-leaved Sundew (*Drosera rotundifolia*). The tarn itself contains stoneworts (*Chara* species) in its shallower eastern side, and is fringed by reedswamp and fen communities which include the Great Fen-sedge

FIG 211. Sunbiggin Tarn, a marl lake to the south of Great Asby Scar, with the much smaller Cow Dub Tarn in the distance.

(*Cladium mariscus*) at its highest known site in Britain. The calcareous grassland and heathland found on the drier soils include an unusual herb-rich community of Heather with an understorey including Wood Anemone (*Anemone nemorosa*), perhaps the closest equivalent to the chalk heath communities of southern England. Pastures on the Orton and Crosby Ravensworth Fells are also noted for the occurrence of Alpine Bartsia (*Bartsia alpina*), also found in Great Close Mire, and Viviparous Bistort (*Persicaria vivipara*). The extension of the National Park would bring another very rare plant to the Dales flora, the Leafless Hawk's-beard (*Crepis praemorsa*), unknown in Britain until 1988 when it was found by Geoffrey Halliday on a bank amongst meadow plants. Recent surveys there by Jeremy Roberts have shown that 99 per cent of the population consists of non-flowering rosettes extending for hundreds of metres along a stream, strongly suggesting it is native and not introduced (Kevin Walker, personal communication).

Sunbiggin Tarn was also noted for its large breeding colony of Black-headed Gulls (*Chroicocephalus ridibundus*), which was allowed to grow to *c.*8,000 pairs by 1989, causing eutrophication of the tarn and surrounding mire and heath communities. But the population then declined rapidly to only 46 pairs in 2000 (Ratcliffe, 2002), and there is little sign of a breeding colony there today. The tarn is noted for breeding populations of some waterfowl including Gadwall (*Anas strepera*) and occasionally Wigeon (*A. penelope*), one of the rarer breeding birds of the Dales.

The final part of the proposed northern extension would include Wild Boar Fell and Mallerstang, both with strong affinities with the landscape already in the Yorkshire Dales National Park to the south and east, including Baugh Fell and the extensive upland commons forming part of the same topographical unit. Mallerstang is the name given to the dramatic glaciated trough which contains the headwaters of the River Eden (Fig. 212). The valley and its dale sides are bounded by the upland summits of High Seat to the east and Wild Boar Fell to the west. Wild Boar Fell, with its long and level summit plateau and stepped profile, has affinities with Ingleborough and Pen-y-ghent to the south, and at 708 metres it would be the fourth-highest hill in the enlarged National Park. The shallow slopes on the gritstone-capped hills were once covered in blanket bogs, now strongly eroded in places, but in others showing signs of recolonisation. Traditionally managed species-rich meadows are a feature of Mallerstang, and the frequent presence of field barns also helps to provide a landscape reminiscent of areas already within the National Park. The valley contains The Clouds SSSI, an area of limestone pavement particularly known for evidence of the effects of ice flow on rock surfaces, but also containing rare ferns, notably Rigid Buckler-fern and Holly-fern (*Polystichum lonchitis*).

FIG 212. Mallerstang Valley at the head of the River Eden, looking north.

The western extension would include part of Firbank Fell, but the major area is Middleton, Barbon, Casterton and Leck Fells together with, at their foot, a narrow strip of land to the east and west of the Lune including a stretch of the river and its floodplain. Firbank Fell forms part of the western slope of the Lune Gorge and includes areas of upland heath and blanket mire with semi-natural woodland in the valley. The narrow strip further down the valley also has semi-natural woodlands along the narrow gills on the valley sides, and, on the low fells to the west of the river, a mosaic of small tarns, mires and wet grasslands which includes Burns Beck Moss, a Cumbria Wildlife Trust reserve. The Middleton, Barbon, Casterton and Leck Fells fall into two parts. The area to the southeast comprising Leck, Barbon High Fell and Casterton Fell is underlain by the Yoredale and Great Scar limestones, with the lower slopes covered in loess or glacial drift. The obvious karst features here are sink holes and limestone pavements, but beneath are caves linking this area to the adjacent area of the National Park. Beneath Casterton, Leck and Ireby Fells lies a single cave system, the Three Counties cave system, with more than 90 kilometres of interconnected passages and a proven hydrological link to the 22 kilometres of passages below Kingsdale within the existing National Park (see Chapter 10). To the north,

FIG 213. Barbondale. The Dent Fault runs along Barbondale. The steep slope in the background is formed of Silurian greywackes with the foreground composed of glacial till covering Great Scar Limestone.

Middleton Fell is on Silurian rocks, with the dramatic former glaciated valley of Barbondale to its south (Fig. 213). The Dent Fault runs through the eastern part of this dale, and the dale is probably also linked to the Three Counties cave system.

In terms of two of the three longer-term aspirations (to 2040) in the Yorkshire Dales National Park Management Plan (providing a distinctive living cultural landscape, and home to the finest variety of wildlife in England), it is hard to see that the proposed extension, if approved, would do other than enhance these aims. The extension includes essentially small, often ancient villages embedded in a largely pastoral landscape. The pattern of in-bye land around the valley farmsteads, sometimes containing field barns, and usually surrounded by dry-stone walls, and the more extensive grazing of the fell sides and hill tops is essentially common in all these areas. This is also true both historically and at the present day in respect of agricultural techniques and the breeds of cattle and sheep employed, perhaps most notably of Swaledale and Dalesbred sheep. Hay time was every bit as vital in the areas covered by the extension as it was to farmers in the Dales. As for the second aspiration, the extension certainly does enhance the wildlife interest. It would add two National Nature Reserves and many SSSIs. It would add species not found in the National Park including the Leafless Hawk's-beard and the Scotch Argus. It would add another rare marl lake surrounded by mires, calcareous grassland and heath communities with similarities to, but with differences from, those occurring at Malham. And the same could also be said of the several fine examples of limestone pavements, including those at Great Asby Scar and The Clouds. The species-rich hay meadows, notably those at Bowder Head and Piper Hole Meadow, also would add fine examples of this now very rare English habitat.

But the third aspiration, 'resistant and responsive to the impacts of climate change, storing more carbon each year than it produces', is perhaps the most problematic. The extension would include only small villages. The nearby small towns of Kirkby Lonsdale and Kirkby Stephen, and even the old railway village of Tebay close to the Lune Gorge, are excluded. So although the National Park would increase by about 20 per cent in area, there would not be a commensurate percentage increase in population adding to the carbon emissions. This suggests that, other things being equal and excluding visitors' vehicle emissions, the extension would improve the National Park's carbon balance. And the extension does include areas of blanket bog which potentially provide further major carbon stores. However, some of the mires in the proposed northern extension are badly eroded and probably now act as net carbon sources rather than stores. Where the erosion has only left peat islands, as on parts of Wild Boar Fell, there is little chance of restoring the mires, and on those moors with extensive erosion channels, even with grip blocking, it will take considerable effort and perhaps many years to convert them to major carbon sinks again. However, the emphasis on bog regeneration and increasing native broadleaved woodland cover, if applied to the extension, would not only increase carbon storage, but also enhance wildlife conservation.

Resilience of plant and animal communities to climate change is perhaps more difficult to assess, although an extended National Park might result in opportunities for increasing the connectivity of habitats through the landscape. The most likely scenario is that the Dales will become warmer and wetter as we move towards the middle of the century. This will favour mire communities if the increased precipitation is greater than any increase in evaporation from plants and soils, and would for instance increase bog growth and carbon storage and extend the areas of springs, flushes and valley mires. A rise in temperature will encourage some species with a current southern distribution in England to extend their ranges northward, particularly the more mobile species such as the insects. But mean temperature can increase without relieving a major constraint on species distribution – for example, if the incidence of frosts, particularly perhaps late frosts, is not reduced. It is the extremes rather than the means which affect plant distributions, and not just annual ones, so that perhaps even a one-in-a-hundred-year serious frost event could reverse the northward advance of some species. And one group of species at least, relics of the Dales flora and fauna of the Late-glacial Interstadial, the arctic–alpines, have nowhere to go in a warmer climate. Many occur only on a few isolated north- and east-facing limestone cliffs near the summits of Ingleborough and Pen-y-ghent from where there is no prospect of escape to higher and cooler habitats in a warmer, wetter world. Conversely, if global warming were to result in significant effects on ocean thermohaline circulation, then the climate of Britain could change, possibly rapidly, to become much colder, which would favour these relict arctic–alpine communities.

Under most climate scenarios, the best that can be done in conservation terms is to redouble efforts to join up isolated habitat fragments both inside and outside the National Park, to allow plants and animals the possibility of ready passage through the landscape. This process will be enhanced by the current emphasis on increasing the connectivity of habitats in the landscape, of which perhaps the best example can be seen in current efforts by the Yorkshire Millennium Trust and others to increase the areas of deciduous woodland and their connectivity. Rivers and becks provide connectivity where they have not been adversely affected by pollution or by manmade barriers such as weirs. Again, efforts to improve water quality and to remove barriers to fish movements are increasing this connectivity. And efforts to improve water quality by conservation of the riparian zone – for example by connecting gill woodlands along a dale – are also helping to improve the potential for terrestrial organisms to move through the landscape.

END NOTE

What will the Yorkshire Dales look like a hundred years from now, in the first decades of the twenty-second century? Prediction is of course fraught with difficulty, but it is hard to imagine that the residents and the many visitors down the years would want to see the landscape character change very much from what we see at present. There will be a greater area of deciduous woodland, although perhaps not with Ash as a major component of either ancient or newly created woodland areas. Indeed, Ash might revert to being a very minor component as the result of Ash-dieback, and particularly so if another eastern invader, the Emerald

Ash Borer (*Agrilus planipennis*), is accidentally introduced into Britain – as seems quite possible. This bark beetle is causing the widespread death of ash species since its introduction to North America, where it was first recorded in 2002. It has already killed more trees there than there are Ash trees in the whole of Britain and Ireland (Rackham, 2014). While the composition of woodland in the Dales may perhaps change radically, and some modest expansion in area will occur, it will remain very much a minor component of the National Park. However, such expansion as will take place will probably result in areas of woodland being better connected through the landscape.

The villages will have seen some modest expansion in dwellings and businesses, but probably not an expansion of quarrying or a return of the major mineral extraction of past centuries, unless such a change is politically and economically driven. More probably it will continue largely to be a managed landscape for cattle and sheep production, field sports, nature conservation and leisure, as it is at present. Looking back, we can see that the balance between these activities has changed over the last 60 years, with the marked growth of leisure and nature conservation, and it is quite likely that this balance will have changed again in another 60 years.

It is doubtful whether agriculture will ever be sustainable in the British uplands without government support, and yet agriculture over the centuries has largely shaped the Dales landscape as we see it today. So to maintain the present character of the National Park, agricultural activity will have to be sustained in some form, even in a world without subsidies – which is a quite plausible scenario looking into the future. If the prediction is correct that future generations will want to see a similar landscape in the next century, then the question becomes, How can this be achieved? And, for naturalists, a related question is how to achieve this whilst enhancing or at the very least sustaining current biodiversity. The simple answer is by long-term commitment of successive governments to appropriate environmental stewardship or similar schemes, and their acceptance by farmers and landowners. But politics is rarely simple in a changing and unpredictable world, and it is possible that increased animal production in the uplands will again be required in future. If so, the only certainty is that adverse effects on biodiversity are inevitable. Even Defra's proposed application of the most recent of the European Union's CAP reforms may have some adverse effects. Changes in the Area Payments in the Single Payment Scheme may result, for a number of years at least, in more intensively managed farming of the more productive dale bottoms of lower Swaledale, lower Wensleydale, lower Wharfedale and upper Airedale on the edges of the National Park, with possible adverse effects on biodiversity and landscape features.

In addition to any politically driven changes, models predict that the Dales climate will have become warmer and wetter at the beginning of the next century. This has implications both for agriculture and for wildlife. The growing season will have been extended, and perhaps arable crops will have become more important in the more sheltered lower dales than they have been in recent centuries. On the fells, warmer soils and air temperatures may have led to increased grassland productivity if nutrients are not limiting, and Bracken will have advanced up the hillsides on freely drained soils. Where the blanket mires have been restored, active growth and carbon storage will have been resumed, with *Sphagnum* species dominating the bog surfaces, and many fewer exposed gulleys will be present than we see today. However, greater amounts of precipitation may also have exacerbated erosion processes, negating gains in carbon storage. In freely drained soils, increased leaching rates may have led to greater nutrient impoverishment, strongly restricting plant growth despite the warmer temperatures, and perhaps resulting in the spread of acidic soil communities at the expense of mesotrophic ones. Some spread of waterlogged soils and flushes may also have occurred, with greater river flows both above and below ground.

One thing is certain, plant and animal populations will not have remained unchanged a hundred years from now. Looking back over the last 60 years or so, we have seen how animal populations in particular have changed, and we can confidently predict that they will continue to change into the future even if the climate remains much as it is today and current management treatments continue to be applied. It is possible that long-lost species such as the Corncrake (*Crex crex*) and the Pine Marten (*Martes martes*) may have made a comeback by the twenty-second century, and long-persecuted raptors such as the Hen Harrier (*Circus cyaneus*) may have re-established breeding populations following legal enforcement. But it is equally possible that the battle against introduced species such as the Grey Squirrel (*Sciurus carolinensis*) and the American Signal Crayfish (*Pacifastacus leniusculus*) will have been lost, with perhaps the associated loss of native Red Squirrel and White-clawed Crayfish (*Austropotamobius pallipes*). The arrival of new invasive species may have continued to pose a threat to native species. One such example is the pending invasion of Muntjac Deer (*Muntiacus reevesi*) causing potentially unpredictable effects, particularly on the Dales woodland. Some long-distance bird migrants may have continued to decline because of factors far beyond the Dales; for example, the Yellow Wagtail (*Motacilla flava*) may have been lost despite optimal management in its former breeding habitats, while Ash-dieback and the Emerald Ash Borer may have significantly altered the woodland structure and biodiversity, resulting in other changes in bird, mammal and insect populations.

To the majority of visitors none of these changes would be noticeable. It is the landscape which is the main attraction for them, and so long as this remains more or less the same and the villages are contained, all will be well in their eyes. But to naturalists, both amateur and professional, the wide variety of habitats with their great wealth of plant and animal communities are a major attraction, and will remain so. They will continue to encourage and support appropriate conservation measures. One hundred years on, this continued commitment will probably have resulted in a greater area of the Dales being managed as nature reserves than is the case today, whatever the agricultural demands. One can also predict that the National Park will remain one of the most important 'laboratories' in Britain for the study of ecological and environmental processes – a laboratory where north meets south along the Pennine chain, attracting students and researchers from across the country to solve both old and new questions, and to understand more about the natural world in all its many complexities.

References and Further Reading

Alexander, R. W., Burek, C. V. & Gibbs, H. M. (2005). The effect of grike orientation and depth upon microclimate. *Malham Tarn Research Seminar 2005*, 50–51.

Allen, T. (2012). The true length unravelled. *Descent*, **224**, 24–25.

Altringham, J. D. & Glover, A. (2013). Bats in the caves. In: *Caves and Karst of the Yorkshire Dales 1* (ed. T. Waltham & D. Lowe). British Cave Research Association, Buxton, 219–224.

Andrews, M. (1988). Some Trichopteran larvae of mid and upper Wharfedale. *The Naturalist*, **113**, 41–57.

Angell, R. L., Butlin, R. K. & Altringham, J. D. (2013). Sexual segregation and flexible mating patterns in temperate bats. *PLoS ONE*, **8** (1), e54194.

Anon. (1785–86). A survey with Maps of Lands within the Manors of Malham-Moors and East Malham in the Parish of Kirkby-Malhamdale and County of York, now the property of Thos Lister Esq. In the possession of the National Trust, York.

Appleyard, I. (1994). *Ring Ouzels of the Yorkshire Dales*. Maney and Sons, Leeds.

Atherton, I, Bosanquet, S. & Lawley, M. (eds.) (2010). *Mosses and Liverworts of Britain and Ireland: a Field Guide*. British Bryological Society, Plymouth.

Baddeley, J. A., Thompson, D. B. A. & Lee, J. A. (1994). Regional and historic variation in the nitrogen content of *Racomitrium lanuginosum* in Britain in relation to atmospheric nitrogen deposition. *Environmental Pollution*, **84**, 189–196.

Baillie, S. R., Marchant, J. H., Leech, D. I., Renwick, A. R., Eglington, S. M., Joys, A. C., Noble, D. G., Barimore, C., Conway, G. J., Downie, I. S., Risely, K. & Robinson, R. A. (2012). *Bird Trends 2011*. BTO Research Report no. 609. British Trust for Ornithology, Thetford.

Baines, D. (1988). The effects of improvement of upland grassland on the distribution and density of breeding wading birds (Charadriiformes) in northern England. *Biological Conservation*, **45**, 221–236.

Baines, D. (1989). The effects of improvement of upland, marginal grasslands on the breeding success of lapwings *Vanellus vanellus* and other waders. *Ibis*, **131**, 497–506.

Baines, D. (1996). The implications of grazing and predator management on the habitats and breeding success of black grouse *Tetrao tetrix*. *Journal of Applied Ecology*, **33**, 54–62.

Barlow, S. E. (2013). The effects of invertebrates on the plant communities in upland hay meadows. PhD thesis, University of Newcastle-upon-Tyne.

Bartley, D. D., Jones, I. P. & Smith, R. T. (1990). Studies of the Flandrian history of the Craven District of the Yorkshire lowlands. *Journal of Ecology*, **78**, 611–632.

Beale, C. M., Burfield, I. J., Sim, I. M. W., Rebecca, G. W., Pearce-Higgins, J. W. & Grant, M. C. (2006). Climate change may account for the decline in British Ring Ouzels *Turdus torquatus*. *Journal of Animal Ecology*, **75**, 826–835.

Bell, M. V. (1979). The status of Golden Plover *Pluvialis apricaria* and Dunlin *Calidris alpine* in Upper Wharfedale. *The Naturalist,* **104**, 95–100.

Bibby, C. J. (1986). Merlins in Wales: site occupancy and breeding in relation to vegetation. *Journal of Applied Ecology*, **23**, 1–12.

Birks, J. D. S. & Kitchener, A. C. (1999). *The Distribution and Status of the Polecat* Mustela putorius *in Britain.* Vincent Wildlife Trust, Ledbury.

Blackstock, N. & Ashton, P. A. (2001). A re-assessment of the putative *Carex flava* agg. (Cyperaceae) hybrids at Malham Tarn (v.c. 64): a morphometric analysis. *Watsonia*, **23**, 505–516.

Blackstock, N. & Ashton, P. A. (2010). Genetic markers and morphometric analysis reveal past hybridisation and introgression in putative *Carex flava* L. *s. str.* (Cyperaceae) hybrid populations. *Plant Systematics & Evolution*, **287**, 37–47.

Bonesi, L. & Macdonald, D. W. (2004). Impact of released Eurasian otter on a population of American mink: a test using an experimental approach. *Oikos*, **106**, 9–18.

Boyd, W. & Shuffrey, W. A. (1893). *Littondale: Past and Present.* Jackson, Leeds.

Bradley, A. (2014). Farming in a national park. In: *The Yorkshire Dales National Park: a Celebration of 60 Years* (C. Speakman). Great Northern Books, Ilkley, 101–107.

Bradshaw, M. E. (1964). Studies on *Alchemilla filicaulis* Bus. *sensu lato* and *A. minima* Walters. III. *Alchemilla minima. Watsonia*, **6**, 76–81.

Brennan, M. & Brennan, T. (2013). *The Hungry Hushes: Exploring the Visible Remains of Lead Mining in Swaledale in General and Arkengarthdale in Particular.* Caroline Brannigan, Richmond.

Broughton, R. K., Hill, R. A., Bellamy, P. E. & Hinsley, S. A. (2011). Nest sites, breeding failure and causes of non-breeding in a population of British Marsh Tits *Poecile palustris*. *Bird Study*, **58**, 229–237.

Brown, L. E., Holden, J. & Palmer, S. (2014). *Effects of Moorland Burning on the Ecohydrology of River Basins. Key Findings from the EMBER Project.* University of Leeds.

Bryce, D. (1962). Chironomidae (Diptera) from freshwater sediments with special reference to Malham Tarn (Yorks). *Transactions of the Society of British Entomologists*, **15**, 41–54.

Bubb, D. H., Thom, T. J. & Lucas, M. C. (2005). The within-catchment invasion of the non-indigenous signal crayfish *Pacifastacus leniusculus* (Dana) in upland rivers. *Bulletin Français de la Pêche et de la Pisciculture*, **376–377**, 665–673.

Bubb, D. H., O'Malley, O. J., Gooderham, A. C. & Lucas, M. C. (2009). Relative impacts of native and non-native crayfish on shelter use by an indigenous benthic fish. *Aquatic Conservation*, 19, 448–455.

Bullock, P. (1971). The soils of the Malham Tarn area. *Field Studies*, **3**, 381–408.

Burt, T. P. & Horton, B. P. (2003). The climate of Malham Tarn. *Field Studies*, **10**, 635–652.

Cabot, D. (2009). *Wildfowl.* New Naturalist 110. Collins, London.

Calladine, J., Baines, D. & Warren, P, (2002). Effects of reduced grazing on population density and breeding success of black grouse in northern England. *Journal of Applied Ecology*, **39**, 772–780.

Cameron, R. A. D. (1978). Terrestrial snail faunas of the Malham, England UK area. *Field Studies*, **14**, 715–718.

Caseldine, C. J., McGarry, S. F., Baker, A., Hawksworth, C. & Smart, P. L. (2008). Late Quaternary speleothem pollen in the British Isles. *Journal of Quaternary Science*, **23**, 193–200.

Chiverell, R. C., Oldfield, F., Appleby, P. O., Barlow, D, Fisher, E., Thompson, R. & Wolff, G. (2008). Evidence for changes in Holocene sediment flux in Semer Water and Raydale, North Yorkshire, UK. *Geomorphology*, **100**, 70–82.

Clapham, A. R. (1954). Summer meeting at Malham Tarn. *Journal of Ecology*, **42**, 574–579.

Clark, W. E. & Roebuck, W. D. (1881). *A Handbook of the Vertebrate Fauna of Yorkshire: Being a Catalogue of British Mammals, Birds, Reptiles, Amphibians and Fishes.* Lovell Reeve, London.

Clunas, A. J. & Shorrock, B. (1990). The birds around Malham Tarn. *The Naturalist*, **116**, 73–91.

Clutton-Brock, J. (1989). Five thousand years of livestock in Britain. *Biological Journal of the Linnean Society*, **38**, 31–37.

Condliffe, I. (2009). Policy change in the uplands. In: *Drivers of Environmental Change in the Uplands* (ed. A. Bonn, T. Allott, K. Hubacek & J. Stewart). Routledge, Abingdon, 59–89.

Cooper, E. A. & Proctor, M. C. F. (1998). Malham Tarn National Nature Reserve: the vegetation of Malham Tarn Moss and Fens. *Field Studies*, **9**, 277–312.

Corkhill, P. (1996). Raising *Cypripedium calceolus* from flask. *Orchid Review*, **104**, 348–352.

Costa, M., Fernandes, C., Birks, J. D. S., Kitchener, A. C., Santos-Reis, M. & Bruford, M. W. (2013). The genetic legacy of the 19th-century decline in the British polecat: evidence for extensive introgression from feral ferrets. *Molecular Ecology*, **22**, 5130–5147.

Coulson, J. C. (1988). The structure and importance of invertebrate communities on peatland and moorland, and effects of environmental and management changes. In: *Ecological Change in the Uplands* (ed. M. B. Usher & D. B. A. Thompson). Blackwell Scientific Publications, Oxford, 365–380.

Court, I. (2000). *Birds of Conservation Concern in the Yorkshire Dales National Park.* Yorkshire Dales National Park Authority, Grassington.

Court, I. R. (2014). Butterfly transect monitoring in the Yorkshire Dales National Park in 2013. In: *Yorkshire Dales National Park Authority Conservation Research & Monitoring Report No. 25.* Yorkshire Dales National Park Authority, Grassington.

Court, I. R. & Bentley, G. (2011). The results of hair tube survey work to determine the presence of Red Squirrel *Sciurus vulgaris* and Grey Squirrel *Sciurus carolinensis* in woodland sites in the north-west of the Yorkshire Dales National Park. *The Naturalist*, **136**, 163–169.

Court, I. R. & Fawcett, H. (2008). The distribution of red squirrels *Sciurus vulgaris* in the Yorkshire Dales National Park between 1990 and 2006. *The Naturalist*, **133**, 55–66.

Court, I. R. & Whitaker, T. M. (2013). Butterfly transect monitoring in the Yorkshire Dales National Park in 2012. In: *Yorkshire Dales National Park Authority Conservation Research & Monitoring Report No. 24.* Yorkshire Dales National Park Authority, Grassington.

Court, I. R. & White, I. (2015). *Dormouse monitoring in Freeholders' Wood 2014.* People's Trust for Endangered Species & Yorkshire Dales National Park Authority, Grassington.

Court, I. R., Irving, P. V. & Carter, I. (2004a). Status and productivity of peregrine falcons in the Yorkshire Dales between 1978 and 2002. *British Birds*, **97**, 456–463.

Court, I. R., Irving, P. V., Slator, D., Smith, J. & Staker, C. (2004b). Status of Eurasian wigeon in the Yorkshire Dales National Park in 2003 and a review of historical breeding records. *The Naturalist*, **129**, 81–84.

Craske, R. M., Fishburn, E., Hodgson, B. A. & Moore, E. M. (1979). Semer Water: twenty years later. *The Naturalist*, **104**, 105–108.

Crawford, A. (2010). *Fifth Otter Survey 2009–10.* Environment Agency, Bristol.

Cribb, P. (1993). The lady's slipper orchid revisited. *Bulletin of the Alpine Garden Society*, **61**, 304–309.

Currant, A. & Jacobi, R. M. (2001). A formal mammalian biostratigraphy for the late Pleistocene of Britain. *Quaternary Science Reviews*, **20**, 1707–1716.

Curtis, J. T. (1943). Germination and seedling development in 5 species of *Cypripedium* L. *American Journal of Botany*, **30**, 199–206.

Curtis, W. (1777–87). A catalogue of certain plants growing wild chiefly in the environs of Settle, in York, observed in months vii and viii, 1782. *Flora Londinensis*, appendix, **1B**. White & Son, London.

de la Hey, D. C. (2008). The importance of birds in the diet of otter *Lutra lutra* on Shapwick Heath. *Bioscience Horizons*, **1**, 143–147.

Dennis, I. A., Macklin, M. G., Coultard, T. J. & Brewer, P. A. (2003). The impact of the October–November 2000 floods on contaminant metal dispersal in the River Swale catchment, North Yorkshire, U.K. *Hydrological Processes*, **17**, 1641–1657.

Disney, R. H. L. (1974). A midge (Diptera: Ceratoponidae) new to Britain that is abundant in the limestone pavement of the Yorkshire Pennines. *Entomologist's Monthly Magazine,* **110**, 227–228.

Disney, R. H. L. (1980). Records of flower visiting by scuttle flies (Diptera: Phoridae) in the British Isles. *The Naturalist,* **105**, 45–50.

Disney, R. H. L. (1986). Two new species of scuttle fly (Diptera: Phoridae) from Malham Tarn, North Yorkshire. *The Naturalist,* **111**, 113–121.

Done, A. & Muir, R. (2001). The landscape history of grouse shooting in the Yorkshire Dales. *Rural History,* **12**, 195–210.

Dougall, T. W., Holland, P. K. & Yalden, D. W. (2010). The population biology of Common Sandpipers in Britain. *British Birds,* **103**, 100–114.

Douglas, M. (2013). Juniper in Cumbria. *Conserving Lakeland,* **63**, 8–9.

Evans, S. (2004). *Waxcap-grasslands: an Assessment of English Sites.* English Nature Research Report 555. English Nature, Peterborough.

Ewing, S. R., Rebecca, G. W., Heavisides, A., Court, I. R., Lindley, P., Ruddock, M., Cohen, S. & Eaton, M. A. (2011). Breeding status of merlins *Falco columbarius* in the UK in 2008. *Bird Study,* **58**, 379–389.

Farrell, L. (1999). *Cypripedium calceolus* L. In: *British Red Data Books 1. Vascular Plants* (ed. M. J. Wigginton), 3rd edition. Joint Nature Conservation Committee, Peterborough.

Farrer, R. (1908). *My Rock Garden.* Edward Arnold, London.

Fleming, A. (1998). *Swaledale: Valley of the Wild River.* Edinburgh University Press, Edinburgh.

Fletcher, K., Aebischer, N. J., Baines, D., Foster, R. & Hoodless, A. N. (2010). Changes in breeding success and abundance of ground-nesting birds in relation to the experimental deployment of legal predator control. *Journal of Applied Ecology,* **47**, 263–272.

Frankland, J. N. (2001). *A Flora of Craven.* North Craven Heritage Trust, Settle.

Freeman, S. N. & Crick, H. Q. P. (2003). The decline of the spotted flycatcher *Muscicapa striata* in Britain. *Ibis,* **145**, 400–412.

Froberg, L., Stoll, P., Baur, A. & Baur, B. (2011). Snail herbivory decreases cyanobacterial abundance and lichen diversity along cracks of limestone pavements. *Ecosphere,* **2**, 1–43.

Fryer, G. (1993). *The Freshwater Crustacea of Yorkshire.* Yorkshire Naturalists' Union & Leeds Philosophical & Literary Society, Leeds.

Gamble, D. & St Pierre, T. (eds.) (2010). *Hay Time in the Yorkshire Dales: the Natural, Cultural & Land Management History of Hay Meadows.* Yorkshire Dales Millennium Trust, Scotforth Books, Lancaster.

Gamble, D., Perry, C. & St Pierre, T. (2012). *Hay Time Final Report.* Yorkshire Dales Millennium Trust.

Garnett, M. H., Ineson, P. & Stevenson, A. C. (2000). Effects of grazing and burning on carbon sequestration in a Pennine blanket bog. *The Holocene,* **10**, 729–736.

Gilbert, O. L. (1980). Juniper in Upper Teesdale. *Journal of Ecology,* **68**, 1013–1024.

Gilbert, O., Goldie, H., Hodgson, D., Marker, M., Pentecost, A., Proctor, M. & Richardson, D. (2006). *The Ecology of Cowside Beck, a Tributary of the River Skirfare in the Malham Area of Yorkshire.* Field Studies Council, Settle.

Giller, P. S. & Malmqvist, B. (1998). *The Biology of Streams and Rivers.* Oxford University Press, Oxford.

Gilmour, M., Currant, A., Jacobi, R. M. & Stringer, C. (2007). Recent TIMS dating results from British Late Pleistocene vertebrate faunal localities: context and interpretation. *Journal of Quaternary Science,* **22**, 793–800.

Glover, A. M. & Altringham, J. D. (2008). Cave selection and use by swarming bat species. *Biological Conservation,* **141**, 1493–1504.

Goldie, H. S. (1993). The legal protection of limestone pavements in Great Britain. *Environmental Geology,* **21**, 160–166.

Goodenough, A. E., Elliot, S. C. & Hart, A. G. (2009). The challenges of conservation for declining migrants: are reserve-based initiatives during the breeding season appropriate for Pied Flycatchers *Ficidula hypoleuca*? *Ibis,* **151**, 429–439.

Graham, F. (2013). *YDNPA Fungi Survey 2013.* Yorkshire Dales National Park Authority, Grassington.

Gregory, R. D., Wilkinson, N. I., Noble, D. G., Robinson, J. A., Brown, A. F., Hughes, J., Procter, D. A., Gibbons, D. W. & Galbraith, C. A. (2012). The population status of birds in the United Kingdom, Channel Islands and Isle of Man: an analysis of conservation concern 2002–2007. *British Birds*, **95**, 410–450.

Halliday, G. (1997). *A Flora of Cumbria.* University of Lancaster, Lancaster.

Hardy, E. (1960). The lady's slipper orchid in Britain. *Bulletin of the Alpine Garden Society*, **28**, 35–39.

Hartley, M. & Ingilby, J. (1956). *The Yorkshire Dales.* J. M. Dent & Sons, London.

Hartley, M. & Ingilby, J. (1968). *Life and Tradition in the Yorkshire Dales.* J. M. Dent & Sons, London.

Haysom, K. A. & Coulson, J. C. (1998). The Lepidoptera fauna associated with *Calluna vulgaris* and effects of plant architecture on abundance and diversity. *Ecological Entomology*, **23**, 377–385.

Hazelwood, E. (1971). Mammals. In: *The Naturalist's Yorkshire* (ed. W. A. Sledge). The Dalesman, Clapham, 8.

Hewson, C. M. & Noble, D. G. (2009). Population trends of breeding birds in British woodlands over a 32 year period: relationships with food, habitat use and migratory behaviour. *Ibis*, **151**, 464–486.

Hey, T. (1949). The lost slipper of the Dales. *The Dalesman*, **11**, 185–186.

Hickling, R., Roy, D. B., Hill, J. K., Fox, R. & Thomas, C. D. (2006). The distribution of a wide range of taxonomic groups are expanding polewards. *Global Change Biology*, **12**, 450–455.

Hodgetts, N. D. & Blockeel, T. L. (1992). *Thamnobryum cataractarum*, a new species from Yorkshire with observations on *T. angustifolium* and *T. fernandesii*. *Journal of Bryology*, **17**, 251–262.

Holden, J., Shotbolt, L., Bonn, A., Burt, T. P., Chapman, P. J., Doughill, A. J., Fraser, E. D. G., Hubacek, K., Irvine, B., Kirkby, M. J., Reed, M. S., Prell, C., Stagl, S., Stringer, L. C., Turner, A. & Worrall, F. (2007). Environmental change in moorland landscapes. *Earth-Science Reviews*, **82**, 75–100.

Holmes, P. F. (1960). The birds of Malham Moor. *Field Studies*, **1**, 49–60.

Holmes, P. F. (1965). The natural history of Malham Tarn. *Field Studies*, **2**, 199–122.

Honeyman, A. (1985). Studies in the Holocene vegetational history of Wensleydale. PhD thesis, University of Leeds.

Hopkins, D. (1998). *Environmental Effects of Drought and Abstractions on River Wharfe Fisheries, Summer 1997.* Fisheries Science Report no. D1/98. Environment Agency North East Region.

Howard, A. J., Macklin, M. G., Black, S. & Hudson-Edwards, K. A. (2000). Holocene river development and environmental change in Upper Wharfedale, Yorkshire Dales, England. *Journal of Quaternary Science*, **15**, 239–252.

Howes, C. A. (1976). The decline of the otter in South Yorkshire and adjacent areas. *The Naturalist*, **101**, 3–12.

Howes, C. A. (1980). Aspects of the history and distribution of polecats and ferrets in Yorkshire and adjacent areas. *The Naturalist*, **105**, 3–13.

Howes, C. A. (1985a). Pine marten. In: *Yorkshire Mammals* (ed. M. J. Delany). University of Bradford, Bradford, 141–145.

Howes, C. A. (1985b). Polecat. In: *Yorkshire Mammals* (ed. M. J. Delany). University of Bradford, Bradford, 154–155.

Howes, C. A. (1985c). Otter. In: *Yorkshire Mammals* (ed. M. J. Delany). University of Bradford, Bradford, 169–174.

Howes, C. A. (2013) Dial 'P' for polecat: the return of the polecat *Mustela putorius* to Yorkshire. In: *Back from the Edge: The Fall and Rise of Yorkshire's Wildlife* (ed. M. Atherden, C. Handley & I. D. Rotherham). PLACE/South Yorkshire ECONET, York St John University, 20–28.

Howes, C. A. (2014). Historical records of some mammals of the Whitby District and adjacent areas of Cleveland and the North York Moors. *The Naturalist*, **139**, 82–101.

Hughes, P. D. M., Lomas-Clarke, S. H., Schulz, J. & Barber, K. E. (2008). Decline and localized extinction of a major raised bog species across the British Isles: evidence for associated land-use intensification. *The Holocene*, **18**, 1033–1043.

Hulme, M. F. & Cresswell, W. (2012). Density and behaviour of whinchats *Saxicola rubetra* on African farmland suggests that winter habitat conditions do not limit European breeding populations. *Ibis*, **154**, 680–692.

Ingram, H. A. P., Anderson, M. C., Andrews, S. M., Chinery, J. M., Evans, G. B. & Richards, C. M. (1959). Vegetation studies at Semerwater. *The Naturalist*, **94**, 113–127.

Ivemy-Cook, R. B. (1965). The vegetation of solution cups in the limestone of the Burren, Co. Clare. *Journal of Ecology*, **53**, 437–444.

Johnson, D. (2008). *Ingleborough: Landscape and History*. Carnegie Publishing, Lancaster.

Kull, T. (1999). *Cypripedium calceolus* L. *Journal of Ecology*, **87**, 913–924.

Langley, P. J. W. & Yalden, D. W. (1977). The decline of the rarer carnivores in Great Britain during the nineteenth century. *Mammal Review*, **7**, 95–116.

Langston, R. H. W., Smith, T., Brown, A. F. & Gregory, R. D. (2006). Status of breeding Twite *Carduelis flavirostris*. *Bird Study*, **53**, 55–63.

Laurie, T. C. (2012). Relict woodland on the cliffs and within the waterfall ravines of Swaledale – an introduction. In: *Trees Beyond the Woods Conference Proceedings*. Sheffield, 217–244.

Lawton, J. H. & Woodroffe, G. L. (1991). Habitat and the distribution of water voles: why are there gaps in a species' range? *Journal of Animal Ecology*, **60**, 79–91.

Lees, F. A. (1888). *The Flora of West Yorkshire with a Sketch of the Climatology and Lithology in Connection Therewith*. Lovel Reeve, London.

Lenton, E. J., Channing, P. R. F. & Jefferies, D. J. (1980). *Otter Survey of England 1978–79*. Nature Conservancy Council, London.

Livett, E. A., Lee, J. A. & Tallis J. H. (1979). Lead, zinc and copper analyses of British blanket peats. *Journal of Ecology*, **67**, 865–891.

Lord, T. C. (2013). The chronology of the Later Upper Palaeolithic recolonisation of Yorkshire: new results from AMS radiocarbon dating of objects from caves in the Yorkshire Dales. *Prehistoric Yorkshire*, **50**, 14–18.

Lord, T. C. & Howard, J. (2013). Cave archaeology. In: *Caves and Karst of the Yorkshire Dales 1* (ed. T. Waltham & D. Lowe). British Cave Research Association, Buxton, 239–251.

Lord, T. C., O'Connor, T. P., Siebrandt, D. C. & Jacobi, R. M. (2007). People and large carnivores as biostratinomic agents in Lateglacial cave assemblages. *Journal of Quaternary Science*, **22**, 681–694.

Lousley J. E. (1950). *Wild Flowers of Chalk and Limestone*. New Naturalist 16. Collins, London.

Lovis, J. D. (1976). Lady's slipper orchid (*Cypripedium calceolus* L.): a plea for help in its conservation. *The Naturalist*, **101**, 55–57.

Lund, J. W. G. (1961). The algae of the Malham Tarn district. *Field Studies*, **1**, 85–119.

Lundberg, J., Lord, T. C. & Murphy, P. J. (2010). Thermal ionization mass spectrometer U-Th dates on Pleistocene speleothems from Victoria Cave, North Yorkshire, UK: implications for palaeoenvironment and stratigraphy over multiple glacial cycles. *Geosphere*, **6**, 379–395.

Lurz, P. W. W. & South, A. B. (1998). Cached fungi in non-native conifer forests and their importance for red squirrels (*Sciurus vulgaris* L.). *Journal of Zoology*, **246**, 468–471.

Lynch, A. H., Hamilton, J. & Hedges, R. E. M. (2008). Where the wild things are: aurochs and cattle in England. *Antiquity*, **82**, 1025–1039.

Lynes, M. (2014). *Alchemilla minima*: a review. Report to the Yorkshire Dales National Park Authority.

Malam, D. S. (1985a). American mink. In: *Yorkshire Mammals* (ed. M. J. Delany). University of Bradford, Bradford, 156–160.

Malam, D. S. (1985b). Rabbit. In: *Yorkshire Mammals* (ed. M. J. Delany). University of Bradford, Bradford, 73–78.

Manley, G. (1979). Temperature records on Fountains Fell with some Pennine comparisons. *Field Studies*, **5**, 85–92.

Marchant, J. H., Hudson, R., Carter, S. P. & Whittingham, P. A. (1990). *Population trends in British Birds*. British Trust for Ornithology, Tring.

Mather, J. R. (1974). *The 1974 Yorkshire Bird Report*. Yorkshire Naturalists' Union, Leeds.

Mather, J. R. (1986). *The Birds of Yorkshire.* Croom Helm, London.

McClymont, E. L., Mauquoy, D., Yeloff, D., Broekens, P., van Geel, B., Charman, D. J., Pancost, R. D., Chambers, F. M. & Evershed, R. P. (2008). The disappearance of *Sphagnum imbricatum* from Butterburn Flow, UK. *The Holocene,* **18**, 991–1002.

Meek, E. R. & Little, B. (1977). The spread of Goosander in Britain and Ireland. *British Birds,* **70**, 229–237.

Millward, D. (1988). *A Flora of Wensleydale.* Yoredale Natural History Society.

Milne, R. & Brown, T. A. W. (1997). Carbon in the vegetation and soils of Great Britain. *Journal of Environmental Management,* **49**, 413–433.

Mitchell, R. J., Bailey, S., Beaton, J. K., Bellamy, P. E., Brooker, R. W., Broome, A., Chetcuti, J., Eaton, S., Ellis, C. J., Farren, J., Gimona, A., Goldberg, E., Hall, J., Harmer, R., Hestor, A. J., Hewison, R. L., Hodgetts, N. G., Hooper, R. J., Howe, L., Iason, G. R., Kerr, G., Littlewood, N. A., Morgan, V., Newey, S., Potts, J. M., Pozsgai, G., Ray, D., Sim, D. A., Stockan, J. A., Taylor, A. F. S. & Woodward, S. (2014a). *The Potential Ecological Impact of Ash-dieback in the U.K.* JNCC Report 483. JNCC, Peterborough.

Mitchell, R. J., Broome, A., Harmer, R., Beaton, J. K., Bellamy, P. E., Brooker, R. W., Duncan, R., Ellis, C. J., Hestor, A. J., Hodgetts, N. G., Iason, G. R., Littlewood, N. A., Mackinnon, M., Pakeman, R., Pozsgai, G., Ramsey, S., Riach, D., Stockan, J. A., Taylor, A. F. S. & Woodward, S. (2014b). *Assessing and Addressing the Impacts of Ash-dieback on UK Woodlands and Trees of Conservation Importance (Phase 2).* Natural England Commissioned Reports 151. Natural England, Peterborough.

Mitchell, W. A. (2013). Glaciation and Quaternary evolution. In: *Caves and Karst of the Yorkshire Dales 1* (ed. T. Waltham & D. Lowe). British Cave Research Association, Buxton, 29–64.

Mitchell, W. R. (1985a). Red deer. In: *Yorkshire Mammals* (ed. M. J. Delany). University of Bradford, Bradford, 186–194.

Mitchell, W. R. (1985b). Roe deer. In: *Yorkshire Mammals* (ed. M. J. Delany). University of Bradford, Bradford, 206–215.

Mitchell, W. R. (1985c). Fallow deer. In: *Yorkshire Mammals* (ed. M. J. Delany). University of Bradford, Bradford, 200–206.

Mitchell, W. R. (1985d). Sika deer. In: *Yorkshire Mammals* (ed. M. J. Delany). University of Bradford, Bradford, 194–199.

Morecroft, M. D., Bealey, C. E., Beaumont, D. A., Benham, S., Brooks, D. R., Burt, T. P., Critchley, C. N. R., Dick, J., Littlewood, N. A., Monteith, D. T., Scott, W. A., Smith, R. I., Walmsley, C. & Wason, H. (2009). The UK Environmental Change Network: emerging trends in the composition of plant and animal communities and the physical environment. *Biological Conservation,* **142**, 2814–2832.

Morris, J. E. (1901). *The North Riding of Yorkshire.* Methuen & Co., London.

Moses, C. A. & Smith, B. J. (1993). A note on the role of the lichen *Collema auriforma* in solution basin development on a Carboniferous limestone substrate. *Earth Surface Processes Landforms,* **18**, 363–368.

Nelson, T. H. (1907). *The Birds of Yorkshire. Being an Historical Account of the Avi-Fauna of the County.* A. Brown & Sons, London.

Newborn, D. & Baines, D. (2012). Enhanced control of sheep ticks in upland sheep flocks: repercussions for red grouse co-hosts. *Medical and Veterinary Entomology,* **26**, 63–69.

Newborn, D. & Foster, R. (2002). Control of parasite burdens in wild red grouse *Lagopus lagopus scoticus* through the indirect application of anthelmintics. *Journal of Applied Ecology,* **39**, 909–914.

Newton, I. (2010). *Bird Migration.* New Naturalist 113. Collins, London.

Newton, I. (2013). *Bird Populations.* New Naturalist 124. Collins, London.

Nunez, R., Spiro, B., Pentecost, A., Kim, A. & Coletta, P. (2002). Organo-geochemical and stable isotope indicators of environmental change in a marl lake, Malham Tarn, North Yorkshire, U.K. *Journal of Palaeolimnology,* **28**, 403–417.

O'Brien, M., Green, R. E. & Wilson, J. (2006). Partial recovery of corncrake *Crex crex* in Britain 1993–2004. *Bird Study,* **53**, 213–224.

O'Connor, T. & Lord, T. (2013). Cave palaeontology. In: *Caves and Karst of the Yorkshire Dales 1* (ed. T. Waltham & D.

Lowe). British Cave Research Association, Buxton, 225–238.

Ormerod, S. J. & Tyler, S. J. (1991). The influence of stream acidification and riparian land use on the feeding ecology of Grey Wagtails *Motacilla cinerea* in Wales. *Ibis*, **133**, 53–61.

Ormerod, S. J., Allenson, N., Hudson, D. & Tyler, S. J. (1986). The distribution of breeding dippers (*Cinclus cinclus* (L.) Aves) in relation to stream acidity. *Freshwater Biology*, **16**, 501–507.

Pearce-Higgins, J. W. & Yalden, D. W. (2004). Habitat selection, diet, arthropod availability and growth of a moorland wader: the ecology of European Golden Plover *Pluvialis apricaria* chicks. *Ibis*, **146**, 335–346.

Pearce-Higgins, J. W., Dennis, P., Whittingham, M. J. & Yalden, D. W. (2010). Impacts of climate on prey abundance account for fluctuations in a population of a northern wader at the southern edge of its range. *Global Change Biology*, **16**, 12–23.

Pearsall, W. H. (1930). Biological Survey of the River Wharfe. *Journal of Ecology*, **18**, 273.

Pearsall, W. H. (1941). The 'mosses' of the Stainmore District. *Journal of Ecology*, **29**, 161–175.

Pearsall, W. H. (1950). *Mountains and Moorlands*. New Naturalist 11. Collins, London.

Peay, S., Guthrie, N., Spees, J., Nilsson, E. & Bradley, P. (2009). The impact of signal crayfish (*Pacifastacus leniusculus*) on the recruitment of salmonid fish in a headwater stream in Yorkshire, England. *Knowledge and Management of Aquatic Ecosystems*, **394–395**, 12, 1–15.

Pentecost, A. (1981). The tufa deposits of the Malham district of North Yorkshire. *Field Studies*, **5**, 365–387.

Pentecost, A. (1984). The growth of *Chara globularis* and its relationship to calcium carbonate deposition in Malham Tarn. *Field Studies*, **6**, 53–58.

Pentecost, A. (1992). Carbonate chemistry of surface waters in a temperate karst region: the southern Yorkshire Dales, UK. *Journal of Hydrology*, **139**, 211–232.

Pentecost, A. (1998). Phosphorus fractionation in the sediments of Malham Tarn, North Yorkshire. *Field Studies*, **9**, 337–342.

Pentecost, A. (2009). The marl lakes of the British Isles. *Freshwater Reviews*, **2**, 167–197.

Pentecost, A. (2010). Some 'lamp floras' from tourist caves in northern England. *Cave and Karst Science*, **37**, 93–98.

Pentecost, A. (2013). Travertine and tufa. In: *Caves and Karst of the Yorkshire Dales 1* (ed. T. Waltham & D. Lowe). British Cave Research Association, Buxton, 111–116.

Pentecost, A. & Zhang, Z. (2001). The distribution of plants in Scoska Cave, North Yorkshire and their relationship to light intensity. *International Journal of Speleology*, **30A**, 27–37.

Pentecost, A. & Zhang, Z. (2004). The distribution of plants in Scoska Cave, North Yorkshire, and their relationship to light intensity. *Cave and Karst Science*, **31**, 19–22.

Pentecost, A., Coletta, P. & Haworth, E. Y. (2013). Recent changes in the Holocene diatom flora of a karstic lake: Malham Tarn, North Yorkshire, UK. *Cave and Karst Science*, **40**, 56–61.

Percival, E & Whitehead, H. (1930). Biological survey of the River Wharfe II. Report on the invertebrate fauna. *Journal of Ecology*, **18**, 286–302.

Peterken, G. (2013). *Meadows*. British Wildlife Publishing, Gillingham.

Piearce, T. G. (1975). Observations on the fauna and flora of Ingleborough Cavern, Yorkshire. *Transactions of the British Cave Research Association*, **2**, 107–115.

Piearce, T. G. & Cox, M. (1977). The distribution of unpigmented and pigmented *Gammarus pulex* L. in two streams in northern England. *The Naturalist*, **102**, 21–23.

Pigott, C. D. (1978). Climate and vegetation. In: *Upper Teesdale: the Area and its Natural History* (ed. A. R. Clapham). Collins, London, 102–121.

Pigott, C. D. & Pigott, M. E. (1963). Late-glacial and Post-glacial deposits at Malham, Yorkshire. *New Phytologist*, **63**, 317–334.

Pigott, D. (2012). *Lime-Trees and Basswoods: a Biological Monograph of the Genus* Tilia. Cambridge University Press, Cambridge.

Pigott, M. E. & Pigott, C. D. (1959). Stratigraphy and pollen analysis of Malham Tarn and Tarn Moss. *Field Studies*, **1**, 84–101.

Porter, J. L. (1994). A study of the ecology of Aspleniums in limestone grikes. *Fern Gazette,* **14**, 245–254.

Pounder, E. J. (1989). *Classic Landforms of the Northern Dales 10.* The Geographical Association (in conjunction with the British Geomorphological Research Group), Sheffield.

Prince, S. D. (1976). The effect of climate on grain development in barley at an upland site. *New Phytologist,* **76**, 377–389.

Proudlove, G. (2013). Subterranean biology. In: *Caves and Karst of the Yorkshire Dales 1* (ed. T. Waltham & D. Lowe). British Cave Research Association, Buxton, 199–218.

Proudlove, G. S., Wood, P. J., Harding, P. T., Horne, D. J., Gledhill, T. & Knight, L. R. F. D. (2003). A review of the status and distribution of the subterranean aquatic Crustacea of Britain and Ireland. *Cave and Karst Science,* **30**, 53–74.

Ptyxis Ecology (2012). *Montane Eyebright Survey.* Yorkshire Dales National Park Authority, Grassington.

Rackham, O. (2006). *Woodlands.* New Naturalist 100. Collins, London.

Rackham, O. (2014). *The Ash Tree.* Little Toller Books, Toller Fratrum.

Raistrick, A. (1953). The lead mines of Upper Wharfedale. *Bulletin of Economic and Social Research,* **5**, 1–16.

Raistrick, A. (1955). *Mines and Miners of Swaledale.* The Dalesman, Clapham.

Raistrick, A. (1967). *Old Yorkshire Dales.* David & Charles, Newton Abbot.

Raistrick, A. (1968). *The Pennine Dales.* Eyre & Spottiswoode, London.

Raistrick, A. & Blackburn, K. B. (1938). Linton Mires, Wharfedale. Glacial and Post-glacial history. *Proceedings of the University of Durham Philosophical Society,* **10**, 24–31.

Raistrick, A. & Jennings, B (1965). *A History of Lead Mining in the Pennines.* Longmans Green, London.

Ramchunder, S. J., Brown, L. E. & Holden, J. (2013). Rotational vegetation burning effects on peatland stream ecosystems. *Journal of Applied Ecology,* **50**, 636–648.

Ratcliffe, D. (2002). *Lakeland: the Wildlife of Cumbria.* New Naturalist 92. Collins, London.

Rebecca, G. W. & Bainbridge, I. P. (1998). The breeding status of the Merlin *Falco columbarius* in Britain in 1993–94. *Bird Study,* **45**, 172–187.

Rivers, N. M., Butlin, R. K. & Altringham, J. D. (2005). Genetic population structure of Natterer's bats explained by mating at swarming sites and philopatry. *Molecular Ecology,* **14**, 4299–4312.

Robinson, L. (2008). The discovery of *Alopecurus borealis* and *Carex vaginata* in the Yorkshire Dales (v.c. 65) with observations on *Saxifraga hirculus. BSBI News,* **107**, 6–7.

Rodwell, J. S. (ed.) (1991a). *British Plant Communities. 1, Woodlands and Scrub.* Cambridge University Press, Cambridge.

Rodwell, J. S. (ed.) (1991b). *British Plant Communities. 2, Mires and Heaths.* Cambridge University Press, Cambridge.

Rodwell, J. S. (ed.) (1992). *British Plant Communities. 3, Grasslands and Montane Communities.* Cambridge University Press, Cambridge.

Rodwell, J. S. (ed.) (1995). *British Plant Communities. 4, Aquatic Communities, Swamps and Tall-herb Fens.* Cambridge University Press, Cambridge.

Rodwell, J. S. (ed.) (2000). *British Plant Communities. 5, Maritime Communities and Vegetation of Open Habitats.* Cambridge University Press, Cambridge.

Rothwell, J. J., Evans, M. G., Daniels, S. M. & Allott, T. E. H. (2008). Peat soils as a source of lead contamination to upland fluvial systems. *Environmental Pollution,* **153**, 582–589.

Round, F. E. (1953). An investigation of two benthic algal communities in Malham Tarn, Yorkshire. *Journal of Ecology,* **41**, 174–197.

Rushton, S. P., Lurz, P. W. W., Gurnell, J., Nettleton, P., Bruemmar, C., Shirley, M. D. F. & Sainsbury, A. W. (2006). Disease threats posed by alien species: the role of poxvirus in the decline of the native red squirrel in Britain. *Epidemiology and infection,* **134**, 521–533.

Seaward, M. R. D. & Pentecost, A. (2001). The lichen flora of the Malham Tarn area. *Field Studies,* **10**, 57–92.

Senior, P., Butlin, R. K. & Altringham, J. D. (2005). Sex and segregation in temperate bats. *Proceedings of the Royal Society B*, **272**, 2467–2473.

Shaw, R. C. (1956). *The Royal Forest of Lancaster*, Guardian Press, Preston.

Shefferson, R. P., Weiss M., Kull, T. & Taylor D. L. (2005). High specificity generally characterises mycorrhizal association in rare lady's slipper orchids, genus *Cypripedium*. *Molecular Ecology*, **14**, 613–626.

Shorrock, B. & Sutton, R. (2012). *Malham Tarn Wildlife & Weather Report 2011*. Malham Tarn Field Centre, Settle.

Shorrock, B & Sutton, R. (2014). *Malham Tarn Wildlife & Weather Report 2013*. Malham Tarn Field Centre, Settle.

Silvertown, J. W. (1982). Measuring plant distribution in limestone pavements. *Field Studies*, **5**, 651–662.

Silvertown, J. W. (1983). The distribution of plants in limestone pavements: tests of species interactions and niche separation against null hypotheses. *Journal of Ecology*, **71**, 819–828.

Sim, I. M. W., Gregory, R. D., Hancock, M. H. & Brown, A. F. (2005). Recent changes in the abundance of British upland breeding birds. *Bird Study*, **52**, 261–275.

Sim, I. M. W., Burfield, I. J., Grant, M. C., Pearce-Higgins, J. W. & Brooke, M. de L. (2007). The role of habitat composition in determining breeding site occupancy in a declining Ring Ouzel *Turdus torquatus* population. *Ibis*, **149**, 374–385.

Sim, I. M. W., Ludwig, S. C., Grant, M. C., Loughrey, J. L., Rebecca, G. W. & Redpath, S. (2013). Seasonal variation in foraging conditions for Ring Ouzels *Turdus torquatus* in upland habitats and their effects on juvenile habitat selection. *Ibis*, **155**, 42–54.

Siriwardena, G. M. (2006). Avian nest predation, competition and the decline of British Marsh Tits *Parus palustris*. *Ibis*, **148**, 255–265.

Sket, B. (2008). Can we agree on an ecological classification of subterranean animals? *Journal of Natural History*, **42**, 1549–1563.

Sledge, W. A. (1936). The aquatic vegetation of Malham Tarn. *The Naturalist*, **71**, 217–219.

Smith, D. I. & Atkinson, T. C. (1977). Underground flow in cavernous limestones with special reference to the Malham area. *Field Studies*, **4**, 597–616.

Smith, K. W. (2005). Has the reduction in nest-site competition from Starlings *Sturnus vulgaris* been a factor in the recent increase in Great Spotted Woodpecker *Dendrocopos major* number in Britain? *Bird Study*, **52**, 307–313.

Smith, R. S. & Jones, L. (1991). The phenology of mesotrophic grassland in the Pennine dales: historic hay cutting dates, vegetation variation and plant species phenologies. *Journal of Applied Ecology*, **28**, 42–59.

Smith, R. S., Buckingham, H., Bullard, M. J., Shiel, R. S. & Younger, A. (1996). The conservation management of mesotrophic (meadow) grassland in northern England. 1. Effects of grazing, cutting date and fertilizer on the vegetation of a traditionally managed sward. *Grass and Forage Science*, **51**, 278–291.

Smith, R. S., Shiel, R. S., Millward, D. & Corkhill, P. (2000). The interactive effects of management on the productivity and plant community structure of an upland meadow: an 8-year trial. *Journal of Applied Ecology*, **37**, 1029–1043.

Smith, R. S., Shiel, R. S., Millward, D., Corkhill, P. & Sanderson, R. A. (2002). Soil seed banks and the effects of meadow management on vegetation change in a 10-year meadow field trial. *Journal of Applied Ecology*, **39**, 279–293.

Smith, R. S., Shiel, R. S., Bardgett, R. D., Millward, D., Corkhill, P., Rolph, G., Hobbs, P. J. & Peacock, S. (2003). Soil microbial community, fertility, vegetation and diversity as targets in the restoration management of a meadow grassland. *Journal of Applied Ecology*, **40**, 51–64.

Soper, J. & Dunning, F. W. (2005). Structure and sequence of the Ingleton Group basement to the Central Pennines of northern England. *Proceedings of the Yorkshire Geological Society*, **55**, 241–261.

Speakman, C. (2014). *The Yorkshire Dales National Park: a Celebration of 60 Years*. Great Northern Books, Ilkley.

Stace, C. (2010). *New Flora of the British Isles*, 3rd edition. Cambridge University Press, Cambridge.

Stevens, C. J., Dise, N. B., Mountford, J. O. & Gowing, D. J. (2004). Impact of nitrogen deposition on species richness of grasslands. *Science*, **347**, 1876–1879.

Stewart, A. & Drewitt, A. (1989). Botanical survey of the Yorkshire Dales National Park (N. Yorks.) 1985–88. Unpublished report for the Yorkshire Dales National Park and the Nature Conservancy Council.

Stubbington, R., Dunscombe, M. P. & Gledhill, T. (2008). Occurrence of *Antrobathynella stammeri* (Jakobi, 1954) (Crustacea: Syncarida: Bathynellidae) in the hyporheic zone of two English karst rivers. *Cave and Karst Science*, **35**, 59–62.

Summerhayes, V. S. (1951). *Wild Orchids of Britain*. New Naturalist 19. Collins, London.

Swales, S. (1987). The vegetational and archaeological history of the Ingleborough Massif, North Yorkshire. PhD Thesis, University of Leeds.

Sweeting, M. M. (1973). *Karst Landforms*. Columbia University Press, New York.

Talling, J. F. & Parker, J. C. (2002). Seasonal dynamics of phytoplankton and phytobenthos, and associated chemical interactions, in a shallow upland lake (Malham Tarn, northern England). *Hydrobiologia*, **487**, 167–181.

Tallis, J. H. (1991). Forest and moorland in the South Pennine uplands in the mid-Flandrian period: III. The spread of moorland local, regional and national. *Journal of Ecology*,**79**, 401–415.

Taylor, E. W. (1956). A summary of our knowledge of Yorkshire mammals, 1881–1955. *The Naturalist*, **81**, 37–44.

Telfer, M. W., Wilson, P., Lord, T. C. & Vincent, P. J. (2009). New constraints on the age of the last ice sheet glaciation in NW England using optically stimulated luminescence dating. *Journal of Quaternary Science*, **24**, 906–915.

Thomas, C. D. (2010). Climate, climate change and range boundaries. *Diversity and Distributions*, **16**, 488–495.

Trudgill, S. T. (1985). Field observations of limestone weathering and erosion in the Malham district, North Yorkshire. *Field Studies*, **6**, 201–236.

Tuke, J. (1794). *General View of the Agriculture of the North Riding of Yorkshire*. MacMillan, London.

Turner, J. & Hodgson, J. (1979). Studies in the vegetational history of the northern Pennines I. Variations in the composition of the early Flandrian forests. *Journal of Ecology*, **67**, 629–646.

Usher, M. B. (1980). An assessment of conservation values within a large Site of Special Scientific Interest in North Yorkshire, England, U.K. *Field Studies*, **5**, 323–348.

Usher, M. B. & Gardener, S. M. (1988). Animal communities in the uplands: how is naturalness influenced by management. In: *Ecological Change in the Uplands* (ed. M. B. Usher & D. B. A. Thompson). Blackwell, Oxford, 75–82.

Utley, J. T. (1936). Notes on the bird population in Wensleydale (VC 65), summer 1936. *The Naturalist*, **61**, 219–220.

Vera, F. W. M. (2000). *Grazing Ecology and Forest History*. CABI International, Wallingford.

Vickery, J. (1991). Breeding density of Dippers *Cinclus cinclus*, Grey Wagtails *Motacilla cinerea* and Common Sandpipers *Actitis hypoleucos* in relation to the acidity of streams in south-west Scotland. *Ibis*, **133**, 178–185.

Vincent, P. (1995). Limestone pavements in the British Isles: a review. *Geographical Journal*, **161**, 265–274.

Vincent, P. J., Lord, T. C., Wilson, M. W. & Wilson, P. (2011). Early Holocene colluviation in northwest England: new evidence for the 8.2 ka event in the terrestrial record? *Boreas*, **40**, 105–115.

Wallage, Z. E., Holden, J. & Macdonald, A. T. (2006). Drain-blocking: an effective treatment for reducing dissolved organic carbon loss and water colour in drained peatland. *Science of the Total Environment*, **367**, 811–821.

Waltham, A. C. & Tillotson, A. C. (1989). *The Geomorphology of Ingleborough*. Nature Conservancy Council, Peterborough.

Waltham, T. (1987). *Karst & Caves in the Yorkshire Dales National Park*. Yorkshire Dales National Park Committee, Grassington.

Waltham, T. (2007). *The Yorkshire Dales: Landscape and Geology*. Crowood Press, Marlborough.

Waltham, T. (2013). Karst geomorphology. In: *Caves and Karst of the Yorkshire Dales 1* (ed. T. Waltham & D. Lowe). British Cave Research Association, Buxton, 65–92.

Waltham, T. & Lowe, D. (eds.) (2013). *Caves and Karst of the Yorkshire Dales 1*. British Cave Research Association, Buxton.

Ward, S. D. & Evans, D. F. (1976). Conservation assessment of British limestone pavements based on floristic criteria. *Biological Conservation*, **9**, 217–233.

Warren, P., Baines, D. & Aebischer, N. J. (2011). The extent and impact of shooting on black grouse *Tetrao tetrix* in northern England. *Wildlife Biology*, **17**, 11–15.

Warren, R. D., Waters, D. A., Altringham, J. D. & Bullock, D. J. (2000). The distribution of Daubenton's bats (*Myotis daubentonii*) and pipistrelle bats (*Pipistrellus pipistrellus*) (Verspertilionidae) in relation to small-scale variation in riverine habitat. *Biological Conservation*, **92**, 85–91.

Waters, C. & Lowe, D. (2013). Geology of the limestones. In: *Caves and Karst of the Yorkshire Dales 1* (ed. T. Waltham & D. Lowe). British Cave Research Association, Buxton, 11–28.

Watson, A. & Moss, R. (2008). *Grouse: the Natural History of British and Irish Species*. New Naturalist 107. Collins, London.

Watt, A. S. (1955). Bracken versus heather: a study in plant sociology. *Journal of Ecology*, **35**, 490–506.

Webb, S. (2013). Limestone pavements. In: *Caves and Karst of the Yorkshire Dales 1* (ed. T. Waltham & D. Lowe). British Cave Research Association, Buxton, 93–110.

Webb, S. & Glading, P. (1998). The ecology and conservation of limestone pavement in Britain. *British Wildlife*, **10**, 103–113.

Webster, J. A. (2001). A review of the historical evidence of the habitat of the pine marten in Cumbria. *Mammal Review*, **31**, 17–31.

Wehr, J. D. & Whitton, B. A. (1983). Accumulation of heavy metals by aquatic mosses 2. *Rhynchostegium riparioides*. *Hydrobiologia*, **100**, 261–284.

Wheeler, B. D., Shaw, S. C. & Meade, R. (2005). Eco-hydrological characteristics of the Malham Tarn mires. *Fourth Malham Tarn Research Seminar*, pp. 10–24. Field Studies Council, Malham.

White, I. & Court, I. R. (2012). The Hazel Dormouse release project in the Yorkshire Dales National Park. *The Naturalist*, **137**, 82–88.

White, P. C. L., McClean, C. J. & Woodroffe, G. L. (2003). Factors affecting the success of an otter (*Lutra lutra*) reinforcement programme, as identified by post-translocation monitoring. *Biological Conservation*, **112**, 363–371.

White, R. (2005). *The Yorkshire Dales, a Landscape Through Time*. Great Northern Books, Ilkley.

Whitaker, T. M. (2014). Mapping changes of the Dark-green Fritillary (*Argynnis aglaja* L.) (Lepidoptera, Argynninae) in Yorkshire VC64 2000–2010. *The Naturalist*, **140**, 112–117.

Whittaker, T. D. (1823). *An history of Richmondshire, in the North Riding of the County of York, together with those parts of the Everwicshire of Domesday which form part of the Wapentakes of Lonsdale, Ewecross and Amunderness*. Longman, Hurst, Rees, Orme & Brown, London.

Williamson, K. (1968). Bird communities in the Malham Tarn region of the Pennines. *Field Studies* **2**, 651–668.

Willoughby, C. A. (1968). *Cypripedium calceolus* L. in Littondale. *The Naturalist*, **93**, 109–111.

Wilson, A. (1992). *Geology of the Yorkshire Dales National Park*. Yorkshire Dales National Park Committee, Grassington.

Wilson, P., Barrows, T. T., Lord, T. C. & Vincent, P. J. (2012). Surface lowering of limestone pavement as determined by cosmogenic (36Cl) analysis. *Earth Surface Processes and Landforms*, **37**, 1518–1526.

Wood, T. G. (1967). Acari and Collembola of moorland soils from Yorkshire, England. 1. Description of sites and their populations. *Oikos*, **18**, 102–117.

Woodroffe, G. L. (1994). Status and distribution of the otter (*Lutra lutra*) in North Yorkshire. *The Naturalist*, **119**, 23–35.

Woodroffe, G. L., Lawton, J. H. & Davidson, W. L. (1990). The impact of feral mink *Mustela vison* on water voles *Arvicola terrestris* in the North Yorkshire Moors National Park. *Biological Conservation*, **51**, 49–62.

Woof, C. & Jackson, E. (1988). Some aspects of the water chemistry in the area around Malham Tarn, North Yorkshire. *Field Studies*, **7**, 159–187.

Wright, G. N. (1986). *The Yorkshire Dales.* David & Charles, Newton Abbot.

Wright, P. M. (2005). *Merlins in the Southern Dales.* Tarnmoor Publications, Skipton.

Yalden, D. W. (1999). *The History of British Mammals.* T & A. D. Poyser Ltd, London.

Yalden, D. W. & Yalden, P. E. (1989). *Golden Plovers and Recreational Disturbance.* Nature Conservancy Council, Edinburgh.

Yallop, A. R., Thacker, J. I., Thomas, G., Stephens, M., Clutterbuck, B., Brewer, T. & Sanmer, C. A. D. (2006). The extent and intensity of management burning in the English uplands. *Journal of Applied Ecology,* **43**, 1138–1148.

Yallop, A. R., Clutterbuck, B. & Thacker, J. (2010). Increase in humic dissolved organic carbon (hDOC) export from upland peat catchments. *Climate Research,* **45**, 43–56.

Yorkshire Dales Biodiversity Forum (2011). *Nature in the Dales: 2020 Vision. The Second Biodiversity Action Plan for the Yorkshire Dales National Park.* Yorkshire Dales National Park Authority, Grassington.

Yorkshire Dales National Park Authority (2000). *Nature in the Dales: a Biodiversity Action Plan for the Yorkshire Dales.* Yorkshire Dales National Park Authority, Grassington.

Yorkshire Dales National Park Authority (2006). *A Summary Report of Yorkshire Feather-moss* Thamnium cataractarum *Survey Work in the Yorkshire Dales National Park 2005.* Yorkshire Dales National Park Conservation Research and Monitoring Report No. 3. Yorkshire Dales National Park Authority, Grassington.

Yorkshire Dales National Park Authority (2013). *Yorkshire Dales National Park Management Plan 2013–2018.* www.yorkshiredalesmanagementplan.org.uk.

Yorkshire Dales National Park Authority (2014). *Nature in the Dales: 2020 Vision, the Second Biodiversity Action Plan for the Yorkshire Dales National Park, 2013 Trends and Status Review.* Yorkshire Dales National Park Authority, Grassington.

Yorkshire Dales Upland Bird Study Group (2006). *A Review of Breeding Birds in the Yorkshire Dales Bird Study Group Recording Area 1992–2004.* Yorkshire Dales Upland Bird Study Group.

Letter to Joan Duncan from Bob Jarman, 15 June 1962 (Natural England archive).

Letter to Joan Duncan from Bob Jarman, 12 June 1967 (Natural England archive).

Letter to Elizabeth and Brian Shorrock from Norman Frankland, 19 December 1975.

Letter to Ben Mercer from Eric Hardy, 26 June 1990 (Natural England archive).

Letter to Ben Mercer from Eric Hardy, 28 May 1992 (Natural England archive).

Letter to John Lee from John Lovis, 8 September 2011.

Message to John Lee from Philip Oswald, 19 September 2011.

Index

SPECIES INDEX

Page numbers in **bold** include illustrations.

GENERAL INDEX

Page numbers in **bold** include illustrations.

The New Naturalist Library

1. *Butterflies* — E. B. Ford
2. *British Game* — B. Vesey-Fitzgerald
3. *London's Natural History* — R. S. R. Fitter
4. *Britain's Structure and Scenery* — L. Dudley Stamp
5. *Wild Flowers* — J. Gilmour & M. Walters
6. *The Highlands & Islands* — F. Fraser Darling & J. M. Boyd
7. *Mushrooms & Toadstools* — J. Ramsbottom
8. *Insect Natural History* — A. D. Imms
9. *A Country Parish* — A. W. Boyd
10. *British Plant Life* — W. B. Turrill
11. *Mountains & Moorlands* — W. H. Pearsall
12. *The Sea Shore* — C. M. Yonge
13. *Snowdonia* — F. J. North, B. Campbell & R. Scott
14. *The Art of Botanical Illustration* — W. Blunt
15. *Life in Lakes & Rivers* — T. T. Macan & E. B. Worthington
16. *Wild Flowers of Chalk & Limestone* — J. E. Lousley
17. *Birds & Men* — E. M. Nicholson
18. *A Natural History of Man in Britain* — H. J. Fleure & M. Davies
19. *Wild Orchids of Britain* — V. S. Summerhayes
20. *The British Amphibians & Reptiles* — M. Smith
21. *British Mammals* — L. Harrison Matthews
22. *Climate and the British Scene* — G. Manley
23. *An Angler's Entomology* — J. R. Harris
24. *Flowers of the Coast* — I. Hepburn
25. *The Sea Coast* — J. A. Steers
26. *The Weald* — S. W. Wooldridge & F. Goldring
27. *Dartmoor* — L. A. Harvey & D. St Leger Gordon
28. *Sea Birds* — J. Fisher & R. M. Lockley
29. *The World of the Honeybee* — C. G. Butler
30. *Moths* — E. B. Ford
31. *Man and the Land* — L. Dudley Stamp
32. *Trees, Woods and Man* — H. L. Edlin
33. *Mountain Flowers* — J. Raven & M. Walters
34. *The Open Sea: I. The World of Plankton* — A. Hardy
35. *The World of the Soil* — E. J. Russell
36. *Insect Migration* — C. B. Williams
37. *The Open Sea: II. Fish & Fisheries* — A. Hardy
38. *The World of Spiders* — W. S. Bristowe
39. *The Folklore of Birds* — E. A. Armstrong
40. *Bumblebees* — J. B. Free & C. G. Butler
41. *Dragonflies* — P. S. Corbet, C. Longfield & N. W. Moore
42. *Fossils* — H. H. Swinnerton
43. *Weeds & Aliens* — E. Salisbury
44. *The Peak District* — K. C. Edwards
45. *The Common Lands of England & Wales* — L. Dudley Stamp & W. G. Hoskins
46. *The Broads* — E. A. Ellis
47. *The Snowdonia National Park* — W. M. Condry
48. *Grass and Grasslands* — I. Moore
49. *Nature Conservation in Britain* — L. Dudley Stamp
50. *Pesticides and Pollution* — K. Mellanby
51. *Man & Birds* — R. K. Murton
52. *Woodland Birds* — E. Simms
53. *The Lake District* — W. H. Pearsall & W. Pennington
54. *The Pollination of Flowers* — M. Proctor & P. Yeo
55. *Finches* — I. Newton
56. *Pedigree: Words from Nature* — S. Potter & L. Sargent
57. *British Seals* — H. R. Hewer
58. *Hedges* — E. Pollard, M. D. Hooper & N. W. Moore
59. *Ants* — M. V. Brian
60. *British Birds of Prey* — L. Brown
61. *Inheritance and Natural History* — R. J. Berry
62. *British Tits* — C. Perrins
63. *British Thrushes* — E. Simms
64. *The Natural History of Shetland* — R. J. Berry & J. L. Johnston

65. *Waders* — W. G. Hale
66. *The Natural History of Wales* — W. M. Condry
67. *Farming and Wildlife* — K. Mellanby
68. *Mammals in the British Isles* — L. Harrison Matthews
69. *Reptiles and Amphibians in Britain* — D. Frazer
70. *The Natural History of Orkney* — R. J. Berry
71. *British Warblers* — E. Simms
72. *Heathlands* — N. R. Webb
73. *The New Forest* — C. R. Tubbs
74. *Ferns* — C. N. Page
75. *Freshwater Fish* — P. S. Maitland & R. N. Campbell
76. *The Hebrides* — J. M. Boyd & I. L. Boyd
77. *The Soil* — B. Davis, N. Walker, D. Ball & A. Fitter
78. *British Larks, Pipits & Wagtails* — E. Simms
79. *Caves & Cave Life* — P. Chapman
80. *Wild & Garden Plants* — M. Walters
81. *Ladybirds* — M. E. N. Majerus
82. *The New Naturalists* — P. Marren
83. *The Natural History of Pollination* — M. Proctor, P. Yeo & A. Lack
84. *Ireland: A Natural History* — D. Cabot
85. *Plant Disease* — D. Ingram & N. Robertson
86. *Lichens* — Oliver Gilbert
87. *Amphibians and Reptiles* — T. Beebee & R. Griffiths
88. *Loch Lomondside* — J. Mitchell
89. *The Broads* — B. Moss
90. *Moths* — M. Majerus
91. *Nature Conservation* — P. Marren
92. *Lakeland* — D. Ratcliffe
93. *British Bats* — John Altringham
94. *Seashore* — Peter Hayward
95. *Northumberland* — Angus Lunn
96. *Fungi* — Brian Spooner & Peter Roberts
97. *Mosses & Liverworts* — Nick Hodgetts & Ron Porley
98. *Bumblebees* — Ted Benton
99. *Gower* — Jonathan Mullard
100. *Woodlands* — Oliver Rackham
101. *Galloway and the Borders* — Derek Ratcliffe
102. *Garden Natural History* — Stefan Buczacki
103. *The Isles of Scilly* — Rosemary Parslow
104. *A History of Ornithology* — Peter Bircham
105. *Wye Valley* — George Peterken
106. *Dragonflies* — Philip Corbet & Stephen Brooks
107. *Grouse* — Adam Watson & Robert Moss
108. *Southern England* — Peter Friend
109. *Islands* — R. J. Berry
110. *Wildfowl* — David Cabot
111. *Dartmoor* — Ian Mercer
112. *Books and Naturalists* — David E. Allen
113. *Bird Migration* — Ian Newton
114. *Badger* — Timothy J. Roper
115. *Climate and Weather* — John Kington
116. *Plant Pests* — David V. Alford
117. *Plant Galls* — Margaret Redfern
118. *Marches* — Andrew Allott
119. *Scotland* — Peter Friend
120. *Grasshoppers & Crickets* — Ted Benton
121. *Partridges* — G. R. (Dick) Potts
122. *Vegetation of Britain & Ireland* — Michael Proctor
123. *Terns* — David Cabot & Ian Nisbet
124. *Bird Populations* — Ian Newton
125. *Owls* — Mike Toms
126. *Brecon Beacons* — Jonathan Mullard
127. *Nature in Towns and Cities* — David Goode
128. *Lakes, Loughs and Lochs* — Brian Moss
129. *Alien Plants* — Clive A. Stace and Michael J. Crawley